PREPARATIVE METHODS
OF POLYMER CHEMISTRY

Preparative
Methods of
Polymer Chemistry

Wayne R. Sorenson *and* Tod W. Campbell
Research Chemist   *Research Manager*
Pioneering Research Division Textile Fibers Department
E. I. du Pont de Nemours & Company, Inc.

19 61

INTERSCIENCE PUBLISHERS, INC., NEW YORK
Interscience Publishers Ltd., London

INTERSCIENCE PUBLISHERS, INC., 250 Fifth Avenue, New York 1, New York

For Great Britain and Northern Ireland:
INTERSCIENCE PUBLISHERS LTD., 88/90 Chancery Lane,
London W. C. 2, England

PRINTED IN THE UNITED STATES OF AMERICA
BY MACK PRINTING COMPANY

PREFACE

The purpose of this book is to provide a reference work containing detailed procedures for the synthesis and handling of a wide variety of polymer types. Although such information is readily available for most low-molecular-weight organic compounds, in the case of polymers it is scattered over a large number of more or less (usually less) accessible journals and patents. We have therefore assembled here the procedures involved in the laboratory preparation of most of the known classes of polymers. In cases where the original literature did not provide sufficient detail, supplementary information is given based on our own experience and that of our colleagues. In many instances this has involved a careful checking of the preparation and the procedures may therefore be used with confidence in their operability.

Since the preparation of useful high-molecular-weight polymers requires that considerable attention be paid to the purification of monomers, solvents, and other reaction intermediates, as well as the choice of suitable equipment and reaction conditions, such information is provided in the different procedures wherever necessary.

As indicated in Chapter 1 (Introduction) it is also our hope that the book might be of use as a supplementary text for a laboratory course in polymer chemistry or an advanced organic synthesis course.

As is always the case, we are indebted to our colleagues, without whose unselfish contribution of time and knowledge this book would not have been possible. We would like to offer special thanks to Professor C. S. Marvel of the University of Illinois and Professor H. Mark of Brooklyn Polytechnic Institute, for their unfailing enthusiasm and encouragement. We are also indebted to Warren Watanabe of Rohm and Haas, J. P. Schroeder, John Wynstra and R. K. Walton of the Union Carbide Plastics Company, and C. G. Overberger of Brooklyn Polytechnic Institute, for most helpful reviews of various portions of the book.

Of our colleagues at the du Pont Company, we would like to thank Fred Billmeyer, Roger A. Hines, Alfred C. Webber and Neil Keiser, all of the Polychemicals Department, L. P. Hubbuch of the Fabrics and Finishes Department and A. C. Stevenson and C. M. Barringer of the Elastomers Department for most helpful comments and suggestions.

We would like to thank the management of our own Textile Fibers Department for permission to write this book. To the following of our colleagues in the Textile Fibers Department, our gratitude for encouragement, technical assistance and many trenchant comments: Jim Van Oot, Sid Maerov, Norton Higgins, Emerson Wittbecker, Fred Sweeny, John Schaefgen, Vic Shashoua, Bill Statton, Frank Moody, Tom Mackey, Helen Anderson, Fran Cramer, Bob Taylor, Al Goodman, Herman Marder, Wayne Hill, Paul Morgan, Ray Tietz, Lup Jung, Ralph Beaman, and Hal Bonner.

Thanks are due to Dan Sauers, Walt Brown, and Norm Van Hove for help in preparing the illustrations.

Finally, our special thanks to Tena Evlom, Mary Joan Reese, Hilda Smith, and Jean Iannarone, who waded through reams of illegible scribblings, stacks of incoherent records, and numerous revisions to produce the final manuscript.

Wayne R. Sorenson
Tod W. Campbell

CONTENTS

CHAPTER 1

Introduction

The organic chemist today is fortunate in the abundance of literature available on the preparative methods for organic compounds. In any moderately well equipped library, it will not take long to locate a detailed laboratory procedure for preparing at least a prototype of a compound in question, if not the exact compound itself.

In polymer chemistry, to the contrary, the worker has been limited to the scattered original research and patent literature to find procedures for the synthesis of polymers. Detail is frequently lacking; laboratory directions are often dismissed in a sentence or two and are useful only to the skilled, experienced worker. The chemist in search of a good method for making a specific polymer, or detailed examples of a variety of polymer-forming reactions, has not had a single convenient reference source, let alone the many that the organic chemist can refer to for synthetic methods.

In the subsequent chapters of this work, the primary intention is to provide such a reference work, containing detailed procedures for the synthesis of a wide variety of polymer types. Most of the known classes of polymers are represented, as are most of the known organic polymer-forming reactions. These procedures were selected from the literature, and have been, in most instances, supplemented with the detail necessary to make them useful as relatively small-scale laboratory preparations.

Descriptions of equipment, purification and/or synthesis of intermediates, manipulative techniques, and typical physical properties of the products have been presented in the majority of the preparations. The organization of the syntheses that follow is necessarily arbitrary. We will not attempt to justify the order of presentation over the many other possible schemes. Detailed indexes, based on intermediates,

1

reaction type, and polymer class, have been provided to assist the reader. In most cases, the naming of polymers follows the standard organic practice of using either IUC or trivial nomenclature, depending on which provides the more handleable, descriptive name, from which the structure can be deduced.

TABLE 1.1. Polymer Preparations

	Reference	
Polymer	Chapter	Prep-aration
6–6 Nylon	3	2
Methoxymethyl 6–6 nylon	3	3
"Nylon rope trick"	3	21
Poly(hexamethylene-*m*-benzenedisulfonamide)	3	27
Poly(4,4′-oxydiphenyleneurea/2,4-tolyleneurea)	3	36
Poly[methylenebis(4-phenyleneurea)]	3	43
Poly(tetramethylene hexamethylenedicarbamate)	3	53
Poly[ethylene methylene bis(4-phenylenecarbamate)]	3	55
Poly(ethyleneterephthalate)	3	56
Poly[2,2-propanebis(4-phenylene isophthalate-co-terephtha-late)]	3	63
Poly(ethylene tetrasulfide)	3	73
Polystyrene	4	94
Polyacrylonitrile	4	100
	4	90
Poly(vinyl acetate)	4	104
Poly(vinyl alcohol)	4	107
Poly(methyl methacrylate)	4	121
Poly(vinyl isobutylether)	4	138
Poly(4-methyl-1-pentene)	4	151
GRS rubber	4	174
Polyisoprene	4	177
Polycaproamide	5	190
Poly(bischloromethyloxetane)	5	217
Polyoxymethylene	6	232
Poly(*N*-butyl-1-nylon)	6	235
Polyester resin	7	251

The basis for selection of preparations has been the first-hand experience of the authors and of our associates, who have been consulted on each phase of the book. (We have endeavored to properly acknowledge this debt in the preface.) This has been tantamount to a "checking" of a majority of the preparations, with a consequent high degree of operability attached to each experiment.

The term "polymer" means many things to many people. In its broadest sense, it includes the tars and resins left in still pots, and the brown, viscous results of unsuccessful syntheses. Again, the term may be applied to low molecular weight products containing more than two of the same repeat unit.

In this book, the term "polymer" is reserved exclusively for a substance of sufficiently high molecular weight such that the properties have become reproducibly fixed. It will be found that the preparation of polymers, as so defined, requires much skill in purification of intermediates, and much attention to technique.

The usefulness of this work is intended to be two-fold. First, it should serve as a reference book for chemists who are involved in some phase of polymer synthesis and handling. Second, it should be a useful adjunct to a laboratory course on the preparation and handling of polymers, or an advanced organic synthesis course. A number of representative polymer-forming reactions are within the necessary time and equipment limitations of the usual organic laboratory course and could be included as examples of typical organic reactions applied to the synthesis of polymers. Other polymer-forming reactions offer unique opportunities for the demonstration of organic reactions having no parallel in the chemistry of simple molecules. The polymerization of monoisocyanates and of vinyl monomers are examples of such reactions.

Table 1.1 is a list of polymer preparations suggested as being particularly suitable for inclusion in an advanced laboratory course. These are chosen as representative of significant polymers, polymer-forming reactions, and polymerization systems.

CHAPTER 2

Preparation, Fabrication, and Characterization of Polymers

Although the reactions used in the preparation of polymers are usually identical to those used in synthesis of small molecules, the high molecular weight of the polymeric products and the physical result of chain size and interactions give polymers the properties that set them apart. Consequently, they often require special methods of handling and characterization which are quite different from those used with small molecules.

I. Techniques for Preparing and Handling Polymers

In addition to the usual experimental methods, the following represent techniques of particularly wide application to the laboratory synthesis of polymers.

1. USE OF VAPOR BATHS

It is sometimes necessary to heat polymerization reactions for long periods of time at constant temperature. One of the most convenient ways to do this is by means of a vapor bath (Fig. 2.1). The large (2 × 15 in.) test tube is filled about one-fourth full, and is then heated to boiling. The vessel to be heated is suspended in the vapors and soon reaches a constant temperature.

Table 2.1 is a partial list of materials which may be used as vapor baths for temperature control. Although most of these have been used and found to be effective, stabilities for long use vary widely. Since some tend to superheat or change with use, it is recommended that the actual vapor temperature be checked routinely.

TABLE 2.1. Liquids for Vapor Baths

Compound	Boiling point, °C.	Compound	Boiling point, °C.
Water	100	Diethylene glycol	245
Toluene	111	Diphenyl	255
n-Butanol	117	Diphenyl ether	259
Perchloroethylene	121	Diphenylmethane	265
Methyl "Cellosolve"[a]	125	o-Chlorodiphenyl	268
Chlorobenzene	133	Diphenylmethane-	
Ethyl "Cellosolve"	135	o-hydroxydiphenyl (60/40)	270
m-Xylene	139	Methyl naphthyl ether	275
Anisole	152	Biphenyl/diphenylene	
Cyclohexanone	156	oxide (25/75)	275
Cyclohexanol	160	Acenaphthene	277
Phenetole	166	Triethylene glycol	282
Butyl "Cellosolve"	171	Dimethyl phthalate	283
p-Cymene	176	Diphenylethane	284
o-Dichlorobenzene	179	o-Hydroxydiphenyl	285
Phenol	181	Diphenylene oxide	288
Decahydronaphthalene	190	Fluorene	295
Ethylene glycol	197	Benzophenone	305
m-Cresol	202	p-Hydroxydiphenyl	308
Tetrahydronaphthalene	206	Hexachlorobenzene	310
Naphthalene	218	"Arochlor" 1242[b]	325
Methyl salicylate	222	o-Terphenyl	330
Butyl "Carbitol"[a]	231	"Arochlor" 1248	340
n-Decyl alcohol	231	Anthracene	340
Methylnaphthalene	242	"Arochlor" 1254	365
		Anthraquinone	380

[a] Trademarks for Union Carbide's ether solvents.
[b] Trademark for Monsanto's chlorinated aromatic hydrocarbon.

2. Purification of Reagents

Although purification of reagents is not peculiar to polymer chemistry alone, it is mentioned here since it is essential for the success of practically any polymerization. Solids should be recrystallized to a constant, and sharp, melting point, and liquids should be fractionated to give a product with a single gas chromatographic peak if possible. The ultimate proof of purity is, however, successful polymerization. Specialized techniques will be mentioned in the appropriate places.

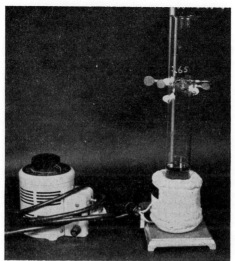

Fig. 2.1. A vapor bath.

3. SEALED TUBE REACTIONS

Sealed tubes are used quite frequently in the synthesis of polymers, probably more so than in conventional organic syntheses. They are used both for the preparation of condensation polymers by melt-polymerization, and for the polymerization at moderate temperatures of vinyl monomers. A typical tube is shown in Fig. 2.2, together with the long-stemmed funnel used to add either liquids or finely divided solids without contaminating the upper part of the tube where the final seal is to be made. These tubes are made of hard glass, either from standard wall, or extra heavy, glass tubing. Since these tubes must be completely strain-free to withstand high internal pressures, it is recommended that they be purchased commercially, or fabricated by a competent glass blower.

When sealed, the polymer tube represents a potential bomb, which can do much damage if treated improperly. Figure 2.3 shows the appearance of a steel sleeve used to enclose the lower part of a polymer tube, after "something went wrong." Admittedly, Fig. 2.3 represents an extreme not often met. For most purposes, enclosing the tube in a sleeve of glass cloth (Fig. 2.4) will offer sufficient protection if the tube is enclosed completely and the ends of the sleeve tied shut. Tubes

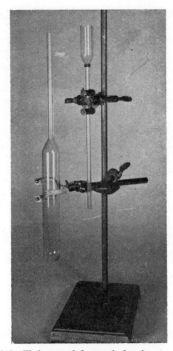

Fig. 2.2. Tube used for sealed tube reactions.

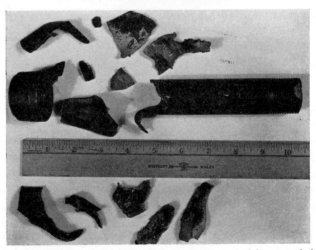

Fig. 2.3. Result of explosion of a sealed tube protected by a steel sleeve.

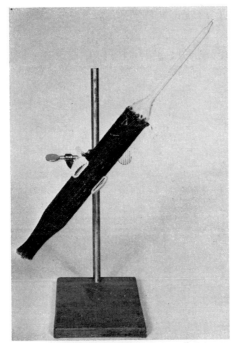

Fig. 2.4. Tube shielded with sleeve of glass cloth.

shielded in this manner and shock-loaded at 2000 p.s.i. from a nitrogen cylinder have shattered, but were completely contained. Steel sleeves also may be used for protection.

A. Vinyl Polymerization in Sealed Tubes

Vinyl polymerizations may be adversely affected by oxygen, and many vinyl monomers are low boiling. To prevent access of oxygen and loss of monomer, it is convenient to seal the polymerization mixture in a glass polymer tube under nitrogen. The tube is then immersed in a constant temperature bath and mechanically shaken or tumbled during the course of the polymerization. For monomers which boil close to room temperature, commercially available pressure bottles, or carbonated beverage bottles, may be used in place of the sealed tube.(See Chapter 4, Section II-1). Sealed tubes should not be used for large-scale preparations. Tubes should not exceed 250–300 ml. capacity and should not be filled more than one-half full.

B. Condensation Polymerization in a Sealed Tube

Most high-temperature polycondensation reactions are carried out in sealed tubes in the absence of air to minimize oxidative color formation and loss of materials. Polyamides, polyesters, and a few polyurethanes, as well as some miscellaneous polymers, may be made in this way.

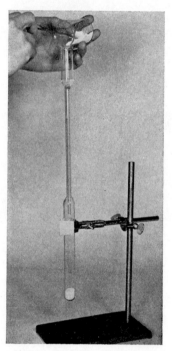

Fig. 2.5. Addition of nylon salt to a polymer tube.

By way of illustration, a polyamide would be prepared as follows (21). A quantity of "nylon salt" (Chapter 3 Preparation 1) is added to the tube through a funnel (Fig. 2.5) such that the tube is not more than one-third filled. The tube is constricted with an oxygen torch, alternately evacuated with an oil pump, flushed with nitrogen several times, and finally sealed under vacuum. The tube is heated, either in a vapor bath (Fig. 2.1) (dangerous with sealed tubes) or, better, in a salt bath, a heavy metal container holding a mixture of

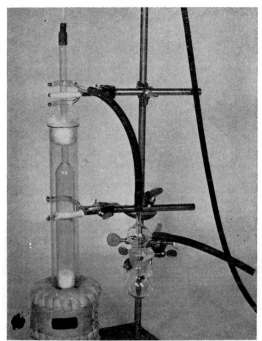

Fig. 2.6. Distillation from a polymer tube.

fused inorganic salts at a predetermined temperature.   Several eutectic
salt mixtures may be obtained commercially, and they are convenient
and safe to use.   For reasons of safety, the glass tube, either heated in
a vapor bath or a salt bath, should be contained in a sleeve of glass
cloth (see Section 3 and Fig. 2.4) or in a steel tube, with the open end
directed away from the operator.   After the heating cycle, the tube,
containing water and a nonvolatile prepolymer is cooled, opened under
nitrogen, and equipped with a capillary and a side arm for distillation
(Fig. 2.6), either sealed on, or attached by heavy-walled pressure tubing.
The nitrogen inlet should extend to the bottom of the polymer tube,
below the surface of the prepolymer; if necessary, the tube may be
heated under nitrogen to liquefy the polymer so the tip of the inlet can
be introduced into the liquid.   The tube is now evacuated, and nitrogen bubbled in for a prescribed time at a given temperature.   The
progress of polymerization often can be judged quite accurately by the
rate of rise of the nitrogen bubbles in the liquid.   Toward the end, the

rate will be exceedingly slow.   When the polymerization is considered to be complete, the mixture is cooled and treated as described in specific experiments in later chapters.

C. Use of Pipe Autoclave

An alternative to the above procedure, a pipe autoclave (Fig. 2.7) may be used in place of the glass tube (11).   The ingredients (e.g., the nylon salt) are placed in a suitable liner, which may be a glass test tube or an aluminum cylinder with a closed end.   The latter can be made from heavy foil and Sauereisen cement.   The liner and contents are placed in the autoclave, and the prescribed polymerization cycle is carried out as in Section B.   A nitrogen bubbler cannot be used.

Fig. 2.7. Pipe autoclave.

D. Safety

The hazards involved in using sealed tubes are described above. It is essential to realize the potential hazards, and take all possible precautions.   For this reason, the operator routinely should manipulate the sealed tube behind a safety shield, and should wear heavy leather gauntlets covering the hand and forearms.   As with all laboratory work safety glasses should be worn.

4. USE OF HIGH SPEED HOME MIXERS IN LABORATORY PREPARATION OF POLYMERS

The technique of interfacial polymerization (chapter 3) has made possible the synthesis of a variety of polymers which could not be made in other ways. Basically, this technique involves the reaction of a diacid chloride dissolved in an inert solvent, immiscible with water with, for example, a diamine in water containing an acid acceptor. Since the reaction occurs at the interface between the two solvents, it is desirable to make the interface as large as possible to speed the polymerization and minimize side reactions.

One of the most convenient ways of doing this on a laboratory scale is to use a home blender, such as the Waring Blendor, or the Osterizer. The aqueous diamine solution is placed in the jar of the blender, and the motor turned on. The diacid chloride solution is run rapidly into the jar in a thin stream, and is dispersed throughout the aqueous solution. Polymerizations run in this way are usually complete in a matter of seconds. Numerous examples will be found in Chapter 3. Note that household blenders must be modified to permit the use of flammable solvents, since otherwise a fire hazard exists.

5. USE OF RESIN KETTLES

Resin kettles (Fig. 2.8) are essentially equivalent to three-necked flasks, and may be used to advantage in place of them, since unlike the three-necked flask, the top can be separated from the bottom.

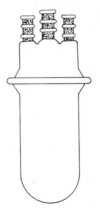

Fig. 2.8. Resin kettle.

When one is dealing with hard, tough polymers, or very viscous solutions or gels, use of a resin kettle may obviate the necessity for breaking the reaction vessel to remove the product. Resin kettles are widely available commercially in a variety of sizes.

6. USE OF HYPODERMIC SYRINGES

In many vinyl polymerizations, particularly those proceeding by ionic mechanisms, it is necessary to add, for example, a catalyst to a very cold, anhydrous monomer under completely anhydrous and anaerobic conditions. This can be done conveniently by equipping the polymerization vessel with a serum-type stopper free of sulfur, etc., which would act as an inhibitor. The catalyst, or other ingredient, then is injected quantitatively through this closure from a graduated hypodermic syringe (Fig. 2.9).

Fig. 2.9. Use of hypodermic syringe for catalyst transfer.

7. ISOLATION OF POLYMERS

Polymerizations may yield the desired polymer as a solution, a suspension, a gel-like mass consisting of polymer swollen by solvent, an emulsion, a hard, solid lump, or an easily filtered, granular solid. The first five conditions require special consideration.

A. Polymer Solution

A polymer solution may be fabricated directly. If it is desired to isolate the polymer, however, the solution should be mixed with a liquid which is a nonsolvent for the polymer, but is miscible with the polymer solvent. The precipitation should be done with vigorous agitation to prevent formation of large lumps of polymer, which could enclose unprecipitated solution. Washing the polymer to remove last traces of solvent, byproducts, and monomer can be done in a high-speed mixer, as in Section 4. Solvent also may be removed by soaking in nonsolvent, followed by heating in a vacuum oven.

B. Suspensions and Emulsions

Colloidal suspension often are obtained from vinyl polymerizations. The suspensions are broken by addition of anionic material, such as alum, sodium chloride, hydrochloric acid, etc. The polymer usually precipitates as a curd, like cottage cheese, which is filtered, washed thoroughly with water, and dried. Other nonfilterable suspensions can be separated by centrifugation.

C. Gel-Like Mass

Occasionally, an interfacial polymerization may yield an emulsion of polymer solution (or highly swollen gel) in water. This is best broken by stream distillation, or addition of an organic nonsolvent for the polymer.

Gel-like masses of precipitated polymer are best soaked or stirred vigorously in a nonsolvent for the polymer to remove the gelling agent and give a filterable solid. Alternatively, the solvent may be evaporated or removed by steam to leave a solid lump (Section D).

D. Solid Lump

Polymer obtained in a solid lump often may be fabricated from this form. However, for convenience in handling and extracting possible impurities, the polymer may first be cut up into smaller lumps, using a heavy knife and hammer, or a small hatchet. These small pieces are then fed into a Wiley mill and cut to any desired fineness. This latter operation may cause trouble if the heat generated in the mill is sufficient to fuse the polymer. This fairly common problem can be solved by grinding dry ice together with the polymer.

8. DISSOLVING OF POLYMERS

Many polymers are soluble in organic media; it is customary to determine routinely the solubility spectrum of new polymers as they are obtained (Section III). However, there are two features of polymer solutions which make them different from ordinary solutions of organic compounds. The polymers, because of their great size may dissolve slowly, and the solutions, so obtained, are extremely viscous.

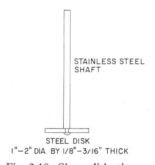

STAINLESS STEEL
SHAFT

STEEL DISK
I"–2" DIA. BY I/8"–3/16" THICK

Fig. 2.10. Shear-disk stirrer.

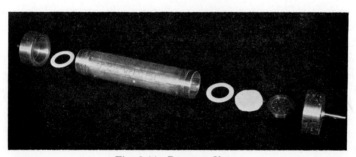

Fig. 2.11. Pressure filter.

A surprising increase in the rate of polymer dissolution can be brought about by the use of a shear-disk stirrer (Fig. 2.10), which consists simply of a steel shaft terminated by a steel disk, and rotated at high speed.   Once the solution is obtained, it cannot be freed of impurities by ordinary filtration unless it is very dilute.   A pressure filter (Fig. 2.11) must be used for viscous solution.   This consists of, from left to right in the figure, a cap to be attached to a compressed air source, screwed onto the body of the filter, with a gasket of an inert material in between.   On the bottom of the tube is another cap with an exit tube, preceded by a perforated metal disk (slotted underneath), a piece of filter cloth, and another inert gasket.   This equipment may be operated at 20–50 p.s.i., and will clean up very viscous solutions.

Soluble polymers obtained in any form may be purified by preparing a solution which is then filtered, or centrifuged, and precipitated in a nonsolvent with vigorous stirring to give a granular product.

II. Fabrication of Polymers

A complete treatment of the fabrication of polymers would require a book at least the size of this one.   It is the intent of this chapter to describe only the simplest and most elementary polymer fabricating methods.

Polymer fabrication may be classified roughly into two categories: melt methods and solution methods.

1.   MELT METHODS

In this method, the polymer is heated until molten, formed into a desired shape, then cooled.   This technique is applicable only to polymers that are stable at the temperatures involved.

A. Melt-Pressing of Films

For the preparation of small pieces of polymer film in the laboratory, a press (such as shown in Fig. 2.12) may be used.

The platens of the press are heated electrically to a temperature close to the polymer melt temperature, previously determined, according to Section III.   The polymer is placed in a small pile in the center of a 4″ × 4″ sheet of aluminum foil, (copper if the temperature is to be over 250°C.) (Fig. 2.13).   It is covered with another piece of foil, and the sandwich is placed between the platens of the press.   If

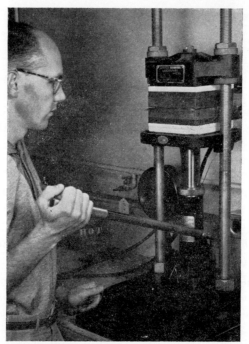

Fig. 2.12. Laboratory press.

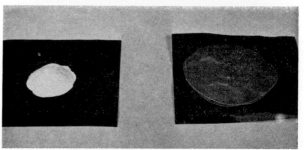

Fig. 2.13. Preparation of a film.

desired, the thickness of the film may be predetermined by the use of metal shims or templates, which may be sandwiched between the pieces of foil.

The platens are brought together by the hydraulic jack, and a pressure of 2–5000 p.s.i. is applied for about 30 sec. The pressure is released, the foil removed and cooled in water, or on a cold metal plate. The two pieces of foil are separated, and the film sample (Fig. 2.13) removed.

If the film is not clear and completely coalesced, the temperature may not be high enough. If the film is too thin and shows evidence of excessive flow, or degradation, the press is too hot. Occasionally, a film will be difficult to remove from the foil. If the polymer is not affected by alkali or acid, the foil may be dissolved away. Separation also is aided by prior spraying of the foil with a mold lubricant, or by placing the sandwich under cold water.

Much useful information can be obtained on a film sample. Thus the qualitative strength (or lack of it) will give an indication of whether the polymer has been prepared in a useful molecular weight or not.

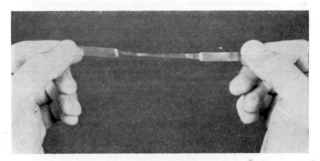

Fig. 2.14. Cold-drawing a film.

Drawability (Fig. 2.14) can be demonstrated on strips of film, and pieces of drawn film are very useful for determining the crystalline melting point of a polymer (Section III).

If a commercial press, such as is shown, is not available, a fairly satisfactory substitute can be made. Mount two electric irons, with tops and handles removed, face to face in a large vise mounted perpendicularly. Wire the irons in parallel and control the temperature with a rheostat capable of handling the required wattage. Temperature may be measured by thermocouples in wells drilled in the bases of the irons. This apparatus may be calibrated, and a plot of rheostat setting versus temperature mounted conveniently nearby. No way of measuring pressure applied is available, but experience will allow the operator to have a reasonable feel for the apparatus.

B. *Preparation of Molded Objects*

The preparation of molded objects such as bars, circular chips, cups, etc., may be done either by injection or compression molding.

Injection molding is done by an apparatus consisting of a molding chamber, into which molten polymer may be forced. Such an apparatus for simultaneously making eight molded bars is shown in Figs.

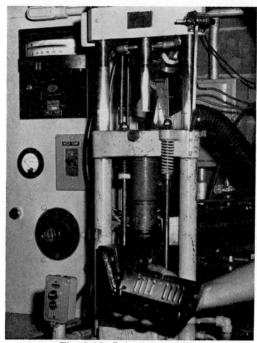

Fig. 2.15. Injection molding.

2.15 and 2.16. The molding chamber (Fig. 2.16) consists of two heavy plates hollowed in the desired shapes, with each compartment connected to the others by channels, through which the molten polymer may flow, and to a channel through which the molten polymer is forced into the mold. The objects so obtained (in this case, small test bars) are all connected. They are separated by cutting away the connecting polymer.

Even the simplest such machine represents a considerable capital outlay. Larger machines suitable for the production of larger and more

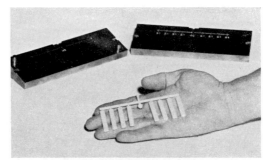

Fig. 2.16. Injection molding.

Fig. 2.17. Apparatus for compression molding of bars.

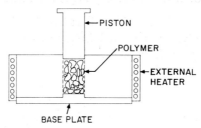

Fig. 2.18. Apparatus for compression molding disks.

complicated objects are quite costly and will be found only in laboratories specializing in this type of work or in commercial injection molding factories.

Compression molding of simple objects such as bars and chips may be done with simple and readily available equipment. In compres-

Fig. 2.19. Arbor press.

sion molding, an apparatus such as is shown in Fig. 2.17 for bars or Fig. 2.18 for disks or plugs may be used. The polymer is placed in the mold, on top of the bottom plate, and the piston is inserted. The mold is heated externally with, for example, an electric strip heater to fuse the polymer, and pressure is applied to the piston to compact the polymer. The pressure may be applied either by a press, such as is shown in Fig. 2.12, or by an Arbor press (Fig. 2.19). The apparatus is cooled, the bottom plate and the piston removed, and the molded object knocked out.

C. Melt Extrusion of Polymer to Fibers

The simplest method for making short lengths of fiber is by manual spinning. The polymer is melted in a test tube, and threads removed with a glass rod (Fig. 2.20).

The simplest mechanical method for converting polymer to continuous lengths of fiber is to place it in a heavy walled, heated steel cylinder, equipped with a piston driven by a hydraulic ram, and a spinneret, a small disk drilled with one or more holes (Fig. 2.21).

A photograph of the spinning cell is shown in Fig. 2.22 and the motor driven wind-up, equipped with a cylindrical, removable bobbin in Fig. 2.23. The bobbin (Fig. 2.24) is normally perforated for soaking or other after treatment of the yarn, an operation usually limited to solvent-spun yarns (Section II-2-B).

The polymer should be compacted before placing it in the cylinder of the extruder to minimize entrapment of air, which would cause

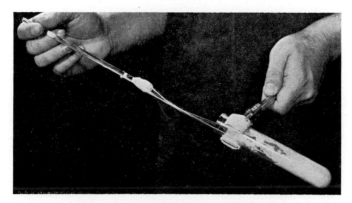

Fig. 2.20. Manual spinning of fibers.

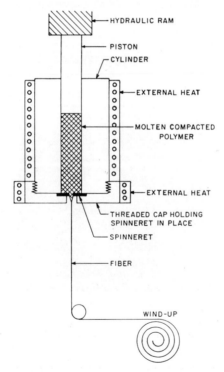

Fig. 2.21. Melt-spinning apparatus.

Fig. 2.22. Melt-spinning cell.

Fig. 2.23. Winding up melt-spun yarn.

discoloration as well as produce bubbles in the extruded filament. The finely divided polymer may be compacted to a cylindrical plug in a heated mold such as is shown in Fig. 2.18.   The plug is then dropped into the cylinder of the melt spinning apparatus.   A simpler, but less

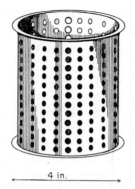

Fig. 2.24. Perforated bobbin.

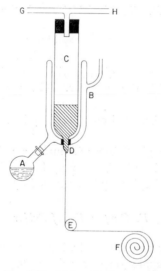

Fig. 2.25. Melt-spinning apparatus.

effective, method is to press the polymer to a rather thick film, then cut disks from the film with a sharp cork borer of the proper diameter to fit snugly in the barrel of the spinner. A stack of disks 1–2 in. in height will produce enough fiber for preliminary evaluation.

The production of melt-spun fibers also can be carried out using equipment described by Hardy (31) and shown in Fig. 2.25. In the figure, (C) is a 1 in. diameter glass tube drawn down to a stout capillary at one end.   It is surrounded by a double walled glass jacket (B) heated with the vapor of a boiling liquid from an attached flask (A). The jacket is constructed with an aperture at its base to permit the capillary jet (D) to pass through when desired.   By adjusting the height of the jet relative to the aperture, it is possible to regulate the temperature of the jet when extruding filament.   The jet is sealed initially to enable the vessel charged with polymer to be evacuated and filled with nitrogen (G, H).   When the polymer is melted, the tip of the jet is cut off and a filament pulled out.   True extrusion is impractical, but it is possible to produced continuous filament under a moderate pressure of nitrogen.   The fiber can be passed over a guide roll (E), and wound up on a spool (F).

D. *Plasticized Melt Fabrication*

Occasionally, a polymer shows very high melt viscosity, or perhaps some instability at the temperature of fusion.   In such a case, it is often possible to blend the polymer with a plasticizer, a high boiling liquid compatible with the polymer.   The plasticized polymer can then be melt-fabricated at much lower temperatures.   A number of vinyl polymers are fabricated commercially in this way, for example, Saran fibers.

The presence of a plasticizer will make a polymer more flexible. If this is desirable, the plasticizer may be left in the polymer after fabrication.   Otherwise, it may be extracted by an organic solvent.

E. *Compounding of Rubber*

Elastomers usually are not used without incorporation of a variety of additives, and preparation of a rubber stock involves mixing the additives with the raw polymers.   This is usually accomplished on a rubber mill, which has two massive heated rolls set parallel with only narrow separation, similar in appearance to a clothes wringer.   These rolls turn in opposite directions, but at different speeds so that material on the mill is subjected to repeated kneading and shearing action.

The additives used cover a wide range of products, the exact nature of which will depend upon the polymer used and the ultimate end use of the product.   The following partial list represents the types of additives which may be used.

1. A vulcanizing agent, such as sulfur, together with an accelerator, such as mercaptobenzthiazole and an activator, or retarder.

2. Fillers—carbon black is very useful, and increases tensile properties, and elasticity. Other fillers include silica and various clays.

3. Pigment—if a filler other than carbon black is used, the product can be given a desired color by mixing in a pigment.

4. Softeners—plasticizers to improve workability.

5. Antioxidants—such as phenyl-β-naphthylamine, to protect the polymer from oxidative deterioration, both during processing and in service.

For further details, the reader is referred to one of the many excellent books on synthetic rubber, for example, references 10 and 18 of Chapter 4.

2. SOLUTION METHODS

When a polymer cannot be melted, or is unstable at its melting point, a common technique for fabrication is to form a viscous solution in a volatile solvent, then cast to a film or spin to a fiber. Massive articles (corresponding to molded objects) cannot be made from solution, since removal of solvent becomes very difficult, and form retention is almost impossible.

A. Casting Films

Solutions for casting sould be prepared by methods suggested in Section I. They should be quite viscous to prevent the cast solution from "running" or spreading over the casting surface. Concentrations

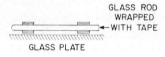

Fig. 2.26. A doctor knife.

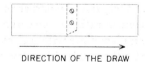

DIRECTION OF THE DRAW

Fig. 2.27. A doctor knife.

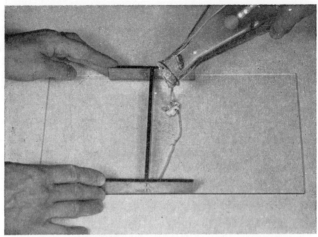

Fig. 2.28. Solution-casting a film.

Fig. 2.29. Solution-casting a film

of the order of 20% are usually satisfactory, although much will depend on polymer properties.   Only the trial and error method eventually will produce the optimum concentration.   To cast a film, a viscous polymer solution is spread onto a glass plate with a doctor knife.   This may be a glass rod wrapped at either end with a few turns of tape to give a uniform clearance when the rod is passed over the solution (Fig. 2.26).

Fig. 2.30. Using a casting table.

Fig. 2.31. Using a casting table.

More precise work can be done with the knife shown in Figs. 2.27, 2.28, 2.30–2.32. It is made of brass or stainless steel, with the cross bar ground back from the runners at an angle to give the desired thickness and clearance.

The operation of film casting is shown in Fig. 2.28. The prepared plate is placed in a forced draft oven to dry, at a temperature well below the boiling point of the solvent, to avoid bubbling. The dried film is then stripped from the plate (Fig. 2.29).

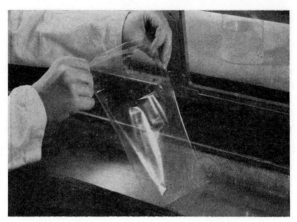

Fig. 2.32. Using a casting table.

More elaborate equipment, suitable for use in a laboratory specializing in polymer work, is shown in Figs. 2.30–2.32. The film is
spread on a chrome-plated casting table with an adjustable doctor
knife. The table is covered with a lid, and may be heated uniformly
with steam. The lid allows an atmosphere rich in solvent to be above
the drying film and prevents too rapid drying of the surface with consequent wrinkling, development of orange peel, etc.

B. Spinning Fibers

There are two well-known methods for converting a polymer solution to fiber. These are dry spinning and wet spinning. In dry
spinning, a viscous polymer solution is forced through a spinneret into
a heated gas (air or nitrogen) which quickly evaporates the solvent,
leaving a polymeric thread. This is very important commercially
(Fig. 2.33). In wet spinning, polymer solution is injected into a
precipitant (nonsolvent), which causes the solution to coagulate into a
thread (Fig. 2.34).

In the laboratory, dry spinning is quite difficult to do because of the
complexity of the process. The simplest set-up for continuous fiber
production, with adequate control of variables, will cost many thou-
sands of dollars. However for the preparation of small amounts of
fiber from easily spinnable polymers, such as acrylonitrile copolymers,
a set-up shown in Fig. 2.35 may be constructed.

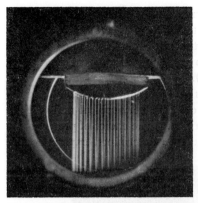

Fig. 2.33. Dry-spinning multifilament.

Fig. 2.34. Wet-spinning.

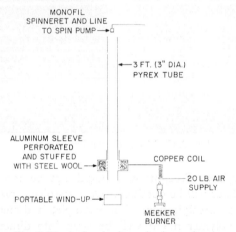

Fig. 2.35. A simple dry-spinning column.

Fig. 2.36. Small-scale wet-spinning.

The column is a 3 ft. piece of Pyrex brand glass, 3 in. in diameter. Hot air is injected without undue turbulence by the scheme shown. Polymer solution is extruded into the hot air, from, for example, a hypodermic syringe such as shown in Fig. 2.9, and collected on a variable speed windup (cf. Fig. 2.23).

Wet spinning on a small scale is more practical, although, again, choice of precipitant, temperature, etc., are very critical and will determine the quality of the fibers obtained. The choice of precipitating bath is particularly critical and must be determined experimentally

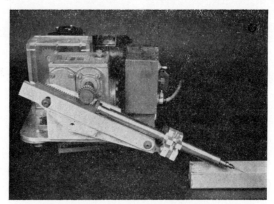

Fig. 2.37. Motor driven hypodermic.

for each situation. Precipitation should not be too abrupt, or a porous, weak fiber will be obtained. A near-solvent may be desirable to allow slower precipitation. For example, a dimethylformamide solution of a polymer might well be spun into dimethylformamide diluted with water. An ordinary hypodermic syringe is useful for preliminary work, the fiber being drawn from the tip with a pair of tweezers (Fig. 2.36). For more precise work, a motor driven, metal hypodermic syringe can be used (Fig. 2.37).

III. Polymer Characterization

1. INTRODUCTION

The many desirable physical properties that are associated with polymeric materials, such as strength, plasticity, elasticity, viscosity, etc., are a direct consequence of the high molecular weight of the molecules composing the material. A related consequence is the need for special techniques to characterize these materials. The problem posed by the much greater molecular size of polymers is complicated further by the molecular inhomogeneity which prevails in as-prepared polymeric materials. Consequently, most of the standard organic characterization procedures must be modified or supplanted.

The characterization of polymers is a task which has been approached in many instances according to the class of polymers being investigated and the needs of the investigators. To cite one example, in amorphous polymers no true melting point can be determined; yet, such a material can be characterized as to the temperature (or temperature range) at which it just softens, or becomes molten, or is moldable, or begins to distort under a defined condition of stress. The same sample of polymer may give a different temperature for each category cited, and, depending on the interest of the investigator, any one of them may constitute a proper characterization of the thermal properties of the material. Thus, the need for citing the conditions of measurement of a given property is essential. Where the property measured is a function of the molecular weight or molecular weight distribution of the sample, these constitute part of the conditions of the measurement in question. Fortunately, most of the physical properties of a given polymer change very little or not at all when a fairly high average molecular weight is reached.

Although a number of highly particularized characterization methods have developed to meet specialized needs, as previously pointed out, a certain few basic properties have been widely used as fundamental starting points for the physical and chemical characterization of polymers. Among the first to be determined are thermal properties, i.e., temperature when polymer becomes molten (PMT), temperature where it softens, crystalline melting point (T_m), and glass transition temperature (T_g). Others are average molecular weight, amount of crystalline and amorphous character, solubility spectrum, and an establishment of chemical structure where any uncertainties may exist. In the following sections, the treatment of some of the above mentioned areas of polymer characterization is primarily from the standpoint of the simplest laboratory methods available for estimating property or value in question. They are intended as a minimum framework of characterization which is applicable to most of the polymers prepared in subsequent chapters.   No detailed theory is presented, since in most cases this has been excellently done by several authors (13,28).   Two works are also available on certain aspects of methods of polymer characterization (1,2).   Detailed test methods are also described in American Society for Testing Materials[1] literature, dealing with a variety of characterization methods.

2. Molecular Weight Determination

The determination of molecular weight in polymeric materials yields a value which is always an average of the molecular weights of the molecules present.   What kind of average is obtained depends on the method of measurement.   The two most common average molecular weights are the number average, $\bar{M}_n$, and the weight average, $\bar{M}_w$. They are defined as:

$$\bar{M}_n = \Sigma NM / \Sigma N$$

$$\bar{M}_w = \Sigma NM^2 / \Sigma NM$$

where N = number of molecules of molecular weight M.

The kind of average obtained depends upon the method used to obtain it.   Osmometry gives a number average (2), while light scattering (2) and ultracentrifuge (52) give weight average molecular weights.   The three above mentioned methods require the use of highly specialized and expensive equipment, and the theory and practice involved has been amply reviewed for each case (see references cited).   They are tools of the specialist in both equipment and training, and consequently outside the intended scope of this Section.   These methods have the advantage of being absolute methods, in that a molecular weight average may be determined without recourse to any previous measurement.   As such, they are the ultimate basis for the use of polymer solution viscosity measurements for the determination of molecular weight (2).

A number of viscosity designations have been defined for dilute polymer solutions.   The terminology involved is in a state of flux presently, but for the sake of consistency the more common usage is adopted here, with the newer, but as yet less used, equivalent term given in parenthesis.   These are as follows:

1. Relative viscosity: $\eta_{rel} = t/t_0$
(Viscosity ratio) t_0 is flow time through a viscometer of a reference liquid, and t is flow time through the same viscometer of a dilute solution of polymer in the reference liquid.

2. Specific viscosity: $\eta_{sp} = \eta_{rel} - 1$
3. Reduced specific viscosity: $\eta_{sp}/C = \eta_{rel} - 1/C$
(Viscosity number)
4. Inherent viscosity: $\eta_{inh} = \ln \eta_{rel}/C$
(Logarithmic viscosity number)
5. Intrinsic viscosity: $[\eta] = \lim_{c \to 0} \eta_{inh} = \lim_{c \to 0} \eta_{sp}/C$
(Limiting viscosity number)

In the above, C is concentration of polymer solution in g./100 ml. of solvent. The units of intrinsic viscosity are deciliters per gram, therefore. The intrinsic viscosity is obtained by extrapolating to zero concentration a plot of either inherent or reduced specific viscosity versus concentration. The above viscosity numbers depend on the solvent, the concentration (except for intrinsic values) and the temperature at which the determination is made, though the latter is usually of little effect within 10–15°C. in a good solvent for the polymer.

A correlation of intrinsic viscosity with molecular weight for linear polymers can be achieved through the empirical equation proposed by Mark and Houwink (37), based on earlier work by Staudinger (45):

$$[\eta] = KM^a$$

where M is molecular weight, and K and a are constants for a particular polymer–solvent system. K and a are determined by the intercept and slope, respectively, for a plot of the log of intrinsic viscosity against the log of molecular weight of fractionated samples of polymer over a wide range of molecular weight values. If unfractionated polymer is used, the molecular weight distribution for each sample over its molecular weight range must be the same. The molecular weights for use in such a plot are determined by one of the absolute methods described earlier, e.g., light scattering. An approximate viscosity

TABLE 2.2 Intrinsic Viscosity–Molecular Weight Relationships

Polymer	Solvent	Temp., °C.	$K \times 10^4$	a	Ref.
Polystyrene	Benzene	25	1.0	0.74	8
Poly(methyl methacrylate)	Butanone	25	0.68	0.72	9
	Acetone	25	0.75	0.70	
Poly(vinyl acetate)	Acetone	25	1.88	0.69	51
Poly(vinyl alcohol)	Water	50	5.9	0.67	44
Natural rubber	Toluene	25	5.0	0.67	19
Poly(ε-caproamide)	Sulfuric acid	25	2.9	0.78	41
Poly(hexamethylenadipamide)	90% Formic acid	—	11	0.72	46
Poly(ethylene terephthalate)	sym-Tetrachloroethane-phenol (50/50 wt.)	25	2.1	0.82	22
Polyisobutylene	Cyclohexane	30	2.6	0.70	27a, 34a
	Diisobutylene	20	3.6	0.64	27a, 34a

average molecular weight, $\bar{M}_v$, (rather than $\bar{M}_w$ or $\bar{M}_n$) is obtained when unfractionated, molecularly heterogeneous polymer is used in a determination using the appropriate K and a. For most high polymers, viscosity average will be much closer to a weight average than a number average molecular weight. The value of a for most polymers has been found to be around 0.7. Where $a = 1$, $\bar{M}_v = \bar{M}_w$.

Thus, by determination of intrinsic viscosity, the magnitude of the polymer molecular weight can be estimated by choosing K and a values from a known polymer–solvent combination which has as much similarity as possible to the polymer–solvent system under consideration (14). Comparison of intrinsic viscosities, measured in the same solvent, of two similar polymers, one of which is of known molecular weight, also can be used to estimate molecular weight (6,38). The qualitative nature of such comparisons must be recognized, however, since minor structural differences may lead to large differences in viscosity.

K and a values for various polymer–solvent combinations are given in Table 2.2.

It should be recalled that the ultimate correlation between intrinsic viscosity and molecular weights via the Mark-Houwink equation rests on determining K and a from samples of polymer having a narrow molecular weight distribution. Fairly homogeneous molecular weight polymer can be obtained by fractionation techniques (2), usually involving the portionwise addition of a nonsolvent to a polymer solution. The fractions obtained in this way must usually be redissolved and refractionated. The fractionation of a polymer can be time consuming; for this reason, K and a values are frequently borrowed from polymers of related structure as described above.

Where it is not necessary to arrive at a numerical value for the molecular weight of a polymer, it is often convenient simply to relate one given sample of polymer to other known samples by means of inherent viscosity or relative viscosity. If it is known, for instance, that poly(vinyl chloride) of a certain inherent viscosity value (under stated conditions) is required in order to achieve a desired level of film properties, it may be sufficient characterization to relate newly prepared poly(vinyl chloride) to anticipated properties by determining only the inherent viscosity of the new sample. In some cases, relative viscosity may have advantages. Table 2.3 shows approximate minimum inherent viscosity values for several classes of polymers, which are usually adequate for preparing fabricated articles with good tensile properties.

TABLE 2.3. Approximate Minimum Inherent Viscosity Values for Fabrication

Polymer class	Inherent viscosity
Polyamides	0.8
Polyurethanes	0.4
Polyureas	0.4
Polyesters	0.5
Vinyl polymers	0.9

In the following procedures for viscosity determinations, per cent solutions are given as g. per 100 ml. of solvent; i.e., 0.5% is 0.5 g. per 100 ml.

A. Determination of Relative Viscosity

Relative viscosity can be taken as the ratio of the flow times of a polymer solution and the pure solvent in the same viscometer and at the same temperature. (Strictly, relative viscosity is the ratio of the kinematic viscosities of solution and solvent. Assuming the same density for dilute solution and solvent, and using the same viscometer for solvent and solution, the ratio of efflux time can be taken as relative viscosity in most cases.)

The following method is specifically designed for determining the relative viscosity of dilute (1% or less) solutions. Relative viscosity values generally are used for calculating the intrinsic or inherent viscosity of a polymer. Relative viscosity is easily determined, but its magnitude is more a function of polymer concentration than it is of molecular weight.

Relative viscosity measurements are conveniently made in a thermostatted bath at 30°C. This temperature is chosen so that the bath always will be above room temperature, even during hot weather, and therefore not require controlled cooling.

For viscometers, Cannon-Fenske, Series 100, 200, 300, 400, and 500, Fisher No. 13-616, or equivalent, are useful in these determinations. It is essential that viscometers be kept free of dust, residues, and other foreign matter.

The solvent to be used will depend on the polymer in question. In general, the solvent should completely dissolve the sample in less than 30 min. It is desirable that the polymer be dissolved at room temperature although heating is permissible if no degradation occurs. Degradation can be noted by determining the viscosity value at intervals of an hour or so.

Weigh 125 ± 1 mg. of the dry sample and transfer it quantitatively to a test tube. If some concentration other than 0.5% is run, use a porportionately larger or smaller sample. Weight liquid samples directly into a test tube.

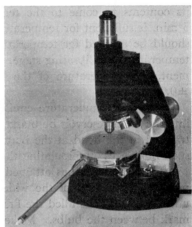

Fig. 2.38. Use of viscometer.   Fig. 2.39. Hot stage microscope.

Accurately measure 25 ± 0.05 ml. of the required solvent into the test tube containing the sample. Manual or mechanical (e.g., spiral rod or disk stirrer, Fig. 2.10 attached to a motor) stirring will usually by required. Instead of a test tube, a small, stoppered Erlenmeyer flask may be used for making the solution. Here, a magnetic stirrer may be used. Solvent must in no case be allowed to evaporate and alter the concentration in any of the operations that follow.

When the sample has completely dissolved, filter about 10 ml. without vacuum through a coarse porosity sintered glass filter into a 50 ml. flask or other suitable container. While the solution is filtering, add about 10 ml. of the solvent used for dissolving the sample to a 50 ml.

beaker.   Select a viscometer through which the solvent will flow in not less than 100 sec. and, preferably, not more than 200 sec.   Hold the viscometer in a vertical, inverted position and immerse the end of the capillary tube in the solvent.   Apply suction to the other (wide) tube until the solvent fills both bulbs and most of the capillary (Fig. 2.38).   Remove from the beaker and while the viscometer is still inverted, allow the liquid in the capillary tube to drain back until the meniscus just reaches the graduation mark around the working capillary.   When the graduation has been reached, quickly invert and wipe the excess liquid off the tube.

Immerse the viscometer in a constant temperature bath in a vertical position.   Allow the viscometer to remain in the bath long enough for its contents to come to the temperature of the bath.   Ordinarily, 5 min. is sufficient for temperatures between 20 and 40°C.; 10 min. should be allowed for temperatures outside this range.   During the temperature equilibrating stage, and later while making the measurement, the temperature of the bath must be held constant within ±0.05°C.

During the temperature equilibrating stage the solvent will drain into the lower reservoir bulb and while doing so a bubble may become trapped in the bend at the bottom of the instrument.   Remove any such bubble by manipulating the solution with a suction bulb.

After the solvent has attained the temperature of the bath, apply pressure to the top of the wide arm (or suction to the capillary) until the liquid has filled the first bulb and is about 1 cm. above the mark between the bulbs.   Make certain that no bubbles are trapped. Allow the liquid to flow freely and determine the time for the meniscus to pass from the upper to the lower mark.

Record this time as the flow time for the solvent.   Draw the liquid up again and measure the flow time, which should agree with the first flow time within 0.2 sec.   If it does not, continue until three flow times agreeing within 0.2 sec. are obtained.

When about 10 ml. of sample solution filtrate has been collected, immerse the same viscometer, which has been cleaned and dried, in the filtrate and fill as described above.   Place in the water bath, allow to come to temperature equilibrium and determine the flow time as described above.   Three values, agreeing within 0.2 sec. for solution flow times, should be obtained.   The relative viscosity is given by:

$$\eta_{rel} = (\text{solution flow time, seconds/solvent flow time, seconds})$$

B. Determination of Inherent Viscosity (45)

Inherent viscosity is calculated from the dilute solution (1% or less) relative viscosity of the polymer.   The relative viscosity is determined as described in the preceding section.

While the nature of the solvent used and the polymer concentration have an influence on inherent viscosity values, the effect is far less than it is on relative viscosity.   In general, the better the solvent, the higher the observed inherent viscosity for a given polymer.   Similarly, the higher the concentration, the lower the observed inherent viscosity. Temperature is important only insofar as it influences solvent power and polymer degradation.   Results obtained at 30 and 25°C. usually agree within the precision of this method.   Results obtained by this method should be precise within 0.04 units, absolute, within the range of 0–5 inherent viscosity units.   The inherent viscosity is calculated as:

$$\eta_{inh} = \ln \eta_{rel}/C$$

where C = concentration of the polymer in grams per 100 ml. of solvent; usually, $C = 0.50$; $\ln \eta_{rel}$ = natural logarithm of the relative viscosity of the dilute (1%, or less) polymer solution.

For polymers of limited solubility at 30°C., it is necessary to use a constant temperature bath held at an elevated temperature.   Polyhydrocarbons such as polyethylene or poly(4-methyl-1-pentene) are satisfactorily soluble only at 130°C. in solvents such as decahydronaphthalene containing 0.2% of an antioxidant such as phenyl-β-naphthalmine.   The polymer is dissolved in decahydronaphthalene at a concentration of 0.1 g. per 100 ml. instead of the usual 0.5 g., using an ethylene glycol monomethyl ether bath at reflux (125°C.) to heat the polymer and solvent.   The solution is filtered through a preheated 200 mesh stainless steel screen into a test tube immersed in the 130 ± 0.1°C. temperature bath.   Ten ml. of the solution is transferred by means of a hot pipet (do not use mouth suction) to a suitable viscometer (a Cannon-Fenske, Series 75) immersed in the bath.   After allowing 10 min. for temperature equilibrium to be established, the inherent viscosity is calculated as described above.

C. Determination of Intrinsic Viscosity

The intrinsic viscosity, $[\eta]$, is given by:

$$[\eta] = \lim_{C \to 0} \eta_{inh} = \lim_{C \to 0}(\eta_{sp})/C$$

Intrinsic viscosity is obtained from plotting inherent viscosity numbers or specific viscosity numbers versus concentration and extrapolating to zero concentration. The viscosity number intercept at zero concentration is taken as the intrinsic viscosity. Customarily, curves for both inherent and specific viscosities versus concentration are plotted. The intrinsic viscosity value obtained should be the same in each case. If they are not, the midpoint between them is usually taken.

The determination of intrinsic viscosity should be based on a minimum of three inherent or specific viscosity measurements at different concentrations. Four or five such measurements are often preferable. Concentrations should be from 0.1 to 0.5 g. per 100 ml. of solvent. The experimental procedures are the same as those given for η_{rel} and η_{inh} in the preceding sections.

Molecular weight estimation by solution viscometry outlined in this section is necessarily brief and nonmathematical, and is designed primarily to present the experimental methods involved. The reader must seek elsewhere for the full theory, implications, and limitations of the subject (2,28,52). Additional experimental procedures, as applied to poly(vinyl chloride) and ethylene polymers, are given in ASTM Standards (3).

D. End Group Methods

Intrinsic viscosity and other physical methods mentioned in the preceding section (osmometry, light scattering, sedimentation, and diffusion) become less reliable for molecular weights below 25,000. End group determinations, where applicable, are useful for molecular weights less than 25,000. Thus, the two approaches are complementary. The latter method, which gives a number average value, depends on the polymer having a terminal group, or groups, on each chain which can be quantitatively measured. When there are no losses of end groups by side reaction, no production of additional end groups by branching, and when all ends can be accurately determined, a direct measure of the number average molecular weight can be made (2,15).

End groups can be determined in specific cases of vinyl polymers through the use of initiators having groups identifiable by functionality (26), elemental analysis (40), or presence of a radioactive element (12). It is essential that the mechanism of the polymerization be known and unambiguous, such that the location of initiator fragments at one or at both ends of the chain can be predicted.

In condensation polymers, where $-CO_2H$ or $-NH_2$ groups are present, direct titration is usually an effective means of end group determination (36,27,48,54). The procedures involve the use of a suitable inert solvent for acidic or basic titration, and consequently depend on the solubility limits of the polymer. Hydroxyl groups in polyesters have been determined by reaction of the $-OH$ with a reagent that subsequently forms a titratable group; i.e., acetic anhydride followed by titration of the acetic acid after hydrolysis of the excess reagent (39), or succinic anhydride followed by titration of the free carboxyl of the succinic half ester (22). Hydroxyls in polyesters also have been determined through infrared methods (49).

The selection of the method to be used for determining a particular group is influenced by the following factors.

a. Solvent. The solvent used must dissolve the polymer but not interfere with the applicable analytical method. For example, formic acid is an excellent solvent for nylon, but the direct acidimetric titration cannot be carried out in it. Generally speaking, the sample need not be highly soluble in the solvent; 0.1% is ordinarily sufficient.

b. Impurities Present. In many cases, the impurities likely to be present in a polymer may be deduced by knowing how it was made. For example, polyamides made by melt polymerization are often free from impurities, while those prepared from acid chlorides usually contain salts which are difficult to remove and seriously interfere in many methods. Methods used for purifying the polymer, and the solvents with which it has been in contact, also must be considered.

c. Other Functional Groups Present. Interfering functional groups must be absent. For example, amine groups interfere with the determination of hydroxyl end groups.

d. Molecular Weight and Structure of the Polymer. If the molecular weight is greater than about 25,000, end group methods are, in general, not very reliable. The degree of cross-linking or branching are other factors which influence both the solubility of the polymer and the end group concentration.

Because the procedure to be used, in any case, depends so much on the individual polymer, no general methods are given here. However, in Chapter 3, Preparation 76, a method of terminal $-OH$ and $-CO_2H$ is given for the low molecular weight polyesters prepared there. This method is used also in the preparation of certain polyester resins in Chapter 7. Also in Chapter 7, a method is described for determining epoxide content (terminal group) in low molecular weight epoxy resins.

E. Other Methods

Both cryoscopic and ebullioscopic methods give a number average molecular weight (15). As the molecular weight of a solute increases, the molar quantity required to give the necessary observable melting point or boiling point change in the solvent becomes greater. Consequently, these methods have generally been restricted to polymers of 30,000 molecular weight or less.

3. Crystallinity in Polymers

It is a feature of polymeric materials that they may be entirely amorphous, partly amorphous and partly crystalline, or almost completely crystalline. The preparation of microscopic single crystals of linear polyethylene has been demonstrated; one crystal lattice exists throughout the polymeric aggregate (25,34). The usual situation is to find that a polymer is entirely amorphous or partly crystalline.

The most effective method of ascertaining the presence and extent of crystallinity in a polymer is x-ray diffraction, which has been one of the most informative and useful physical methods in polymer characterization (43,17). X-ray diffraction, in principle and practice, is beyond the intent of this section.

Crystallinity is a phenomenon more generally observed in polymers which have (a) little or no random chain branching or crosslinking, (b) regularity and symmetry of structure along the backbone of the chain, and (c) polar or highly bonding groups. The effects of these structural features are much the same as they are in simple organic compounds; those effects that tend for the readier packing and mutual attraction of chains favor crystallinity in polymers. Polymers which are amorphous as prepared may sometimes be induced to crystallize, in part, by the action of heat, treatment with a near or partial solvent, slow cooling of the polymer melt, etc. Such treatments may permit the necessary amount of molecular motion in segments of the polymer chain to allow them to attain some of the alignment needed for crystallization. A detailed theoretical treatment of polymer crystallinity has been given by Mandelkern (36).

For polymers that are crystalline, the crystalline melting point, T_m, is taken as that temperature where the last trace of crystallinity disappears under equilibrium conditions. Elaborate techniques have been devised for determining this temperature with considerable accuracy (29). One of the better methods is via the disappearance of a crystalline x-ray diffraction pattern as the temperature is raised. The long heating time required (24 hr. or more) limits the usefulness of the method. The simplest laboratory method is to note the loss of cyrstalline birefringence in a polymer sample using a hot stage polarizing microscope.

A. Determinatin of Crystalline Melting Point (T_m)

The sample is heated on a hot stage microscope (Fig. 2.39), optionally under nitrogen, and the temperature at which the color between crossed optical polarizers disappears is noted.

This procedure is applicable to any fiber, film, or other material which exhibits color (birefringence) when placed between crossed optical polarizers, and does not decompose at elevated temperatures in the relatively short times required.

There are two sources of birefringence in *unoriented* crystalline polymer samples: (a) birefringence due to strain within the sample which is characterized by a brilliant play of colors during the initial heating period and which disappears when the temperature approaches the melting point; and (b) birefringence due to sample crystallinity which is characterized by the bright yellow or white color of the sample which remains until the crystalline melting temperature is reached. This color disappears rapidly over a narrow temperature range and blends with the dark field. Inorganic impurities showing birefringence should be ignored. These are usually very high melting substances and can be easily recognized with a little practice.

For use in this determination, any good microscope equipped with $5\times$ and $10\times$ oculars and objectives, an optical polarizer and analyzer, and an insulated or metal stage is satisfactory. The Unitron Polarizing Microscope, Model MPS (United Scientific Co.), which has been modified to seat the Koefler hot stage accurately, is an example. A less elaborate instrument can be made by modifying a simple student microscope with a disk of Polaroid film on the eyepiece and another over the light source (Fig. 2.39). The optics must be raised by an insert in the mounting to accommodate the hot stage. The procedure below uses the Unitron Microscope, but is the basic operation for any instrument.

Using a film as an example, cut the sample into at least 10 pieces, each about $0.1 \times 1 \times 1$ mm., or smaller. Place the pieces in the center of a slide, taking care that the pieces are close to each other, but not overlapping. Cover the pieces with a cover glass. Place the slide on the stage, turn on the light and using the $5\times$ objective and $10\times$ eyepiece, select a field where the sample particles are well distributed with little bunching or clumping. Place the heat baffle over the slide and cover the stage with the glass cover.

If the approximate melting point of the sample is known ($\pm 10°$C.) adjust the heating rate to give a temperature rise of $0.1°$C. per min. at $20°$C. below the expected value. Allow the sample to anneal for 30 min. under these conditions. This is to relieve internal strains in this sample which may cause birefringence. Then adjust the heating rate to give a temperature rise to $1°$C. per min. Refocus the microscope with the $10\times$ objective and $10\times$ eyepiece, move the analyzer into position and note the temperature at which the first polymer particle blends with the dark background as T_i. Note the temperature at which the last polymer particle disappears as T_f. Disregard any small isolated bright spots which persist well above the temperature at which the bulk of the sample particles have lost their color.

When the approximate melting point of the sample is not known, refocus the microscope, using the $10\times$ objective and $10\times$ eyepiece. Move the analyzer into position. Set the heating rate to give a temperature rise of $10°$ per min. at $250°$C. Note the temperature at which the last sample particle disappears as T_m.

Place the cooling block, which has been precooled in ice water, on the hot stage. Prepare and mount a fresh portion of the sample on the stage as described above. Anneal the sample for 30 min., using the T_m value just determined as its approximate melting point and then determine the melting point as described.

On cooling the melted polymer, crystallinity will usually reappear and the determination can be repeated. If the sample does not become crystalline again on cooling, treatment with an appropriate solvent or mechanical working may reinduce crystallinity. Orientation in a crystalline polymer does not adversely affect determination of the crystalline melting point; in fact, it usually helps, since oriented, crystalline samples are usually brighter and the disappearance of color is more apparent.

Calculation. Let $T_i = $ °C. at which the first sample particle blends with the background; $T_f = $ °C. at which the last sample particle blends with the background:

$$\text{Crystalline Melting Point} = T_m = (T_i + T_f)/2$$

It should be noted that amorphous polymers having some orientation of the molecules (as in a stretched film) will exhibit birefringence under a polarizing microscope. This will dissappear near the glass transition temperature and will not reappear on cooling. It should be noted also that cutting bulk, unoriented polymer will introduce some additional birefringence around the edges due to shear orientation, hence such samples will be more brilliant around the edges when viewed between crossed polarizers.

4. GLASS TRANSITION TEMPERATURE (T_g)

An amorphous polymer can be considered to be a hard glass below a certain temperature; above it, the material is usually soft or rubbery. The temperature that marks this division is the glass transition temperature, T_g, formerly often called the second-order transition temperature (16). Above T_g, a freer movement of parts of the polymer chains can occur. An amorphous polymer is hard and brittle or soft and rubbery, accordingly, as it is below or above its glass transition temperature.

T_g is determined by measuring the change in some physical property of the solid polymer (e.g., thermal coefficient of expansion, specific volume, dynamic modulus of elasticity, heat capacity or dielectric constant) as a function of temperature. A change in slope of the curve so obtained is taken as the glass transition temperature. For most homopolymers having crystalline and amorphous regions it is a general rule of thumb that the glass transition temperature, T_g, is two-thirds of the crystalline melting point, T_m, both expressed in °K. (10). Laterally symmetrical polymers [e.g., polyethylene, poly-(vinylidene fluoride)] appear to have T_g equal to one-half T_m in °K. (15a). Polymers with in-chain carbonyls cannot be laterally symmetrical.

Since the determination of T_g experimentally requires somewhat specialized equipment, no procedure is given here. T_g is a rate phenomenon and not a true physical constant; it is one of the most difficult physical values to determine on polymers with precision. Experimenters using different methods, samples, and interpretation, frequently obtain values on the same polymer that differ markedly. For this reason, the two-thirds or one-half rule is considered here as a reasonable method of estimation. The limitation, of course, is that the polymers have a determinable crystalline melting point.

T_g is of value as an indication of temperatures for drawing films or fibers, and in other aspects of fabrication. Drawing of fibers, for instance, must usually be done at, or somewhat above, T_g. The position of T_g determines the basic character of the polymer, as either a rubber, or plastic, or fiber, depending on whether T_g is substantially above or below the use temperature of a polymer. Table 2.4 shows the approximate glass transition temperature of typical polymers, along with crystalline melting point, T_m, where applicable. If facilities

TABLE 2.4. Glass Transition Temperatures of Some Polymers

Polymer	T_m, °C.	T_g, °C.	$(T_g, °K)/(T_m, °K.)$	Ref.
—CH₂—CH— | Cl	—	75	—	20
—CH₂—CH— | CO₂CH₃	—	0	—	53
cis-CH₂—C=CH—CH₂— | CH₃	27	−72	0.67	10
trans—CH₂—C=CHCH₂— | CH₃	60	−53	0.67	47
—NH(CH₂)₆NHC—(CH₂)₄—C— (O, O)	265	50	0.60	10
—O(CH₂)₂O—C—(CH₂)₄—C— (O, O)	50	−70	0.63	10
—O(CH₂)₂O—C—⟨benzene⟩—C— (O, O)	270	80	0.65	10
—Si—O— | CH₃ | CH₃	—	−123	—	50

for differential thermal analysis are available, this technique may be used for determining both T_g and T_m (35).

A detailed discussion of crystalline melting and glass transition phenomena in polymers has been given by Bunn (18).

5. OTHER THERMAL CHARACTERIZATION METHODS

A. Polymer-Melt Temperature (PMT)

For many polymers, one of the simplest observations that can be made is the temperature at which a polymer sample simply becomes visually soft or molten. The polymer-melt temperature, PMT, is defined as that temperature where a polymer sample becomes molten and leaves a trail when moved across a hot metal surface with moderate pressure (11). A polymer may become rubbery or soften before becoming molten, particularly if largely amorphous. Where a polymer is of very high molecular weight, it may show an anomalously high PMT because of a high melt viscosity. Some polymers decompose before becoming molten. The temperature at which any such behavior occurs should be noted, as well as the best estimate of the PMT, or the PMT range.

This test reveals some practical information about the polymer in terms of fabrication. It can serve as a guide to proper temperatures for molding, melt extruding, melt pressing, and an indication of the thermal stability.

For highly crystalline polymers, the PMT may occur rather sharply, over a narrow range, usually a few degrees below the crystalline melting point. Amorphous polymers exhibit a PMT over a wider temperature range, frequently with noticeable softening at a lower temperature. The PMT may be determined on polymer in any form, e.g., as powder stroked with a spatula along the heated surface, or as a film or solid plug manipulated by hand as in Fig. 2.40, where a modified Dennis bar (see below) is the hot surface. A tendency to thermoset on heating also may be observed in this test on polymers which soften or become molten, the resolidify. On cooling and reheating, such samples are usually found to be infusible.

A convenient apparatus is a modified Dennis bar (23), shown in Fig. 2.41; a temperature gradient between the ends of the bar is measured potentiometrically at a number of points. Such a bar may be used to determine polymer-melt temperatures up to 350–400°C. The

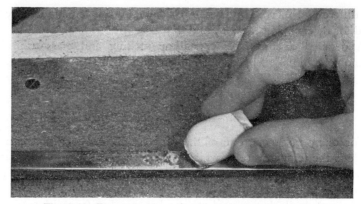

Fig. 2.40. Determination of polymer-melt temperature.

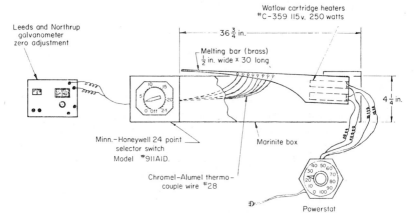

Fig. 2.41. Apparatus for determining PMT.

test is somewhat subjective, particularly for amorphous polymers, but has the advantage of speed and simplicity coupled with the observation of potentially useful thermal behavior of the polymer.

It should be noted that for amorphous polymers no "melting point" can be validly assigned, since melting is a phenomenon restricted to crystalline materials. Polymer-melt temperature means only what was said for it above; it is a temperature or temperature range where a polymer leaves a molten trail under the conditions given. It can be applied, therefore, to amorphous as well as crystalline material.

B. Durrans Mercury Method

In addition to the method described in the preceding section for estimating the polymer-melt temperature, other techniques have been developed that have found specific application to a class of polymers. One of these is the Durrans mercury method (24), which has been used extensively in the characterization of soluble, fusible epoxy resins before they are cross-linked. The method determines the temperature at which a given weight of mercury will break through a resin on which it is placed. The following procedure is recommended for use in characterizing the epoxy resins prepared in Chapter 7.

Three g. of resin is placed in a 17 × 150 mm. test tube and the contents heated to melt the resin. A thermometer is inserted in the melt. After the resin is allowed to cool to room temperature or cooled in ice in order to form a solid plug in the tube, 50 g. of mercury is added to the tube. The tube and contents are then heated in a bath to effect a temperature rise of 2°C. per min. The temperature at which the resin first appears above the surface of the mercury is taken as the softening or melting point. This determination should be done in a hood.

The method can be applied to any class of polymers that are not degraded on heating and which flow sufficiently on heating to allow penetration by the mercury. Standardized conditions (weight of resin and mercury, size of tube, type of thermometer, heating rate, etc.) are necessary for making valid comparisons of different polymer samples. The Durrans mercury method requires no special equipment and can be carried out rapidly with a minimum of subjectivity under standardized conditions.

C. The Vicat Needle Method

For many hard plastic materials, thermal characterization consists in part, at least, of a determination of the temperature at which a given distortion occurs under specified conditions of stress. For example, in the Vicat method (4,32,47), the standard sample (minimum width, $^3/_4$ in. and thickness, $^1/_8$ in.) is heated at a given rate (50°C. per hr.) while a needle (having a point with an area 1 mm.^{2}) under a definite pressure (usually not exceeding 1 Kg.) is applied to the surface of the sample. The temperature at which a 1 mm. penetration of the needle occurs is taken as the softening point or heat distortion point. The test can be applied to polyethylene, polystyrene, and polyacrylics with a presicion of 2°C. For nonrigid poly(vinyl chloride), poly(vinylidene chloride), and some others, the Vicat softening range is too large to permit such precision. A Vicat apparatus may be purchased commercially.

D. Ring and Ball Method

In this method, the softening point of a polymer is determined by noting the temperature at which a sample held within a horizontal ring is forced downward 1 in. by the weight of a steel ball supported by the sample, while the temperature of the sample is being raised in a liquid bath (5). The method is useful for resins of the phenol–formaldehyde and urea–formaldehyde type. The conditions of the test must be fixed from test to test and be closely defined if acceptably reproducible results are to be obtained. The Ring and Ball apparatus may be purchased; a design is given, however, in Ref. 5, along with a description of the method of operation.

6. POLYMER SOLUBILITY

The solubility of a polymer is an important part of its characterization. For polymers that are not melt-stable, fabrication via their solutions is often the only method available. Determination of molecular weight by solution viscosity methods (see Molecular Weight Determination) requires that a suitable solvent be found.

As is to be expected, degree of cyrstallinity and molecular weight of a polymer affect its solubility. For these reasons solubility behavior may vary from sample to sample of a given polymer. As a generalization, the following (Table 2.5) solubility relationships have been recognized. Table 2.5 is not an exhaustive list of solvents or solubilities, but shows some typical examples.

Cross-linked polymers do not show normal solubility. Such polymers may swell under the influence of certain solvents. The fact of swelling by itself is not proof of cross-linking, however, since a polymer on the borderline of solubility may exhibit this behavior. But, when a polymer resists solubility in a number of solvents typical for those of its class, and is infusible as well, it is usually considered to be cross-linked unless there is compelling evidence to the contrary.

TABLE 2.5. Some General Polymer–Solvent Systems

Polymer	Solvent
Polyamides	Acidic solvents; formic acid, *m*-cresol.
Polysulfonamides (having —NH—)	Basic solvents; 10% aqueous sodium hydroxide, dimethyl formamide.
Polyurethanes	Chlorinated solvents; methylene chloride, chloroform, mixtures of methylene chloride or chloroform with 10–20% by weight of methanol.
Polyesters	Chlorinated solvents; trichloroethane, dichlorobenzene; see also polyurethanes.
Vinyl polymers	Ketones, aromatic hydrocarbons, cyclic ethers, esters, chlorinated solvents; see specific examples below.
Poly(vinyl alcohol)	Water.
Poly(vinyl chloride)	Tetrahydrofuran, dioxane.
Poly(vinyl acetate)	Acetone, methyl ethyl ketone.
Polystyrene	Xylene, butyl acetate, carbon tetrachloride.
Polyacrylic and methacrylic esters	Methyl ethyl ketone, tetrahydrofuran.
Polyacrylonitrile	Dimethylformamide, dimethyl sulfoxide, ethylene carbonate.
Hydrocarbon polymers	"Decalin,"[a] benzene, xylene
Most *O*, *N*, or *S* containing polymers (uncross-linked)	Sulfuric acid, occasionally with decomposition.
Resins in soluble stage, before cross-linking	Ketones, acids, alcohols, water, ethers, hydrocarbons, halogenated solvents; see examples below.
Alkyds (phthalic acid–glycerol type; varies with extent and type of modification)	Acetone, methyl ethyl ketone, acetic acid, butyl acetate, toluene.
Phenol–formaldehyde condensates	Alcohol, acetone, "Cellosolve"[b]
Urea or melamine–formaldehyde condensates	Water, butanol, toluene (when resin is partially etherified).
Epoxy	Ethylene dichloride, benzene, dioxane.

[a] Trademark for du Pont's decahydronaphthalene solvent.
[b] Trademark for Union Carbide Corporation's solvent.

Solubility in sulfuric acid is usually a characteristic of polymers with functional groups. Degradation may occur in this and other potent acidic solvents such as trifluoroacetic acid, however.

Solvent mixtures are sometimes more effective than a single solvent; e.g., alcohol–benzene for certain cellulose derivatives, carbon disulfide–

acetone for polyvinyl chloride, and nitromethane–water for polyacrylo-nitrile. Mixed solvents are usually most effective when each compo-nent is a near solvent for the polymer or when the solvents mutually interact as, for example, by hydrogen bonding.

Many of the structural aspects of polymer molecules that affect solubility and melting point are those that affect these same properties in simple organic molecules also. For instance, crystallinity, high symmetry, hydrogen bonding, high polarity, chain stiffness, and stereo-regularity in the chain, contribute to higher melting point and reduced solubility compared to an otherwise similar polymer lacking the fea-ture in question. The following procedure is useful for a rapid, quali-tative determination of solubility.

A small amount of polymer, about 0.1 g., is mixed with about 2 ml. of solvent in a test tube and stirred together thoroughly. An indica-tion of solubility is "schlieren" as the mixture is stirred. Solubility is usually facilitated by the use of polymer in a finely divided state. If no sign of solubility occurs at room temperature, the mixture should be heated gently to the boiling point of the solvent, or near it. If polymer dissolves, the solution should be allowed to cool to see if polymer re-mains in solution or precipitates. If polymer is swollen by a solvent, but not dissolved, related solvents should be checked to see if they will effect solution, either singly or in combination. Swelling without dissolving, even in the most potent solvents for the polymer type, should be taken as an indication of cross-linking. However, many cross-linked resins will have extractable fractions which may be highly branched. These fractions are of relatively low molecular weight in most cases, having not yet reached the cross-linked stage.

TABLE 2.6. Designations for Effect of Solvent on Polymer Sample

0 = Unaffected by hot solvent
1 = Melted or sticky in hot solvent
2 = Partly soluble in hot solvent
3 = Soluble in hot solvent, precipitated cold
4 = Soluble in hot solvent, remains soluble cold
5 = Soluble in cold solvent

Solubility categories of polymers have been suggested by Beaman and Cramer (11) to describe the apparent interaction of polymer and solvent. These are given in Table 2.6.

The theoretical aspects of polymer solubility and solutions are treated by Flory (28), Billmeyer (13), Huggins (33), and Spurlin (42), and will not be considered here.

REFERENCES

1. Adams, C. H., R. J. Bourke, G. B. Jackson, and J. R. Taylor, *Polymer Evaluation Handbook*, Armed Service Technical Information Agency (ASTIA) Document No. AD 110557; Wright Air Development Center Report 56-399.
2. Allen, P. W., ed., *Techniques of Polymer Characterization*, Academic Press, New York, 1959: Butterworths Publications, London, 1959.
3. Am. Soc. Testing Materials, ASTM Standards, Pt. 9, D 1243-58T and D 1601-58T, Philadelphia, 1958, pp. 530 and 534.
4. *Ibid.*, D 1525-58T, p. 406.
5. *Ibid.*, E 28-58T, p. 1893.
6. Bailey, W. J., and H. R. Golden, *J. Am. Chem. Soc.*, **76,** 5418 (1954).
7. Barb, W. G., *J. Polymer Sci.*, **37,** 515 (1959).
8. Bawn, C. E. H., R. F. J. Freeman, and A. R. Kamaliddin, *Trans. Far. Soc.*, **46,** 1107 (1950).
9. Billmeyer, F. W., and C. B. de Than, *J. Am. Chem. Soc.*, **77,** 4763 (1955).
10. Beaman, R. G., *J. Polymer Sci.*, **9,** 470 (1952).
11. Beaman, R. G., and F. B. Cramer, *J. Polymer Sci.*, **21,** 223 (1956).
12. Bevington, J. C., H. W. Melville, and R. P. Taylor, *J. Polymer Sci.*, **14,** 463 (1954); **12,** 449, (1954).
13. Billmeyer, F. W., *Textbook of Polymer Chemistry*, Interscience Publishers, New York, 1957.
14. Blout, E. R., and M. Idelson, *J. Am. Chem. Soc.*, **80,** 4909 (1958).
15. Bonnar, R. N., M. Dimbat, and F. H. Stross, *Number Average Molecular Weights*, Interscience Publishers, New York, 1958.
15a. Boyer, R. F., *J. Appl. Phys.*, **25,** 825 (1954).
16. Boyer, R. F., and R. Spencer, *Advances in Colloid Science*, vol. II, Interscience Publishers, New York, 1946.
17. Bunn, C. W., in R. Hill, ed., *Fibers from Synthetic Polymers*, chapts. 10 and 11, Elsevier, New York, 1953.
18. Bunn, C. W., *ibid.*, chapter 12.
19. Carter, W. C., R. L. Scott, and M. Magat, *J. Am. Chem. Soc.*, **68,** 1480 (1946).
20. Clash, R. F., Jr., and L. M. Rynkiewicz, *Ind. Eng. Chem.*, **36,** 279 (1944).
21. Coffman, D. D., G. J. Berchet, W. R. Peterson, and E. W. Spanagel, *J. Polymer Sci.*, **2,** 306 (1947).
22. Conix, A., *Makromol. Chem.*, **26,** 226 (1958).
23. Dennis, L. M., and R. S. Shelton, *J. Am. Chem. Soc.*, **52,** 3128 (1930).
24. Durrans, T. H., *J. Oil and Colour Chem. Assoc.*, **12,** 173 (1929), *C.A.* **23,** 4355 (1929).
25. Eppe, R., E. W. Fischer, and H. A. Stuart, *J. Poly. Sci.*, **34,** 721 (1959).

26. Evans, M. G., *J. Chem. Soc.*, **1947,** 266.
27. Fijolka, P., I. Lenz, and F. Runge, *Makromol. Chem.*, **23,** 60 (1957).
27a. Flory, P. J., *J. Am. Chem. Soc.* **65,** 372 (1943).
28. Flory, P. J., *Principles of Polymer Chemistry*, Cornell University Press, Ithaca, N. Y., 1953.
29. Flory, P. J., L. Mandelkern, and H. K. Hall, Jr., *J. Am. Chem. Soc,,* **73,** 2532 (1951).
30. Goldberg, A. I., W. P. Hohenstein, and H. Mark, *J. Polymer Sci.*, **2,** 503 (1947).
31. Hardy, D. V. N., *J. Soc. Chem. Ind., Trans.*, **67,** 426 (1948).
32. Houwink R., *Plastomers and Elastomers*, vol. III, p. 53, Elsevier, New York, 1948.
33. Huggins, M. L., *Physical Chemistry of High Polymers*, John Wiley & Sons, New York, 1958.
34. Keller, A., and A. O'Connor, *Discussions Faraday Soc.*, **25,** 114 (1958).
34a. Krigbaum, W. R., and P. J. Flory, *J. Am. Chem. Soc.*, **75,** 1775 (1953).
35. Mackey, T. E., private communication.
36. Mandelkern, L., *Chem. Rev.*, **56,** 903 (1956).
37. Mark, H., *Der Feste Korper*, 1938, 65–104; R. Houwink, *J. prakt. chem.* **1957,** 15 (1940).
38. Marvel, C. S., and R. D. Vest, *J. Am. Chem. Soc.*, **79,** 5771 (1957).
39. Ogg, C. L., W. L. Porter, and C. O. Willits, *Ind. Eng. Chem., Anal. Ed.*, **17,** 394 (1945).
40. Price, C. C., and B. E. Tate, *J. Am. Chem. Soc.*, **65,** 517 (1943).
41. Schaefgen, J. R., and P. J. Flory, *J. Am. Chem. Soc.*, **70,** 2709 (1948).
42. Spurlin, H. M., *J. Poly Sci.*, **3,** 714 (1948).
43. Statton, W. O., ASTM, Spec. Tech. Publication, No. 247, Philadelpia, 1959.
44. Staudinger, H., and H. Warth, *J. prakt. chem.*, **155,** 261 (1940).
45. Staudinger, H., and W. Heuer, *Ber.*, **63,** 222 (1930).
46. Taylor, G. B., *J. Am. Chem. Soc.*, **69,** 635 (1947).
47. Überreiter, K., *Z. phy. Chem.*, **B45,** 361 (1940).
48. Waltz, J. E., and G. B. Taylor, *Anal. Chem.*, **19,** 448 (1947).
49. Ward, I. M., *Trans. Faraday Soc.*, **53,** 1406 (1957).
50. Weir, C. E., W. H. Leser, and L. A. Wood, *Rubber Chem. and Technol.*, **24,** 366 (1951).
51. Wagner, R. H., *J. Polymer Sci.*, **2,** 21 (1947).
52. Weissberger, A., ed., *Technique of Organic Chemistry*, vol. I, part I, Interscience Publishers, New York, 1949.
53. Wiley, R. H., and G. M. Brauer, *J. Poly. Sci.*, **3,** 647 (1948).
54. Zahn, H., and P. Rathgeber, *Melliand Textilber.*, **34,** 749 (1953).

CHAPTER 3

Polycondensation and Hydrogen
Transfer Polymerization

Condensation reactions in organic chemistry are among the most useful reactions for the synthesis of organic compounds, so it is not surprising that many of them have been used successfully in the preparation of high polymers from difunctional molecules. The common attribute of all condensation reactions is the linking together of two molecules with the formation of a new bond, and the elimination of by-product molecule,

$$A + B \longrightarrow A\text{—}B + C$$

where A and B are coreactive functional molecules and C is the by-product. If molecules having two condensable groups each are brought together, polymer will result if the reaction conditions are chosen properly. The polymerizable reactants may be of the AA and BB type, or the AB type. Polymerization would be represented as:

$$n \text{ AA} + n \text{ BB} \longrightarrow [\text{—AA—BB—}]_n + 2n \text{ C}$$

and

$$n \text{ AB} \longrightarrow [\text{—A—B—}]_n + n \text{ C}.$$

The following reactants are examples: AA = hexamethylenediamine, BB = adipic acid, AB = ϵ-aminocaproic acid.

The number of condensation reactions is very large, and many of them have been turned to the formation of polymers. A list of these (Table 3.1) would include the following, which could be used in either of the generalized types of equations above, where A and B represent various functional molecules.

TABLE 3.1

A	B	Polymer formed	C
R—OH	R—CO$_2$H	Polyester	H$_2$O
R—NH$_2$	R—COCl	Polyamide	HCl
R—NH$_2$	R—NH—CO$_2$R	Polyurea	ROH
R—NH$_2$	R—CO$_2$H	Polyamide	H$_2$O
R—OH	R—COCl	Polyester	HCl
R—CO$_2$H	R—CO$_2$H	Polyanhydride	H$_2$O
R—SH	R—Cl	Polythioether	HCl
R—SO$_2$Cl	R—NH$_2$	Polysulfonamide	HCl
R—OCOCl	R—NH$_2$	Polyurethane	HCl
R—NH$_2$	R—NH—COSH	Polyurea	H$_2$S

Polymers formed by such polycondensation reactions are termed "condensation polymers." However, the term "condensation polymer" also includes any polymer whose structure indicates that it could have been prepared by a condensation reaction. For instance, the addition of a diol to a diisocyanate forms a polyurethane which is structurally a condensation polymer by this definition, although it was prepared, not from a condensation, but from an addition reaction without by-product elimination:

$$OCN—R—NCO + HO—R'—OH \longrightarrow$$

$$\left[-NHR—NH-\overset{\overset{\displaystyle O}{\|}}{C}-O—R'—O-\overset{\overset{\displaystyle O}{\|}}{C}- \right]_n$$

It is a condensation polymer because it could conceivably have been prepared from either of the condensation reactions:

$$HO_2C—HN—R—NH—CO_2H + HO—R'—OH$$

$$\longrightarrow \left[-NH—R—NH-\overset{\overset{\displaystyle O}{\|}}{C}-O—R'—O-\overset{\overset{\displaystyle O}{\|}}{C}- \right]_n + H_2O$$

$$H_2N—R—NH_2 + Cl-\overset{\overset{\displaystyle O}{\|}}{C}-OR'—O-\overset{\overset{\displaystyle O}{\|}}{C}-Cl \longrightarrow$$

$$\left[NH—R—NH-\overset{\overset{\displaystyle O}{\|}}{C}-O—R'—O-\overset{\overset{\displaystyle O}{\|}}{C}- \right]_n + HCl$$

In this chapter, then, methods for preparing condensation polymers will be presented which involve true condensation reactions between functional groups, and those reactions which involve the addition of active hydrogen compounds to receptive molecules. The

diol-diisocyanate reaction cited is an example of the latter. Before
beginning a discussion of these polymerization processes, it would be
well to point out that, although the condensation and addition reactions involved are those familiar in principle or practice to most organic chemists, the most important difference, besides the polyfunctionality of the reactants, is that only reactions which proceed in
extremely high yield will form high polymer. While an organic reaction may be considered to be of excellent preparative value if it forms
the desired product in 90% yield, it is immediately clear that in order
to obtain high molecular weight condensation polymers, the yield must
be essentially 100%. (See, however, examples of interfacial polycondensation for exceptions.)   The final few per-cent of reaction brings together
the ends of fairly large molecules to produce the desired very large
molecules. In order to achieve this kind of efficiency, reactions must
be substantially free of chain-terminating side reactions, and the reactants must be of the utmost purity. In most, but not all, polycondensations an exact equivalence of reactants is also required.

Branching may occur in certain types of condensation polymers.
An example of branching is shown below, where, in an isocyanate-
diol addition reaction, a urethane hydrogen along the polymer chain
may add to a terminal isocyanate group of another growing chain:

$$\text{\textasciitilde\textasciitilde}R\!-\!NH\!-\!\overset{\displaystyle O}{\overset{\|}{C}}\!-\!O\text{\textasciitilde\textasciitilde} \;+\; OCN\text{\textasciitilde\textasciitilde} \longrightarrow \text{\textasciitilde\textasciitilde}R\!-\!\underset{\underset{\underset{NH}{|}}{\overset{|}{C}\!=\!O}}{N}\!-\!\overset{\displaystyle O}{\overset{\|}{C}}\!-\!O\text{\textasciitilde\textasciitilde}$$

Such a reaction is not a favored one if any hydroxyl ends still remain;
but, in the presence of excess isocyanate ends, and with sufficient heat,
such a reaction becomes a threat to the linearity of the polymer.   Cross-
linking, the formation of a space network polymer, may result in the
above example or one in which reactants are used with functionality
greater than two, for example a triamine or a tricarboxylic acid (1,2).

The molecular weight distribution in condensation polymers depends on the polymer type, on the kind of polymerization reactions
involved, and on the conditions prevailing during the process.

The quantitative aspects of condensation polymerization, including
kinetics, molecular weight distribution and effect of polyfunctionality

on branching and gelation, have been thoroughly treated elsewhere (1,2,3) and will not be considered.

The polymer preparations in this chapter are arranged as far as possible, according to the polymer class: polyamide, polyurethane, polyurea, etc. Examples of specific polymer-forming reactions (e.g., reaction of an active hydrogen compound with an acid halide) are dispersed throughout the chapter. Discussion of some of the more important condensation and hydrogenation transfer addition reactions precede the first usage of the reaction.

Some examples of reactions on polymers are also included, and follow the preparation of the polymer itself. They point up the applicability of normal organic reactions to polymers as well as demonstrate property changes due to structural alteration.

Because of the similarity of experimental procedure in several instances, certain preparations are repeatedly referred to because of the detailed directions provided. For example, the basic technique of melt polymerization is given for polyamides in the preparation of poly-(hexamethyleneadipamide) and for polyesters with poly(ethylene terephthalate). A number of other polymer preparations use these procedures with variations as required. In most cases, vacuum cycles are necessary and, in some, a sealed tube heating cycle is used which involves considerable pressure build-up. In both cases, sufficient shielding of equipment is an essential and fundamental safety practice. Where direct handling of pressured or evacuated equipment is required, the operator should wear protective gloves and face mask or goggles. The routine use of safety glasses or goggles is a laboratory practice strongly recommended under any circumstances.

I. Polyamides and Related Polymers

The reaction of a primary or secondary amine with a carboxylic acid to form an amide is a well-known organic reaction. The same reaction involving difunctional molecules is a convenient way of preparing polyamides and related polymers. The reaction is carried out, customarily, by heating the reactants together above the melting point of the final product, and driving the process to completion by removing the last traces of water, usually with the assistance of a high vacuum and/or the sweep of an inert gas. This technique is limited to starting materials and products that are stable to heat above their melting points. For polymerization of AA with BB, stoichiometric amounts of reactants are essential, which is assured by the preparation of a balanced salt of the diamine and diacid. In the case of an aminoacid, an AB reactant, the required balance of functionality is a built-in feature of the molecule.

Probably the classic example of a diamine-diacid condensation is the preparation of poly(hexamethyleneadipamide) from hexamethylenediamine and adipic acid (4). The term "nylon" was originally coined as the generic name for all long chain synthetic polyamides, which were then distinguished by adding numbers to the generic title to designate the constituents of the polymers. Thus, the polymer named above became 6-6 nylon, or 6-6 polyamide since there are six carbons in the diamine chain (designated first) and six carbons in the diacid chain. The nylon from tetramethylenediamine and sebacic acid is 4-10, and that from ε-aminocaproic acid is simply 6, the number of carbon atoms in the chain.

As a class, polyamides are high-melting materials whose properties depend, in large part, on the high interchain attraction due to the occurrence of hydrogen bonding sites (both donor, —NH—, and acceptor, —C=O) along the chains. They usually can be made to crystallize easily and are often found to be highly crystalline as prepared. The dependence of melt temperature on structure in polyamides has been cited in several places (2,3,4). In general, the longer the distance between amide groups, the lower the melting point of the polymer. The qualification must be added that as the number of carbons is increased in either the diamine or diacid portion, the melting point decreases in an alternating fashion, with the polymers from intermediates having an odd number of carbons melting lower than those having an even number. Table 3.2 illustrates this point.

The preparation of **6-6 polyamide,** which follows, is typical of the methods used in **melt-polymerization.** Most of the aliphatic poly-

TABLE 3.2

Polyamide	Polymer-melt temperature, °C.	Polyamide	Polymer-melt temperature, °C.
4-6	308	4-10	236
5-6	223	5-10	186
6-6	265	6-10	228

amides can be made by the basic technique described. The most certain way of achieving reactant balance is through the use of the diamine salt of the dicarboxylic acid, as in the following example.

1. Preparation of Hexamethylenediamine-Adipic Acid Salt (6-6 Salt) (22)

In a 250 ml. Erlenmeyer flask is placed 14.60 g. (0.100 mole) adipic acid. The acid is dissolved in 110 ml. absolute ethyl alcohol by warming, and then is cooled to room temperature. A solution of 11.83 g. (0.102 mole) hexamethylenediamine (b.p. 90–92°C./14 mm., m.p. 41–42°C.) in 20 ml. absolute ethyl alcohol is added quantitatively to the adipic acid solution. The mixing is accompanied by spontaneous warming. Crystallization soon occurs. After standing overnight, the salt is filtered, washed with cold absolute alcohol, and air-dried to constant weight. The yield is 25.5 g. (97%). A 2% excess of diamine is used to promote a salt which is rich in diamine, since this is the more volatile component and may be lost during salt drying or during polycondensation. The white crystalline salt melts at 196–197°C. and has a pH of about 7.6, determined on a 1% solution of salt in water, using a pH meter.

A pH tolerance of 0.5 unit is usually acceptable, especially on the high side because of possible diamine loss, as noted above. Salt imbalance may be corrected by recrystallization or the after-addition of a small amount of the indicated component. Salts of low and high pH may be mixed to give a balanced composition of the proper pH.

2. Preparation of Poly(hexamethyleneadipamide) (6-6 Nylon) (22)

$$\left[H_3\overset{+}{N}\!\!-\!\!(CH_2)_6\!\!-\!\!\overset{+}{N}H_3 \right]\left[\overset{-}{O}\!\!-\!\!\overset{\overset{O}{\|}}{C}\!\!-\!\!(CH_2)_4\!\!-\!\!\overset{\overset{O}{\|}}{C}\!\!-\!\!\overset{-}{O} \right] \longrightarrow$$

$$\left[-\!\!NH\!\!-\!\!(CH_2)_6\!\!-\!\!NH\!\!-\!\!\overset{\overset{O}{\|}}{C}\!\!-\!\!(CH_2)_4\!\!-\!\!\overset{\overset{O}{\|}}{C}\!\!- \right]_n + H_2O$$

Twenty grams 6–6 salt is charged into a polymer tube using a polymer tube funnel (See Chapter 2). A constriction is made in the upper half of the neck of the tube with a glass-blowing torch. The tube is connected to a three-way stopcock, which connects to a vacuum pump and a source of low pressure (about 5 p.s.i.) nitrogen. The tube is purged of air by alternately evacuating to about 0.5 mm. and filling with nitrogen. After 3–4 such cycles, the constriction is sealed shut by means of a torch while the tube is evacuated.

The tube is placed in a steel tube open at the top and immersed in a salt bath heated at 215°C. for $1\frac{1}{2}$–2 hours. The heated tube is a potential bomb and should be handled with due care. The salt bath is shielded in the front, with an access door at the side. The hand and arm used to manipulate the tube should be protected with a leather–asbestos glove and a leather gauntlet. The sealed tube step results in the formation of low molecular weight polymer under conditions which prevent escape of volatile diamine. If a shielded salt bath is not available, the tube can be heated in a metal tube immersed in a vapor bath or a Wood's metal bath. The metal shield should surround the tube completely, although it should be open at the top. The entire apparatus should then be shielded additionally, for example with a transparent safety shield.

After completion of this first heating cycle, the sealed polymer tube is removed from the heating bath and allowed to cool to room temperature. Then, the tube is opened behind a barrier after first scoring with a glass-cutting tool. In some melt polycondensations, uncondensed gases such as ammonia or carbon dioxide may be evolved during the sealed tube step, and the cold tubes may be under considerable pressure.

A neck bearing a side arm is sealed onto the polymer tube, the tube is clamped in an upright position and the side arm connected with pressure tubing to a trap which comprises a 50 ml. round-bottomed flask fitted with an adapter. The trap is connected via a three-way stopcock, both to a vacuum pump and to a source of nitrogen. The top of the tube is fitted with a short section of rubber tubing. An inlet comprising a 7–8 mm. o.d. glass capillary tubing drawn out to a fine tip is fitted through the rubber tubing, with the end reaching to the bottom of the polymer tube. The inlet sometimes cannot be brought to the bottom of the tube until the polymer has been remelted. The inlet is connected to a source of low-pressure nitrogen.

The tube is purged of air by alternately evacuating and flushing with nitrogen. It is then heated by a 270°C. vapor bath (See Chapter 2). After 30–60 min. heating at atmospheric pressure, the polymer is gradually brought to high vacuum by manipulating the three-way stopcock. The heating is continued under vacuum of 0.2–1.5 mm. for about 1 hr. The polycondensation is discontinued when visual inspection of the rate of bubble rise indicates that the maximum melt viscosity has been reached.

Nitrogen is introduced through the stopcock, the inlet tube is raised, and the vapor bath is removed. The polymer is cooled under a gentle nitrogen stream entering through the side arm. The tube is wrapped with a towel during cooling to prevent glass from flying if the polymer tube spontaneously cracks. The tough, white, opaque polymer is removed by breaking the tube and separating the adhering glass by hammering and filing. The recovery is about 14 g. (80%). The inherent viscosity (0.5% conc., m-cresol) is about 1.0–1.4. The polymer has a melt temperature of 265°C., and is soluble in formic acid. Fibers and films may be obtained by melt methods or from formic acid solution.

The preceding method of polycondensation sometimes can be used starting with equivalents of diamine and dicarboxylic acid ester, weighed directly in the polymer tube (Preparation 14). In the latter instance, alcohol is removed instead of water. No "balancing" by salt preparation obtains in these instances.

An alternative method for carrying out polyamidations from a nylon salt is to use a pipe autoclave. This is safer and more convenient but does not allow visual observation of the polymerization (11).

Polymers which decompose below their melting points can sometimes be made by powder polymerization. The polycondensation is
carried out to a low molecular weight product and the low polymer is
ground in a suitable mill. Nylon salts of the type described above,
which melt above 225°C., may be powder polymerized directly. The
polycondensation is conducted by heating the ground polymer or
high melting salt under vacuum with a nitrogen bleed to carry away the
volatile by-products. Polymer types other than polyamides also may
be prepared by powder methods. An example of the use of powder
polymerization in the preparation of a polyester is found in Preparation 58.

A method of demonstrating the effect of *N*-**alkylation in polyamides**
is the reaction of the polymer with formaldehyde and methanol to
give a partially *N*-methoxymethylated product. The resultant decrease in amide hydrogen bonding has a profound effect on 6-6 polyamide. The polymer melt temperature is reduced, the solubility
increased to include nonacidic solvents, and the polymer becomes
somewhat rubber-like, depending on the degree of substitution.
The following directions are for an *N*-methoxymethyl 6-6 having about
36% substitution on nitrogen. A small portion of the substitution is
N-methylol. The melt temperature is reduced from 265°C. to 150°C.,
and the polymer is now soluble in 80% aqueous ethanol as well as
in strong acids. The polymer used in this reaction may be prepared
by the methods of the preceding example.

3. The *N*-Methoxymethylation of Poly(hexamethyleneadipamide) (19)

$$\left[-HN(CH_2)_6-NH-\overset{\overset{O}{\|}}{C}-(CH_2)_4-\overset{\overset{O}{\|}}{C}-\right]_n \xrightarrow[CH_3OH]{CH_2O}$$

$$\left[-HN(CH_2)_6-\underset{\underset{\underset{\underset{CH_3}{|}}{\overset{|}{O}}}{\underset{|}{CH_2}}}{N}-\overset{\overset{O}{\|}}{C}-(CH_2)_4-\overset{\overset{O}{\|}}{C}-\right]_n$$

A solution of 60 g. of 6–6 nylon in 180 g. of 90% formic acid is prepared
by stirring at 60°C. To this is added a solution of 60 g. paraformaldehyde
in 60 g. methanol, heated to 60°C. This latter solution is prepared by warming a suspension of paraformaldehyde in methanol to 60°C. and adding a
trace of solid sodium hydroxide, whereupon the solution becomes perfectly

clear. The rate of addition of the paraformaldehyde solution is very slow during the first minute in order not to precipitate the polymer, then is increased so that addition is complete at the end of three minutes. Ten minutes after addition of the paraformaldehyde is begun, another 60 g. of methanol is added rapidly and the reaction allowed to proceed for 30 min. (If a time interval greater than 10 min. elapses before adding the second quantity of methanol, the degree of substitution is increased.) The solution is then poured into 1700 ml. of a water–acetone solution (50:50 by volume), and concentrated aqueous ammonia is gradually added, causing the N-methoxymethylated polymer to precipitate as fine white granules. After filtration, the polymer is washed thoroughly with water and dried over phosphorus pentoxide in a vacuum desiccator. Analysis for methoxyl content by the Zeisel method should give a value of about 7.1%. Analysis for methylol content is carried out by treating a solution of the polymer in 70% ethanol with sodium sulfite and titrating the liberated alkali with acid (72). Methylol content should be about 1.4%. This corresponds to a total amide subsitition of about 36% from methoxymethyl and methylol.

The polymer melt temperature of the modified polyamide is about 150°C. It is soluble in 80% ethanol as well as formic acid and m-cresol. The polymer chain length is essentially unchanged. A film cast from ethanol is elastic, unlike a film of the parent polymer.

Another example of polyamide modification is the **reaction of ethylene oxide with 6-6 nylon** to give a polyamide where some of the nitrogens bear poly(ethylene oxide) chains (35). The product, therefore, is a graft copolymer, with many more of the hydrogen bond sites left intact than in the previous example of a methoxymethyl 6-6 polymer. Despite the large modification of 50% by weight ethylene oxide, the polymer melt temperature is lowered only slightly to around 220°C. (from 265°C.) and solubility is restricted to typical nylon solvents such as formic acid. The effect of the poly-(ethylene oxide) side chain grafts is that of an internal plasticizer, producing a more rubbery, flexible polymer, but one still not possessing distinctly elastic properties. The side-chain effect is manifested in a marked lowering of the glass transition temperature from about 47°C. for unmodified 6-6, to below −40°C. for the modified polymer.

In the following reaction, modification should be as high as 50% by weight. It is necessary to start with polymer of low crystallinity, presumably because of the greater difficulty in penetration of ethylene oxide into crystalline regions. The growth of poly(ethylene oxide) chains rather than formation of N-hydroxyethylated polymer points to the preference of ethylene oxide for reaction with hydroxyl over amide hydrogen.

4. Preparation of Poly(ethylene oxide)-Grafted Poly(hexamethylene-adipamide) (35)

$$\left[-HN-(CH_2)_6-NH-\overset{O}{\overset{\|}{C}}-(CH_2)_4-\overset{O}{\overset{\|}{C}}-NH-\right]_n + m\ CH_2\underset{O}{\overset{}{-}}CH_2 \longrightarrow$$

$$\left[-HN-(CH_2)_6-\underset{(CH_2-CH_2-O-)_mH}{N}-\overset{O}{\overset{\|}{C}}-(CH_2)_4-\overset{O}{\overset{\|}{C}}-\right]_n$$

To insure better reactivity of the polymer, a sample of 6–6 nylon which is of low crystallinity should be used. Amorphous 6–6 can be prepared by heating it to 280°C. in a polymer tube (in a vapor bath) in an atmosphere of nitrogen for a few minutes, then quenching the tube in ice water. (Caution! Use a shield in case the tube shatters.) The polymer should be ground to pass a 30 mesh screen. Ten grams of polymer is placed in a stainless steel bomb and about 50–60 g. of ethylene oxide is then added to the bomb, which should be chilled to minimize loss of the volatile oxide when it is added. The bomb is sealed and heated in an 80°C. thermostated oil bath or jacket behind a barricade for 40 hrs. Shorter times will result in less take-up of the oxide by the polymer. The bomb is cooled in ice, opened with caution, and allowed to warm to vent excess ethylene oxide. The polymer remains as a swollen, rubbery mass, which is washed thoroughly with water (e.g., in a household blender several times), and dried over phosphorus pentoxide at 50°C. in vacuum. The increase in weight may be taken as the amount of ethylene oxide combined as poly(ethylene oxide) side chains. It should amount to about 50% in this case. The polymer melt temperature is then about 220°C., and the inherent viscosity should be only slightly less than that of the starting polymer, as determined in m-cresol for both. Films cast from formic acid are distinctly more flexible than ordinary 6–6 films. The degree of polymerization of the ethylene oxide in the side chains is about 5–7.

The **effect of intermolecular hydrogen bonding** on polyamide properties is again strikingly demonstrated by the difference in properties between poly(hexamethylenesebacamide) and the same polymer where 60% of the amide hydrogens have been replaced with alkyl groups. The following polymerization, where isobutyl is the alkyl substituent on nitrogen, illustrates this. The polymer melt temperature is reduced from 215°C. in 6–10 nylon to 145°C. in the 60% N-alkylated 6-10; and while 6-10 forms fibers similar in properties to those from 6-6 nylon, the N-alkylated polymer forms fibers that are quite elastic.

5. Preparation of N,N'-Diisobutylhexamethylenediamine (91)

$$H_2N—(CH_2)_6—NH_2 + 2\ (CH_3)_2CHC\overset{O}{\underset{H}{\diagdown}} \longrightarrow$$

$$(CH_3)_2CH—CH{=}N—(CH_2)_6—N{=}CH—CH(CH_3)_2 + 2H_2O$$
$$(I)$$

$$(I) \xrightarrow{[H]} (CH_3)_2CHCH_2—NH(CH_2)_6NH—CH_2CH(CH_3)_2$$

To 386 g. (2.0 mole) of a 60% aqueous hexamethylenediamine solution is added with stirring 288 g. (4.0 mole) of distilled isobutyraldehyde. The temperature is kept at 50–5 °C. with an ice bath. The organic dialdimine layer is separated from the water layer and hydrogenated without purification as follows.

Platinum oxide (0.7 g.) is reduced in the absence of the hydrogen acceptor by shaking a suspension of the catalyst in 50 ml. of absolute alcohol with hydrogen for 10 min. in a low-pressure Parr catalytic apparatus equipped with a 1 l. Pyrex bottle. The dialdimine from above is added to the reduced catalyst in ethanol and the hydrogenation is started at 55 p.s.i. pressure and room temperature. When hydrogen is no longer absorbed, the catalyst is removed by filtration and the N,N'-diisobutylhexamethylenediamine is distilled through a 10 in. helices-packed column at reduced pressure. The fraction boiling at 116–117 °C./3 mm. weighs 365 g. (81%), and may be used in the following reaction without further purification.

6. Preparation of N,N'-Diisobutylhexamethylenediamine-Sebacic Acid Salt (DIB6-10 Salt) (92)

To a solution of 48.5 g. (0.24 mole) of sebacic acid in 200 ml. of absolute ethanol is added 56.5 g. (0.246 mole) of N,N'-diisobutylhexamethylenediamine in 100 ml. ether. After mixing the solution thoroughly, about 700 ml. of ether is added. The salt crystallizes on cooling in ice. It is filtered, washed well with ether on the filter, and air dried. The pH of a 1% solution of salt, thus prepared, is about 6.6. The salt is dissolved in 200 ml. of absolute ethanol. The yellow solution is treated with decolorizing charcoal, and after filtration 800 ml. ether containing 10 g. of the N,N'-diisobutylhexamethylenediamine is added. After crystallization the salt is filtered, washed with ether, and dried in a vacuum desiccator. The pH of the salt is then around 7.5. The dry salt melts at 137–138 °C. The yield is 90 g. (See Preparation 1 for determination of pH and comments on obtaining a balanced salt.)

7. Preparation of Hexamethylenediamine-Sebacic Acid Salt (6-10 Salt)

The subject compound can be made by the directions given in the "Preparation of 6–6 Salt," substituting sebacic for adipic acid and using the same molar quantities of reactants. The pH of a balanced 6–10 salt is about 7.6. (See Preparation 1) The melting point of 6–10 salt is 170–172 °C., and the yield by the method described is about 85%.

8. Preparation of a Partially *N*-Isobutylated Poly(hexamethylenesebacamide) (92)

$$\left[\underset{\substack{|\\ \text{i—Bu}}}{\overset{+}{H_2N}}-(CH_2)_6-\underset{\substack{|\\ \text{i—Bu}}}{\overset{+}{NH_2\cdot}}\right]\left[\bar{O}\overset{\overset{O}{\|}}{C}-(CH_2)_8-\overset{\overset{O}{\|}}{C}-\bar{O}\right]$$

$$+\left[\overset{+}{H_3N}-(CH_2)_6-\overset{+}{NH_3}\right]\left[\bar{O}\overset{\overset{O}{\|}}{C}-(CH_2)_8-\overset{\overset{O}{\|}}{C}-\bar{O}\right] \longrightarrow \text{Random copolymer}$$

By the technique and equipment described in the "Preparation of Poly-(Hexamethyleneadipamide)" (Preparation 2), a mixture of 12.90 g. of DIB6–10 salt (0.03 mole) and 6.36 g. 6–10 salt (0.02 mole) is charged to a polymer tube and the tube filled with nitrogen and sealed. It is heated in a 202°C. vapor bath (*m*-cresol) for 16 hr. *N,N'*-dialkyldiamines react more slowly than the corresponding diprimary diamines and a much longer sealed tube heating stage is required. The polymer tube is cooled and opened cautiously. (Observe precautions noted in 6–6 nylon preparation.) A capillary is introduced to the bottom of the tube and the tube flushed with nitrogen. It is then heated in a 218°C. vapor bath (naphthalene) for $\frac{1}{2}$ hr. at atmospheric pressure, when it is transferred to a 275°C. vapor bath (methyl naphthyl ether) for 45 min., still at atmospheric pressure and with a slow nitrogen flow through the capillary. Finally, the pressure is reduced to about 1 mm. for a period of 6 hr. The polymer has a polymer melt temperature of about 145°C. Elastic fibers can be melt fabricated. Films can be cast from 98% formic acid or melt pressed. The inherent viscosity (0.5% conc. in *m*-cresol, 25°C.) is 0.6–0.8.

No salt balance is required when an **aminoacid** undergoes **polymerization.** In a pure compound, equivalence of reactive groups is guaranteed. An example is the polyamide from 11-aminoundecanoic acid (5,97). The monomer is prepared from undecylenic acid, which in turn is a derivative of castor oil. The polymer has an 11-carbon chain between amide nitrogens; the polymer melt temperature, 185–190°C., reflects the lower degree of hydrogen bonding per chain length (cf. polycaproamide) and the odd-numbered carbon skeleton. Solubility is restricted to strong acids and the phenols.

9. Preparation of 11-Aminoundecanoic Acid (5)

$$CH_2{=}CH-(CH_2)_8-CO_2H + HBr \longrightarrow Br-(CH_2)_{10}-CO_2H$$

$$Br(CH_2)_{10}-CO_2H + 2NH_3 \longrightarrow H_2N-(CH_2)_{10}-CO_2H + NH_4Br$$

A solution of 82 g. (0.44 *m*.) undecylenic acid (m.p. 24–25°C.) in 500 ml. of olefin-free hexane is stirred and cooled to 0°C. The hexane solution of the acid should be well exposed to the air in its preparation, and a trace of benzoyl peroxide should also be added. Hydrogen bromide gas is slowly passed into the reaction flask through an inlet tube that dips below the surface of the hexane. A trap should be provided for unabsorbed hydrogen bromide.

When the hydrogen bromide is no longer being absorbed, the mixture is cooled in ice-salt to −20°C. and the solid product separated by filtration. Some hexane can be evaporated if need be to aid precipitation of the product if at −20°C. no solid separates. The crude 11-bromoacid is twice recrystallized from petroleum ether to give a white, crystalline product melting at 50°C.

A mixture of 100 g. (0.38 m.) 11-bromoundecanoic acid, 300 g. of concentrated ammonium hydroxide, and 200 g. ethyl alcohol are stirred together at 30°C. for a total of 4 days. The excess ammonia and the alcohol are distilled at reduced pressure on the steam bath and the residue taken up in 1500 ml. boiling water, which is then cooled in ice. The resulting solid is filtered, washed with water, and, if necessary, recrystallized once more from about 1 l. of boiling water. The melting point of the product, dried in a vacuum oven at 50°C. for 5 hr., then over phosphorus pentoxide in a vacuum desiccator, is 176°C. The yield is about 49 g. (64%).

As an alternative to the above, the bromoacid and ammonia in the above amount may be heated at 60°C. in a bomb for 10 hr. with agitation and worked up as above. The yield is about 40 g. (53%).

10. Preparation of Poly(11-undecanoamide) (5)

$$H_2N-(CH_2)_{10}-CO_2H \longrightarrow \left[-(CH_2)_{10}-\overset{\overset{\displaystyle O}{\|}}{C}-NH- \right]_n + H_2O$$

Twenty-five grams of purified 11-aminoundecanoic acid is charged to a 200 ml. three-necked flask equipped with a stirrer having a stainless steel shaft and paddle, Claisen head for the distillation of water, and a nitrogen inlet. Nitrogen is passed in to purge the air and heating is begun by means of a metal or oil bath. The polymerization is heated at 220°C. for 10 hr. while a current of nitrogen is passed through the flask. After first raising the stirrer from the molten mass, the reaction is cooled under nitrogen and the polymer is removed by breaking the flask.

The polymerization may be run in a polymer tube using smaller quantities (10–15 g.) of aminoacid. A nitrogen inlet capillary to the bottom of the tube provides agitation of the melt. (See Preparation 2 for general directions. No vacuum cycle is needed in the present case.)

The product is obtained in a quantitative yield. Its polymer melt temperature is 185–190°C. The inherent viscosity in m-cresol (0.5% at 35°C.) is about 0.6–0.7. Films may be melt-pressed and fibers may be pulled from a melt of the polymer.

While most amine-acid condensations involve dicarboxylic acids with diamines (AA + BB reactions) or aminoacids with themselves (AB reactions), unusual polymers may be made by reactions involving a combination of these. For instance, hexamethylene bis(iminoacetic acid), a **diaminodicarboxylic acid,** undergoes a **polycondensation**

with itself to form diketopiperazine rings linked through the nitrogens by hexamethylene units (8). The monomer in this case is an AB-BA type, whose reaction can be depicted as:

$$AB{-}BA + AB{-}BA \longrightarrow \left[\begin{matrix} {-}BA \\ | \ | \\ AB{-} \end{matrix} \right]_n$$

Despite the tetrafunctionality of the monomer, a linear polymer is formed because of the ease of formation of the diketopiperazine ring.

11. Preparation of Hexamethylene Bis(iminoacetic Acid) (8)

$$H_2N{-}(CH_2)_6{-}NH_2 + HCN + CH_2O \longrightarrow$$

$$NCCH_2{-}NH{-}(CH_2)_6{-}NHCH_2CN$$

$$NCCH_2NH{-}(CH_2)_6{-}NHCH_2CN + H_2O \longrightarrow$$

$$\overset{\displaystyle O}{\overset{\|}{HO{-}C}}{-}CH_2NH{-}(CH_2)_6{-}NHCH_2{-}\overset{\displaystyle O}{\overset{\|}{C}}{-}OH$$

Caution: Some Hydrogen Cyanide may be Formed.   Run in a Good Hood.

A solution of 72.6 g. (0.62 m.) of hexamethylenediamine in 60 ml. of water is placed in a 1 l. three-necked flask equipped with stirrer, dropping funnel, and condenser. The solution is cooled in ice and the diamine is neutralized by the addition of 127 g. of concentrated (36%) hydrochloric acid. The solution is then maintained at 5–10°C. while 86.8 g. potassium cyanide (1.33 m.) in 120 ml. of water is added at such a rate that the temperature does not exceed 10°C. Then over a 1 hr. period, 97.5 g. of a 38% formalin solution (1.25 m. of formaldehyde) is added with stirring at 5–10°C. The mixture · is stirred 3 hr. further at room temperature after addition. The solution is then filtered and 70 g. potassium carbonate added as a solid. The hexamethylene bis(iminoacetonitrile) separates as an oil, which is removed from the aqueous layer by decantation or by means of a separatory funnel. The oil is then taken up in 200 ml. methanol and the solution dried over anhydrous sodium sulfate, treated with 5 g. of decolorizing charcoal, and filtered. At this point, the bis(iminoacetonitrile) dihydrochloride may be precipitated, if desired, by addition of concentrated hydrochloric acid. After recrystallization from methanol, the dihydrochloride melts at 188–189°C. (dec.).

The crude bis(iminoacetonitrile) is obtained from the above methanol solution, after drying, by distilling the methanol at aspirator pressure through a Claisen head on the steam bath. The compound is freed from inorganic salts by dissolving in 200 ml. absolute ethanol, filtering and removing the ethanol under aspirator pressure. The hexamethylene bis(iminoacetonitrile) is obtained as a crystalline mass, in a yield of 84 g. (60%). This is hydrolyzed by refluxing the bis(iminonitrile) with 160 g. (0.5 m.) of barium hydroxide octahydrate in 3 l. of water for thirteen hours. The mixture is cooled to room temperature and 49 g. (0.5 m.) of concentrated sulfuric acid is added to precipitate barium sulfate, which is removed by filtration.   The filtrate is concentrated on the steam bath at water aspirator pressure until considerable separation of solid has occurred.   This is filtered and ethanol added to the filtrate.   The solid which precipitates is filtered and the combined solids recrystallized from a minimum of hot water by the addition of enough ethanol to induce precipitation.   The hexamethylene bis(iminoacetic acid) is filtered, washed with a little ethanol and dried in a vacuum desiccator over phosphorus pentoxide at 1 mm. pressure.   The yield is about 68 g. (80%); the melting point on rapid heating is 265–266 °C. (dec.) with sintering at 257 °C.

12. Preparation of Poly(N,N'-Hexamethylene-2,5-diketopiperazine) (8)

$$HO-\overset{\overset{O}{\parallel}}{C}-CH_2NH-(CH_2)_6-NHCH_2-\overset{\overset{O}{\parallel}}{C}-OH \longrightarrow$$

$$\left[-(CH_2)_6-N\diagup\diagdown N- \right]_n + 2H_2O$$

In a 100 ml. three-necked flask, with nitrogen capillary inlet tube reaching to the bottom of the flask, short air condenser, and dropping funnel, is placed 15 g. of hexamethylene bis(iminodiacetic acid), and 35 g. of distilled m-cresol containing 0.04 g. phosphoric acid.   The mixture is heated at 180 °C. by means of an oil bath for 30 hr. (not necessarily continuously) while a slow stream of nitrogen is passed through the reaction.   As the solvent is lost by evaporation, additional m-cresol is added from the dropping funnel.   The temperature is then raised to 218 °C. for 20 hr., then the pressure is reduced to 15–20 mm. for 3 hr.   This removes the solvent and leaves a yellow-orange tough plug of polymer.   It is cut up, ground to a powder, and extracted with boiling acetone to remove residual m-cresol.   The inherent viscosity in m-cresol (0.5%, 25 °C.) is about 0.6–1.0.   The polymer melt temperature is around 240 °C., and fibers may be pulled from the melt.   Flexible, tough films may be melt-pressed, which become soft and pliable after water immersion.   The polymer is soluble in formic and acetic acids as well as in m-cresol.

Polyamides can be prepared by **reaction of a diamine with a diester** in a typical aminolysis reaction.   Usually, phenyl esters (or negatively substituted phenyl esters) or methyl esters are selected because of their greater reactivity.   Thiol esters are more reactive than their oxy counterparts.   In the following example, a disubstituted phenyl malonate is used; the unsubstituted or monosubstituted malonates do not condense well with diamines.

13. Preparation of Phenyl Di-n-butylmalonate (76)

$$(n-C_4H_9)_2-C\begin{array}{c}CO_2C_2H_5 \\ CO_2C_2H_5\end{array} \longrightarrow (n-C_4H_9)_2-C\begin{array}{c}CO_2H \\ CO_2H\end{array}$$

$$(n-C_4H_9)_2-C\begin{array}{c}CO_2H \\ CO_2H\end{array} \xrightarrow{PCl_5} (n-C_4H_9)_2-C\begin{array}{c}COCl \\ COCl\end{array}$$

$$(n-C_4H_9)_2-C\begin{array}{c}COCl \\ COCl\end{array} + 2 \underset{\text{(phenol, OH)}}{\bigcirc} \longrightarrow (n-C_4H_9)_2-C\begin{array}{c}CO_2-\bigcirc \\ CO_2-\bigcirc\end{array} + 2HCl$$

In a 1 1. three-necked flask equipped with condenser and dropping funnel, a solution of 123 g. (2.46 m.) of potassium hydroxide in 500 ml. of absolute ethanol is heated to reflux, and 100 g. (0.38 m.) of ethyl di-n-butylmalonate gradually added from the funnel. Hydrolysis takes place almost immediately and some salt precipitates toward the end of the reaction. After complete addition of the ester, the mixture is refluxed for 1–2 hr. It is then cooled to room temperature and acidified with concentrated hydrochloric acid. The resulting mixture is filtered to remove the potassium chloride, which is washed with ether. The filtrate is extracted with ether and the ether extractions and washings combined. The ether solution is extracted with three 200 ml. portions of 10% aqueous sodium carbonate. The sodium carbonate solution is treated with activated charcoal, cooled, and acidified with concentrated hydrochloric acid. After cooling to room temperature, the crystallized di-n-butylmalonic acid is collected on a filter, washed with cold water, and dried at 50°C. in a vacuum oven; yield is about 78 g. (98%); m.p. 160°C.

The di-n-butylmalonic acid (78 g., 0.36 m.) is placed in a 500 ml. three-necked flask and 175 g. (0.84 m.) phosphorus pentachloride added portionwise with occasional cooling of the flask in ice. When the addition is complete and the initial reaction has subsided, the mixture is heated under reflux for $1^1/_2$ hr. Hydrogen chloride is evolved and should be trapped. The phosphorus oxychloride is distilled from the reaction at atmospheric pressure (b.p. 107°C.) through a 10 in. Vigreux column, and the residue fractionated at reduced pressure. The di-n-butylmalonyl chloride boils at 160–178°C./85 mm. The yield is about 48 g. (57%).

Fifty grams (0.2 m.) of the acid chloride is heated with 41 g. (0.44 m.) phenol at a temperature of 200°C. by means of an oil bath until the evolution of hydrogen chloride has essentially ceased, which may require up to 3 hr. The reaction is then fractionally distilled at reduced pressure to give the phenyl ester boiling at 191–192°C./2 mm. The phenyl di-n-butylmalonate melts at 49°C. and can be recrystallized from ethyl alcohol (about 1 g. ester/3 ml. alcohol). The yield is 44 g. (60%).

14. Preparation of Poly(hexamethylenedi-*n*-Butylmalonamide) (76)

$$H_2N—(CH_2)_6—HN_2 + (C_4H_9)_2—C \begin{matrix} CO_2—\langle \rangle \\ \\ CO_2—\langle \rangle \end{matrix} \longrightarrow$$

$$\left[—HN—(CH_2)_6—NH—\overset{O}{\overset{\|}{C}}—\overset{\overset{C_4H_9}{|}}{C}—\overset{O}{\overset{\|}{C}}— \right]_n + 2 \; \langle \rangle OH$$

A carefully weighed mixture of 2.95 g. (0.0254 *m.*) of hexamethylenediamine and 9.20 g. (0.0250 *m.*) of phenyl di-*n*-butylmalonate is placed in a polymer tube, which is then evacuated and filled with nitrogen and finally evacuated as described in the melt preparation of 6–6 nylon (Preparation 2). The tube is sealed while evacuated and is then heated for 14 hr. in a vapor bath at 210°C. The tube is then opened and fitted with a nitrogen capillary bleed reaching to the bottom of the tube and a side arm for distilling. The tube is then heated in a 265°C. bath for 1 hr. at atmospheric pressure, for 15 min. at 30 mm. pressure, and finally for 5 hr. at 3 mm., all with a slow stream of nitrogen passing through the melt. The tube is allowed to cool to room temperature, then opened, and the glass broken away from the polymer plug. Except for mechanical losses in isolation, the yield of polymer is quantitative. The poly-(hexamethylenedibutylmalonamide) has an inherent viscosity of about 0.5–0.7 in *m*-cresol (0.5% conc., 25°C.) and a polymer melt temperature of around 145°C. It can be melt-pressed or dry-cast to strong films from chloroform/methanol (88/12 by weight). The polymer is also soluble in ethanol as well as in the acidic polyamide solvents, e.g., *m*-cresol, formic acid.

From the standpoint of the diacid involved, the most readily aminolyzed esters are generally those from oxalic acid (74). For this reason, plus the fact that oxalic acid decomposes on melting, the preparation of **polyoxamides** usually involves the **reaction of an oxalate ester with a diamine** in some solvent at room temperature. The reaction in most cases is rapid and exothermic and a precipitate of prepolymer of low molecular weight forms. This is then polymerized to high molecular weight material in a melt system. Polyoxamides from short chain diamines (six carbons and less) have proved somewhat difficult to prepare in many instances because of a tendency to decompose at the high melt temperature involved. Polyoxamides have been prepared from such diamines as triethylenetetramine, $H_2NC-H_2CH_2NHCH_2CH_2NHCH_2CH_2NH_2$, which, with an excess of an oxalic ester, apparently gives polyoxamides having cyclic oxamide units in the chain (10), as

$$\left[-CH_2CH_2N \underset{\text{(ring)}}{\overset{O \quad O}{\diagup \diagdown}} N-CH_2CH_2-NH-\overset{O}{\overset{\|}{C}}-\overset{O}{\overset{\|}{C}}-NH- \right]_n$$

Similarly, shorter chain diamines that are laterally substituted have also been used successfully to given melt-stable polyoxamides (77,98). For instance, 3-methoxyhexamethylenediamine forms a polyoxamide having a polymer melt temperature of about 190°C. (77).

In the example below, the polyoxamide of decamethylenediamine is prepared.

15. Preparation of Decamethylenediamine (73)

$$NC-(CH_2)_8-CN \xrightarrow{[H]} H_2N-(CH_2)_{10}-NH_2$$

In a 1 l. hydrogenation bomb are placed 250 g. sebaconitrile, 250 ml. dioxane, and 15 g. Raney cobalt catalyst (as an ethanol paste, below). The bomb is flushed with hydrogen to remove air, and pressured to 500 p.s.i. with hydrogen while at a temperature of 120°C. Hydrogen is pressured into the vessel at regular intervals until no more is taken up. The bomb is cooled to room temperature, bled to atmospheric pressure, and the solution filtered free of catalyst. The dioxane is stripped by distillation on the steam bath at water aspirator pressure using a short column. The residue can be fractionally distilled through an 8 in. helices-packed column at reduced pressure in a stream of nitrogen to give about 160 g. (62%) of decamethylenediamine, boiling at 139–141°C./12 mm. The melting point is 60–61°C. If the hydrogenation is carried out in the presence of 180 g. anhydrous ammonia, yields may be as high as 97%. The diamine should be stored under nitrogen to avoid carbonate formation, and kept free from moisture.

The Raney cobalt catalyst used in this preparation can be prepared (100,104) by suspending 50 g. of finely powdered aluminum-cobalt alloy containing 50% by weight of each metal in 300 ml. boiling water in a 1 l. three-necked flask equipped with condenser and efficient stirrer. A solution of 50 g. sodium hydroxide in 100 ml. water is added slowly with good stirring and the mixture is boiled for 4 hr. After cooling, the supernatant liquid is decanted and the residue refluxed again for 4 hr. with a solution of 50 g. sodium hydroxide in 300 ml. water. The water is again decanted and the catalyst washed free from alkali by repeated stirring with fresh portions of water followed by decantation. The final washing and decantation is with 95% ethanol. The

catalyst is stored under alcohol and should be used as an ethanol paste.   It
is pyrophoric and should be handled with caution.

16. Preparation of Poly(decamethyleneoxamide) (9)

$$H_2N(CH_2)_{10}NH_2 + C_4H_9O\overset{\overset{O}{\|}}{C}-\overset{\overset{O}{\|}}{C}-OC_4H_9 \longrightarrow$$

$$\left[-HN(CH_2)_{10}NH-\overset{\overset{O}{\|}}{C}-\overset{\overset{O}{\|}}{C}-\right]_n + 2C_4H_9OH$$

For use in this preparation, commercial dibutyl oxalate can be freed of
acidic impurities by stirring overnight with 10% by weight of dry calcium
hydroxide under anhydrous conditions.   The mixture is filtered and the
filtrate distilled under reduced pressure, b.p. 84°C./0.85 mm.   Decamethylenediamine is prepared and purified as described in the preceding section.

To a solution of 17.23 g. (0.10 m.) decamethylenediamine in 25 ml. toluene
(dried over sodium) in a 250 ml. three-necked flask equipped with stirrer, adjustable nitrogen inlet tube, and drying tube is added all at once 20.22g.
(0.10 m.) dibutyl oxalate with stirring under nitrogen.   The residual oxalate
ester is washed quickly into the flask with another 15 ml. portion of dry toluene.
Heat is liberated and a white solid begins to form within a very short time.
Stirring is continued until the mass becomes too thick to stir.   The solid is a
prepolymer with an inherent viscosity of about 0.15–0.25 (sulfuric acid, 0.5%
conc., 25°C.).   Two hours after the initial addition, the flask is heated to
270°C. in a Woods' metal bath with a current of nitrogen continually passing
over the reaction mixture.   The nitrogen inlet tube is located immediately
above the reaction mass.   The toluene distills as the temperature is raised.
The 270°C. temperature is maintained for 1 hr., then the polymer is permitted to cool under nitrogen.   A tough, white plug is obtained.   The inherent
viscosity is 0.6–0.7 in sulfuric acid (0.5% conc., 25°C.) and the polymer melt
temperature is around 240°C.   Fibers can be pulled from the melt.

Formation of a mixed polyamide-imide is accomplished by
polymerizing tricarballylic acid with a diamine.   The somewhat
irregular structure of the molecule and the reduced degree of hydrogen
bonding (in contrast to 6-6 polyamide) make the polymers obtained
somewhat low melting.   The polymer from the short chain ethylenediamine, for instance, has a polymer melt temperature of 170°C.
(265°C. for 6-6).   The reaction is another case where ease of ring
formation leads to linear rather than cross-linked polymer, despite
the average functionality of $2^1/_2$ for the reactants.

17. Preparation of Poly(hexamethylenetricarballylamide-imide) (34)

$$\underset{\underset{\displaystyle \underset{O}{\overset{\|}{CH_2C-OH}}}{|}}{HO-\overset{\overset{O}{\|}}{C}CH_2\overset{}{C}H\overset{\overset{O}{\|}}{C}OH} \quad + \ H_2N(CH_2)_6NH_2 \ \longrightarrow$$

$$\left[\underset{\underset{\displaystyle \underset{O}{\overset{\|}{CH_2C}}}{|}}{-HN-\overset{\overset{O}{\|}}{C}CH_2\overset{}{C}H\overset{\overset{O}{\|}}{C}} \right.\hspace{-0.5em} \underset{\displaystyle \hspace{2em}}{\diagdown} \underset{\diagup}{N-(CH_2)_6-} \left. \vphantom{X}\right]_n + \ 3H_2O$$

A mixture of 12.60 g. (0.071 m.) tricarballylic acid and 8.31 g. (0.071 m.) hexamethylenediamine is heated together at 150°C. for 3 hr. in a sealed polymer tube which has been thoroughly flushed with nitrogen. The temperature is then raised to 205°C. for another 2 hr. (This heating of the sealed tube should be conducted behind a suitable shield.) The tube is then cooled and opened and fitted with an adjustable capillary tube as a nitrogen inlet along with a neck with side arm as a vacuum outlet. The tube is then heated at 218°C. while a slow stream of nitrogen is introduced and the pressure is reduced to 1 mm. After two hours, the nitrogen inlet tube is raised from the melt and the tube is cooled under nitrogen. The polymer has an inherent viscosity of about 0.5 in m-cresol (0.5% conc., 30°C.). The polymer melt temperature is around 120°C. Fibers can be drawn from the melt.

For additional details of the experimental procedure involved, see Preparation 2.

The **reaction of diamines with** a diester of pyromellitic acid, **a tetrafunctional compound,** can form linear, soluble **polyimides.** This is an instance where a tetrafunctional compound is capable of producing linear, noncross-linked polymers in reaction with a difunctional intermediate. The ease of intramolecular ring closure in the pyromellitimide system makes this effectively a difunctional molecule. (For an example of linear polymer from a tetramine and diacid, see Preparation 31.) The polymerization is limited to the longer chain diamines in order to obtain melt-stable products. The stiff, inflexible pyromellitimide ring system gives rise to very high melting polymers, despite the lack of hydrogen bonding. This stiffness in the polymer chain is reflected in the higher glass transition temperature of the polyimides; for the polyimide from nonamethylenediamine with pyro·

mellitic anhydride, it is about 100°C., while for 6-6 polyamide it is about 47°C.

18. Preparation of Nonamethylenediamine (27)

$$HO_2C(CH_2)_7CO_2H \xrightarrow{NH_3} NC(CH_2)_7CN$$

$$NC(CH_2)_7CN \xrightarrow{H_2} H_2N(CH_2)_9NH_2$$

In a 500 ml. three-necked flask, equipped with a gas inlet tube and straight distillation head with condenser, is placed a mixture of 250 g. azelaic acid and 10 g. polyphosphoric acid. The temperature is raised to about 115–120°C. by means of a Woods' metal bath to melt the acid. Anhydrous ammonia is passed through the reaction at a fairly rapid rate by means of the gas inlet tube which reaches nearly to the bottom of the flask. The temperature is raised to 290–300°C. for a period of 8 hrs. while the ammonia is added. Aqueous ammonia distills from the reaction. The residue in the flask is fractionated at reduced pressure to give about 150 g. (75%) azaleonitrile, boiling at 145–150°C./2 mm., which solidifies on standing.

Reduction is carried out as described for decamethylenediamine, Preparation 15, at a temperature of 135°C. Nonamethylenediamine is obtained in 70–80% yield; the boiling point is 80–82°C./3 mm.

19. Preparation of Poly(nonamethylenepyromellitimide) (27)

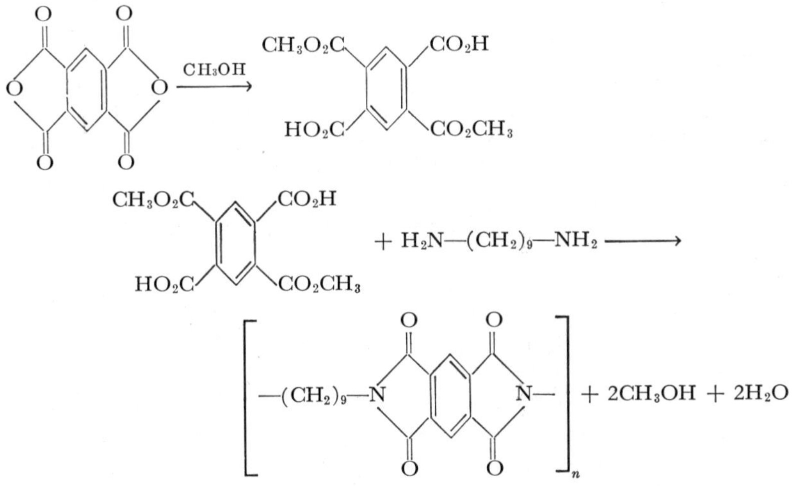

In a 100 ml. three-necked round-bottom flask protected by a drying tube is placed 6.08 g. (0.0279 $m.$) pyromellitic dianhydride and 30 ml. absolute methanol. (Pyromellitic dianhydride may be recrystallized from acetic anhydride.) The mixture is swirled by hand and gently warmed on the steam bath until a clear solution results. Then 4.414 g. (0.0279 m.) non-amethylenediamine is added quantitatively and the methanol distilled on the steam bath. The residual salt, which should be dry enough for easy handling, is transferred by means of a long stemmed funnel to a polymer tube having a side arm. The tube is then fitted with a capillary inlet reaching nearly to the bottom. (See Preparation 2 for general directions on melt-polymerization technique.) The tube is purged by alternate evacuation by means of an oil pump, and admission of nitrogen. At atmospheric pressure and in a slow stream of nitrogen, the temperature is raised to 139 °C. by immersion in a m-xylene vapor bath for 2 hrs., during which time water and methanol are driven off. The polymer tube is then transferred to a 325 °C. vapor bath for another 2 hrs. The tube is cooled after first raising the nitrogen capillary above the level of the melt. The polymer is removed by breaking the tube. The yield of polymer is quantitative except for mechanical losses. The polymer melt temperature is about 325 °C., and the inherent viscosity is 0.8–1.2 in m-cresol (0.5% conc. at 25 °C.). Tough films can be melt pressed at 340 °C.

A "copolymer effect" is observed in condensation polymers **when more than two complementary difunctional molecules are caused to polymerize in a random arrangement** (11). Generally, for random condensation copolymers, properties such as polymer melt temperature and crystalline melting point pass through a minimum at some composition between the homopolymers. Solubility may show a maximum. An exception is to be found in those copolymers having constituents which are isomorphous, i.e., are capable of occupying interchangeably the same crystal lattice. Such copolymers show a linear dependence of physical properties on composition. For example, bis(3-aminopropyl)ether, heptamethylenediamine, and adipic acid give a copolyamide (24) which is isomorphous with the homopolyamide from either diamine and adipic acid.

Complete randomness results from melt-polymerizations through amide interchange reactions (12), but from low temperature, non-reversible polymerization reactions (e.g., the diacid chloride-diamine reaction) ordered copolymers may result. Addition reactions involving hydrogen transfer give either random or block copolymers, depending on the monomers used and the polymerization conditions. The addition of a hydroxy-terminated polyester to a diisocyanate (Preparation 76) is an example of a block copolymer from a hydrogen transfer addition reaction.

In the following preparation of a random copolymer from hexamethylene- and tetramethylenediamines with adipic and sebacic acids, the composition of 0.6 moles of 6-10 and 0.4 moles of 4-6 is used.

This gives the minimum melting composition for the 6-10/4-6 copolymer series. It is nearly the maximum in solubility, being slightly exceeded by the 0.5/0.5 mole ratio copolymer in this respect. Some comparisons with the properties of the homopolymers are shown in Table 3.3 (11).

TABLE 3.3

Polymer	Polymer melt temperature, °C.	Crystalline m.p. (fibers), °C.	80% Ethanol
6-10	228	225	Insoluble
4-6	308	282	Insoluble
6-10/4-6 (0.6/0.4)	155	167	Soluble

20. Preparation of Poly(hexamethylenesebacamide-co-tetramethyleneadipamide) (0.6/0.4 Molar) (11)

0.60 m. 6-10 salt + 0.40 m. 4-6 salt ⟶

$$\left[-HN-R-NH-\overset{\overset{O}{\|}}{C}-R'-\overset{\overset{O}{\|}}{C}- \right]_n + 2H_2O$$

R = $\left(CH_2\right)_4$ and $\left(CH_2\right)_6$; R' = $\left(CH_2\right)_4$ and $\left(CH_2\right)_8$

The preparation of 6-10 salt is described in Preparation 8. The 4-6 salt used here is prepared as described (Preparation 1) for 6-6 salt, using a 2% excess of tetramethylenediamine, which can be purified by distillation in a current of nitrogen and stored under nitrogen to protect it from atmospheric moisture and carbon dioxide. It boils at 158–160°C. at atmospheric pressure, and melts at 27–28°C. The 4-6 salt can be obtained in over 95% yield. The balanced salt melts at 193–194°C., and a 1% aqueous solution has a pH of about 7.1.

The polymerization may be conducted as described for the preparation of 6-6 nylon (Preparation 2) with the following modifications. Due precautions for handling tubes under pressure should be observed.

A mixture of 4.685 g. (0.02 m.) 4-6 salt and 9.553 g. (0.03 m.) 6-10 salt is charged to a polymer tube which is then evacuated and filled with nitrogen. The tube is sealed and heated at 220°C. (methyl salicylate bath) for 2 hr. A side arm is attached and vacuum is then gradually applied over a 15 min. period. The tube is heated for $1^1/_2$ hr. further at 220°C. at a pressure of 1.0 mm., or less, while a slow stream of nitrogen is passed through the melt via a capillary tube. The polymer is cooled under nitrogen after raising the capillary and is obtained as a tough translucent plug by breaking the tube. The copolyamide has a polymer melt temperature of about 170°C., and an inherent viscosity of 0.7–0.8 in m-cresol (0.5% conc. 25°C.). Fibers are slightly crystalline and exhibit a crystalline melting point of 179°C. The polymer is soluble in dimethylformamide, 80% ethanol, and ethylene chlorohydrin, as well as in the acidic polyamide solvents (phenols, formic acid, etc.).

There are, perhaps, no organic reactions that could be considered any more "classical" than the Schotten-Bauman reaction for acylating amines and alcohols, or the Hinsberg method of separating amines. Both involve the reaction of an acid halide with the active hydrogen of an alcohol or amine in the presence of an acid acceptor, and are usually carried out in an aqueous system. These simple, fast reactions have become the basis for an extremely versatile method for synthesizing polymers. (94,7,43,44,52A).

The method for carrying out the reaction on a polymer-forming basis has been termed **"interfacial polycondensation"** (94,52A). The **reaction** apparently takes place **at the interface between** a solution of a **diacid chloride in a water immiscible organic solvent and a water solution of,** for example, **a diamine** containing an acid acceptor. The acid component may be aliphatic or aromatic dicarboxylic chlorides, bischloroformates, or disulfonyl chlorides. The active hydrogen compound may be aliphatic primary or secondary diamines, or diphenols as their sodium salts. Aromatic diamines and aliphatic diols apparently react too slowly to yield high polymer. Hydrolysis of the acyl halide, always a possible side reaction, may compete with the acylation sufficiently in these cases to prevent formation of high polymer.

Exact stoichiometry of reactants is not so important as it is in melt-polycondensations, presumably because of the extremely rapid rate of interfacial polycondensation. In fact, enough excess diamine to act as the acid acceptor may be used in some cases without seriously reducing the molecular weight of the product. This is taken as evidence for a reaction site in the organic phase close to the interface, but apart from the excess diamine. Acid chloride enters the aqueous phase very little, thus avoiding hydrolysis. Reaction is so rapid that lack of precise equivalency of reactants in the solution does not prevent the formation of high molecular weight products at the surface contact of the two liquids.

Although interfacial polycondensation usually is very rapid, proper choice of a solvent system and reactant concentration is essential to ensure sufficient mobility of the growing chain to permit a high molecular weight to be reached.

The great utility of interfacial polycondensation stems from the fact that it is a low temperature process. Thus, polymers that are not stable at their melt temperatures can easily be prepared and unstable reactants can be used where melt-polycondensation would be useless. The method is very rapid, permitting the preparation of polymer in a matter of minutes, once the reactants are in hand. Little in the way of special equipment is needed. Rapid stirring is easily effected by use of a household blender. However, standard laboratory stirrers and flasks often may be used and, as one of the following preparations shows, a beaker may be the only apparatus required. The variety of polymer types that may be prepared is wide: **polyamides, polysulfonamides, polyurethanes** and **polyphenyl esters.** Copolymers that would be difficult to obtain otherwise are easily prepared by interfacial polycondensation, e.g., **copolyamide-urethanes, copolyamide-sulfonamides.** Substantially different reactivities of the different diacid chlorides with the other component may lead to the formation of nonrandom, ordered copolymer (42A). The same will be true if two diamines of differing reactivity are polymerized with one acid chloride or if the reactants are mixed consecutively rather than all at once.

The average molecular weight of polymers from interfacial systems is usually at least as high as that in the comparable melt-prepared polymer and may, in the best of circumstances, be much higher.

Probably the simplest and the most dramatic example of interfacial polycondensation is the preparation of 6-6 or 6-10 nylon by the beaker method of Morgan and Kwolek (53). Their process (aptly called "The Nylon Rope Trick" for its something-out-of-nothing quality) consists simply of carefully pouring an aqueous solution of excess hexamethylenediamine onto a carbon tetrachloride solution of adipoyl or sebacoyl chloride, then steadily pulling away a coherent film of polyamide from the interface. No mixing is required, and the diamine can be used in excess to function as the acid acceptor. With purified intermediates, high molecular weights are obtained ($\bar{M}_n$ of 20,000 or more, and inherent viscosities of 1.8 in m-cresol), but even with as-purchased diamine and diacid chloride film and fiber-forming polymers are produced, but with lower molecular weight. The simplicity in comparison with, and the advantages over, melt-polymerization methods are obvious.

21. Preparation of Poly(hexamethylenesebacamide) (6-10 Nylon) (53)

$$H_2N—(CH_2)_6—NH_2 \ + \ Cl—\overset{\overset{\displaystyle O}{\|}}{C}—(CH_2)_8—\overset{\overset{\displaystyle O}{\|}}{C}—Cl \longrightarrow$$

$$\left[—HN—(CH_2)_6NH—\overset{\overset{\displaystyle O}{\|}}{C}—(CH_2)_8—\overset{\overset{\displaystyle O}{\|}}{C}—\right]$$

A solution of 3.0 ml. sebacoyl chloride in 100 ml. distilled tetrachloroethylene is placed in a 200 ml. tall-form beaker. (The diacid chloride should be distilled material, for best results. The boiling point is 124°C./0.5 mm.; the pot temperature should not exceed 160°C., and the distillation should be as rapid as possible.) Over the acid chloride solution is carefully poured a solution of 4.4 g. hexamethylenediamine in 50 ml. water. (The diamine is

Fig. 3.1. Interfacial spinning with   Fig. 3.2. Interfacial spinning—self-
manual windup.   propelled.

handled most conveniently as a standardized stock solution of about 20% in water. The commercially available solid diamine may also be used without further purification.) The polymeric film which forms at the interface of the two solutions is grasped with tweezers and raised from the beaker as a continuously forming rope. If a mechanical wind-up device is placed above the beaker, the polymer may be wound up continuously (Fig. 3.1) until one of the reactants is exhausted. Figure 3.2 shows how the process can be made to operate automatically. The polymer can be washed several times with 50% aqueous ethanol or acetone and dried in a vacuum oven at 60°C. The product has an inherent viscosity of from 0.4 to 1.8 (*m*-cresol, 0.5% conc. at 25°C.), depending on the reaction conditions. The polymer melt temperature is 215°C. Fibers and films can be obtained from the melt or from formic acid solutions.

The following preparation is an example of the use of an **aromatic diacid chloride** in a **polycondensation with a secondary cyclic diamine,** *trans*-2,5-dimethylpiperazine. The polyamide so formed (from phthaloyl chloride) is devoid of hydrogen bonds, but is still very high melting (>300°C.). The plurality of rings reduces the flexibility of the chain, increasing thereby the temperature required to put all the molecules in the condition of relatively free movement that obtains in the melt. However, because the strong interchain forces due to hydrogen bonding are not present, the polyamides are easily dissolved in a number of solvents.

22. Poly(*N*,*N*'-phthaloyl-*trans*-2,5-dimethylpiperazine) (40)

In a household blender jar is placed 6.50 g. (0.058 m.) of trans-2,5-dimethylpiperazine, 25 ml. methylene chloride, 20 ml. of a 5% "Duponol"* ME solution and 150 ml. of ice water containing 0.10 mole of sodium hydroxide, prepared by diluting a standardized caustic solution. *trans*-2,5-Dimethylpiperazine can be recrystallized from acetone (1 g./ml.); m.p. 117–118°C. To the rapidly stirred system is added all, at one time, 7.2 ml. (0.05 m.) of phthaloyl chloride in 25 ml. methylene chloride. The phthaloyl chloride should be fractionated at reduced pressure. The material boiling at 103°C./ 1.5 mm. through an 8 in., glass helices-packed column gives satisfactory polymer. The polymerization mixture is stirred for 10 min., then poured into 1 1. of water and the methylene chloride boiled away on the steam bath. The polymer is filtered, washed in the blender three times with 200 ml. portions of water, and dried at 70°C. in a vacuum oven. The yield is 10 g. (80%), the polymer melt temperature is 350°C., and the inherent viscosity is 1.0–1.4 in *m*-cresol (0.5% conc. at 25°C.). The polymer is soluble in chloroform, acetic acid, and dioxane-water (82/18 vol.).

* Trademark for du Pont's surface active agent.

Extremely high melting polyamides can be prepared **from short chain** (2–6 carbon atoms) **primary aliphatic diamines** and **terephthaloyl chloride** (70). These polymers require very dilute conditions for best preparation. Because of their insolubility, they precipitate rapidly during polymerization and are unswollen by the reaction solvents used. Consequently, there is a tendency for low molecular weight products to form. The polyterephthalamide from ethylenediamine, whose preparation follows, is soluble in none of the customary polyamide solvents (*m*-cresol, formic acid), but only in the very strong acids, sulfuric and trifluoroacetic. Thus, the ring structure plus a high degree of hydrogen bonding combine to produce a high-melting, difficultly soluble polymer.

23. Preparation of Poly(ethyleneterephthalamide) (70)

$$H_2NCH_2CH_2NH_2 + Cl-\overset{O}{\underset{\|}{C}}-\!\!\!\left\langle\!\!\!\bigcirc\!\!\!\right\rangle\!\!\!-\overset{O}{\underset{\|}{C}}-Cl \longrightarrow$$

$$\left[-HNCH_2CH_2NH-\overset{O}{\underset{\|}{C}}-\!\!\!\left\langle\!\!\!\bigcirc\!\!\!\right\rangle\!\!\!-\overset{O}{\underset{\|}{C}}-\right]_n + 2HCl$$

For the following polymerization, ethylenediamine is purified by drying over potassium hydroxide pellets for 15 hr. It is then fractionated in a stream of nitrogen through a 10 in., glass helices-packed column, taking care to protect the distillate from atmospheric carbon dioxide by means of soda-lime–packed tubes. Ethylenediamine boils at 117°C. at 760 mm. Terephthaloyl chloride can be prepared by refluxing 100 g. of terephthalic acid for 12 hr. in 500 g. of thionyl chloride and 2 ml. pyridine. The excess thionyl chloride is distilled at water aspirator pressure on the steam bath, and the residual acid chloride is distilled under vacuum through a short Vigreux column. The boiling point is 115–116°C. at 3.0 mm. It can be recrystallized from dry hexane (100 g./700 ml.); m.p., 81–82°C.

A solution of 3.78 g. (0.0630 m.) of ethylenediamine, and 0.126 m. of potassium hydroxide from a standardized solution in 4.5 l. of water is placed in an 8 l. stainless steel beaker and stirred by means of an efficient high speed stirrer. A large spatula is mounted vertically at the edge of the beaker with the blade perpendicular to the wall to act as a baffle for more efficient stirring. Next, 12.79 g. (0.0634 m.) of terephthaloyl chloride dissolved in 1 l. of methylene chloride is added rapidly to the stirred solution. The polymerization mixture is stirred for 10 min. at room temperature. The mixture is then filtered and the polymer placed in boiling distilled water to remove absorbed methylene chloride. The product is then filtered and washed twice with boiling distilled water. Finally, the polymer is dried in a vacuum oven at 80°C. to give a yield of 9.0 g. (75%). The polymer has an inherent viscosity of around 1.0

in sulfuric acid (0.5% conc., 30°C.). This corresponds to a weight average molecular weight of about 18,000. The polymer melt temperature is over 400°C. (The first transition above 400°C., determined by differential thermal analysis, is at 455°C., which may represent the polymer melt temperature.) The polymer is soluble in trifluoroacetic acid. Fibers can be dry-spun and films can be dry-cast from such a solution.

The **effect of N-alkyl substitution in polyamides,** with the concurrent loss in interchain hydrogen bonding, is again demonstrated by a comparison of the above polymer with the completely N-ethylated polymer (26). In going to the latter, the polymer melt temperature is decreased over 200°C., and the solubility is raised to such a degree that 80% aqueous ethanol becomes a solvent. The N-substituted polymer is completely amorphous as prepared while the unsubstituted is moderately crystalline.

24. Preparation of N,N'-Diethylethylenediamine (70)

$$ClCH_2CH_2Cl + 2CH_3CH_2NH_2 \xrightarrow{NaOH} CH_3CH_2NHCH_2CH_2NHCH_2CH_3$$

A mixture of 148.5 g. (1.5 m.) ethylene dichloride and 450 g. (10.0 mole) ethylamine are heated together in a stainless steel bomb at 100°C. for 4 hr. The bomb is then allowed to cool, excess ethylamine vented, and the mixture transferred by rinsing with 500 ml. water to a 2-l. separatory funnel. About 500 g. of solid potassium hydroxide is added slowly. The diamine separates as an upper, oily layer; 20 ml. methanol is added to facilitate separation of the layers. The upper layer is separated and dried over potassium hydroxide pellets overnight. It is fractionated at atmospheric pressure through a precision column to give a forerun boiling at 52–138°C. which is discarded, followed by the main fraction, which is the desired dialkyldiamine, boiling at 149–51°C. The diamine is hygroscopic and must be protected from moisture and carbon dioxide of the air. The yield is 58 g. (33%). Also obtained from the distillation is 10–20 g. of N,N',N''-triethyldiethylenetriamine, b.p. 81–2°C./3 mm.

N,N'-Diethylethylenediamine also can be purchased, and purified by distillation (see Chemicals Appendix).

25. Preparation of Poly(N,N'-diethylethyleneterephthalamide) (70)

$$C_2H_5NHCH_2CH_2NHC_2H_5 + ClC(=O)-C_6H_4-C(=O)Cl \longrightarrow$$

$$\left[-N(C_2H_5)CH_2CH_2N(C_2H_5)C(=O)-C_6H_4-C(=O)- \right]_n + 2HCl$$

A solution of 5.8 g. (0.05 m.) of N,N'-diethylethylenediamine and 10.6 g. (0.1 m.) of sodium carbonate in 250 ml. water is stirred rapidly in a household blender. To this, a solution of 10.1 g. (0.05 m.) terephthaloyl chloride in 80 ml. of dry chloroform is quickly added and the resultant mixture is stirred for 10 min. at high speed. The product, consisting of two clear liquids, is heated to expel the chloroform and precipitate the polymer. The mixture is then filtered and the solid washed four times in a blender with water to give, upon drying, 10.1 g. (82% yield) of white polymer with an inherent viscosity of 1.93 in sulfuric acid (0.5% conc., 25°C.). The product has a polymer melt temperature of 230°C. and is soluble in m-cresol, formic acid, chloroform, acetone, and 80% ethanol.

Polysulfonamides can be prepared **from aromatic disulfonyl chlorides and aliphatic diamines** by interfacial polycondensation (78). Aliphatic disulfonyl chlorides give poorer results. Polysulfonamides having hydrogens on the amide nitrogen are in many cases soluble in strong alkali, just as their monomeric organic counterparts. With sodium hydroxide as the acid acceptor in the polymerization, branching and cross-linking can result from reaction of sulfonyl chloride with the sulfonamide anion, although conditions can be chosen to minimize these effects.

$$\text{wwSO}_2\text{—NH}\text{ww} + \text{NaOH} \longrightarrow \text{wwSO}_2\overset{-}{\text{N}}\text{ww}$$

$$\text{wwSO}_2\text{N}\text{ww} \xleftarrow{\quad \text{wwSO}_2\text{—Cl} \quad}$$
$$\underset{\text{SO}_2}{\overset{|}{}}$$

26. Preparation of m-Benzenedisulfonyl Chloride (78)

$$\text{HO}_3\text{S}\text{—} \bigcirc \text{—SO}_3\text{H} \xrightarrow[\text{PCl}_5]{\text{POCl}_3} \text{ClO}_2\text{S}\text{—} \bigcirc \text{—SO}_2\text{Cl}$$

In a 3 l. three-necked flask fitted with a condenser, thermometer, and stirrer is placed 1360 g. (6.55 mole) of ground phosphorus pentachloride and 727 g. of phosphorus oxychloride. To the stirred mixture is added 770 g. (2.94 mole) of m-benzenedisulfonic acid (90%) during 30 min. The temperature is not allowed to exceed 70°C. The mixture is refluxed 3 hr., then phosphorus oxychloride is distilled first at atmospheric pressure and later under vacuum until approximately 700 ml. is collected. The dark colored liquid reaction mixture is poured with stirring into a 5-l. beaker two-thirds full of cracked ice. The cold mixture is stirred about 20 min. and filtered. The solid is dissolved in 1 l. of benzene and washed three times with 250 ml. portions of 5% sodium bicarbonate solution and once with 250 ml. water. After drying over anhydrous calcium sulfate and treating with decolorizing carbon, the filtrate is passed with suction through a $1^1/_4$ in. diameter column packed with 15 in. of activated alumina to remove the last traces of charcoal and to thoroughly dry the solution. The column is washed with 200 ml. benzene. To the solution is added 2500 ml. of olefin-free n-hexane, and the oil which separates is cooled to 20°C. and scratched to cause crystallization. The solid is filtered on a large Buchner funnel and washed twice with 500 ml. portions of olefin-free n-hexane to remove a slight yellow color. After drying in a desiccator containing calcium chloride for 3 hr. using a vacuum pump the solid weighs 553 g. (68%). It melts at 62.0–62.5°C. The filtrate is concentrated to 350 ml., and 500 ml. n-hexane added to give an oil which on seeding gives, after drying, 90 g. of crystalline material, melting at 61–61.5°C. The total yield is 643 g. (80%).

The hexamethylenediamine used in the following polymerization may be purified as described in the preparation of 6-6 nylon (Preparation 2) and weighed directly; or, it may be used in an aqueous solution, about 5–6 N, which has been standardized by titration with hydrochloric acid. Such a solution should be stored under nitrogen.

27. Preparation of Poly(hexamethylene m-benzenedisulfonamide) (78)

$$H_2N\text{—}(CH_2)_6\text{—}NH_2 + ClO_2S\text{—}\langle\text{benzene}\rangle\text{—}SO_2Cl \longrightarrow$$

$$\left[\text{—HN—}(CH_2)_6\text{—NH—}O_2S\text{—}\langle\text{benzene}\rangle\text{—}SO_2\text{—}\right]_n + 2HCl$$

A household blender jar is charged with 145 ml. distilled water, 20 ml. of 10% aqueous "Duponol"* ME solution, 3.016 g. hexamethylenediamine (or enough standardized aqueous diamine solution to give 0.026 m.), and 5.30 g. (0.05 mole) of sodium carbonate. To the stirred solution over a period of 20–30 sec. is added 6.88 g. (0.025 mole) of m-benzenedisulfonyl chloride dissolved in 200 ml. of methylene chloride. The mixture is then stirred 15 min. After adding 100 ml. ethanol, the solid is filtered, washed on the funnel with 400 ml. water, and then washed in the blender with 200 ml. portions of ethanol, acetone, hot water, and acetone again. (Caution! If the blender motor housing has not been modified with a compressed air inlet on the motor housing for flame protection, do not use the flammable solvent washes listed, or else wash the polymer in a beaker.) The sample is dried at 70–75°C. in a vacuum oven overnight to give 4.9 g. polymer (63%). The inherent viscosity (0.5% conc. at 25°C.) measured in sulfuric acid should be about 2.0; in dimethylformamide, 1.5. The polymer melt temperature is about 160–170°C. when amorphous, about 200°C. when crystalline. The polymer is fairly crystalline as prepared; melt pressed films, however, are amorphous.

* Trademark for du Pont's surface active agent.

The polymer is soluble in the above-noted solvents as well as 6–10% sodium hydroxide solutions.

The addition of a carboxylic acid to an isocyanate first forms a mixed carboxylic-carbamic anhydride. In some cases, this intermediate has been isolated. However, in most instances it decomposes directly to the end products, either a mixture of the anhydride of the acid and the urea based on the diamine (path 1); or, the substituted carboxamide plus carbon dioxide (path 2), depending on the reactants used. Further heating of the anhydride-urea mixture forms the substituted carboxamide of the acid and evolves carbon dioxide. Consequently, the eventual course of reaction leads to amide formation with the loss of carbon dioxide (55). The over-all reaction is:

$$RNCO + R'CO_2H \longrightarrow$$

Dicarboxylic acids and diisocyanates or diisothiocyanates have given **polyamides** by this reaction sequence (99). From diisothiocyanates, carbon oxysulfide is evolved, indicating that in the decomposition of the $RNH-C(=O)-O-C(=O)-R'$ mixed anhydride, the carbonyl oxygen in the product amide is derived from that of the acid used. In the following preparation of 10-10 polyamide, the diisocyanate is used; its preparation is given in Preparation 34.

28. Preparation of Poly(decamethylenesebacamide) (10-10 Polyamide) (99)

In a polymer tube purged of air and flushed with nitrogen and having a capillary inlet tube reaching nearly to the bottom is placed a mixture of 7.5 g. sebacic acid and 8.41 g. decamethylenediisocyanate. (See Preparation 2.) The tube is heated at about 170°C. by means of a vapor bath for 1 hr. at atmospheric pressure as nitrogen is passed slowly through the melt which forms. A solid eventually forms during this period. The temperature is raised to 222°C. (methyl salicylate) for 3 hr. The polymer is then cooled under nitrogen. It has an inherent viscosity of about 0.4 in m-cresol (0.5% conc., 25°C.), and is soluble in the usual acidic aliphatic polyamide solvents (e.g., formic acid, phenol). The polymer-melt temperature is about 185°C. Cold drawable fibers may be pulled from the molten polymer.

An unusual example of a hydrogen addition to a double bond to form polymer is the Michael-type **addition of acrylamide to itself** to form poly(β-alanine), or 3-nylon (51). It represents the unusual case of an AB monomer in an anionic, proton transfer addition reaction. Although the polymerization gives a relatively low molecular weight product, it is included here because of the unusual character of the polymerization and the fact that 3-nylon is one of the lower possible homologues of the polyamide series derived from ω-aminoacids. Because of the short chain separation between amide groups the polymer melt temperature (320–330°C.) of 3-nylon is substantially higher than that of 6- or 4-nylon, 215°C. and 255°C., respectively (see chapter on *Ring Opening Polymerizations*). Hydrolysis of the polymer provides a short, high yield synthesis of β-alanine from the commercially available acrylamide.

Acrylamide also can be polymerized by a typical free radical route to vinyl polymer having pendant —$CONH_2$ groups. Polyacrylamide prepared in this way is a water-soluble, high molecular weight material, which forms polyacrylic acid on hydrolysis. (See Chapter 4).

29. Preparation of Poly(β-alanine) (3-nylon) (51)

$$CH_2{=}CH-\overset{\overset{\displaystyle O}{\|}}{C}-NH_2 \xrightarrow{\ Na\ } \left[-CH_2-CH_2-\overset{\overset{\displaystyle O}{\|}}{C}-NH- \right]_n$$

The acrylamide used in this polymerization can be purified by recrystallization from ethyl acetate and sublimation at <1 mm.; the melting point is 85°C. (Use care in handling; acrylamide is toxic!) The dimethylformamide must be dry; it can be distilled from a small quantity of phosphorus pentoxide at reduced pressure.

A solution of 4.4 g. acrylamide (0.062 m.) in 4 ml. dimethylformamide is prepared in a suitable small reaction vessel which is protected from the atmosphere by a nitrogen inlet tube attached to a mercury bubbler to vent nitrogen when the vessel is closed.

The solution is heated to $100\,^{\circ}C$. in an oil bath and 2 drops of 50% dispersion of sodium in xylene, which is approximately 0.018 g. (8×10^{-4} g.a.) of sodium is added. Polymerization occurs and is completed in 3–5 min. The reaction mixture is quenched in water, the polymer filtered and washed with water several times in a blender. The polymer, dried at $70\,^{\circ}C$. for 24 hr. in a vacuum, weighs 3.5–4.0 g. (80–90%), has a polymer melt temperature of 320–$330\,^{\circ}C$., and an inherent viscosity of about 0.33 in 90% formic acid (0.5% conc., $25\,^{\circ}C$.). It is soluble in strong acids, such as formic acid, from which brittle films may be cast.

30. Preparation of β-Alanine (51)

$$\left[-CH_2-CH_2-\overset{\displaystyle O}{\overset{\displaystyle \|}{C}}-NH- \right]_n \xrightarrow{\;H_2O\;} H_2N-CH_2-CH_2-\overset{\displaystyle O}{\overset{\displaystyle \|}{C}}-OH$$

The 3-nylon polymer prepared above is refluxed with an excess of 50% aqueous sulfuric acid for 4 hr. The solution is then neutralized to pH 7 with hot aqueous barium hydroxide. The barium sulfate is filtered and washed twice by trituration with 50 ml. portions of water. The combined water filtrates are evaporated to dryness by heating at water aspirator pressure on the steam bath. The residual syrup crystallizes on cooling to give 80–90% yield of β-alanine, which may be recrystallized from hot methanol. The product melts at 195–$196\,^{\circ}C$.

The preparation of a **soluble, linear polyimide from** the **tetrafunctional pyromellitic dianhydride** (Preparation 19) demonstrates that polycondensation reactants may be more than difunctional and still produce linear, uncross-linked products. Another example of this unusual situation involving a **tetrafunctional amine** rather than acid, is the preparation of the **polybenzimidazole** from 3,3'-diaminobenzidine and sebacic acid (16). The polybenzimidazole structure is a type not heretofore seen in polymers and is a striking example of the application of synthetic organic chemistry to the field of condensation polymers.

31. Preparation of Poly(2,2'-octamethylene-5,5'-bibenzimidazole) (16)

3,3'-Diaminobenzidine tetrahydrochloride (see Chemicals Appendix) is treated with decolorizing charcoal, and recrystallized twice from water by adding concentrated hydrochloric acid. The tetraamine is freed by adding a slight excess of sodium hydroxide in water to the tetrahydrochloride in water (1 g./30 ml.) and cooling. The slightly red solid is filtered, washed with water and dried in a vacuum desiccator over phosphorus pentoxide. The melting point of the free base is 173–174°C. The above operations should be conducted in boiled, oxygen-free water, with as many of the manipulations blanketed by nitrogen as possible, since the tetramine is very sensitive to oxidation.

A mixture of 4.08 g. (0.019 m.) 3,3'-diaminobenzidine and 4.04 g. (0.020 m.) sebacic acid is heated in a polymer tube at atmospheric pressure for $3^1/_2$ hr. at 265°C. by means of a vapor bath (diphenylmethane). A stream of nitrogen is admitted through a capillary reaching to the bottom of the tube. After allowing the melt to cool in nitrogen, the inherent viscosity of the pale yellow polymer is around 1.0 in m-cresol (0.5% conc., 25°C.) and the polymer-melt temperature is about 250–255°C. A temperature of 340–370°C. is required to press films.

Hydrazine may be condensed at high temperature and under pressure **with a dicarboxylic acid, a dicarboxylic ester, a diamine or a dihydrazide** to produce high polymer through formation of the 4-amino-1,2,4-triazole ring (31).

$$HO-\overset{O}{\underset{\|}{C}}-R-\overset{O}{\underset{\|}{C}}-OH + 2NH_2 \cdot NH_2 \longrightarrow -R-\overset{NH_2}{\underset{\substack{N\\ \| \\ N--N}}{\overset{N}{\diagup \diagdown}}}C- + 4 H_2O$$

An advantage is gained in using the dihydrazide of the acid because a vacuum cycle is not needed in the polymerization. The polyamino-triazoles where —R— is —(CH-)$_6$, $_7$, and $_8$ have been melt spun into fibers having good tensile properties and high dyeability with acid dyes (31,52); the presence of basic sites in the polymer accounts for the latter.

The polymer-melt temperatures of the polyaminotriazoles are high (280°C. for that from adipic acid), the lower alkylene polymers (R = —(CH-)—- or -) are water soluble, and the class as a wyole is soluble in the polyamide solvents (m-cresol, formic acid, etc.).

32. Preparation of Sebacic Dihydrazide (28)

$$CH_3O-\overset{O}{\underset{\|}{C}}-(CH_2)_8\overset{O}{\underset{\|}{C}}-OCH_3 + 2N_2H_4 \longrightarrow$$

$$H_2NHN-\overset{O}{\underset{\|}{C}}-(CH_2)_8-\overset{O}{\underset{\|}{C}}-NHNH_2 + 2CH_3OH$$

A solution of 100 g. (2.0 m.) of hydrazine hydrate in 100 ml. methanol is refluxed gently in a 500 ml. three-necked flask equipped with condenser and dropping funnel. (Caution! Hydrazine is toxic.) A solution of 57 g. (0.25 m.) of dimethyl sebacate in 25 ml. methanol is added dropwise. Heating at reflux is continued 1 hr. after addition. The reaction mixture is cooled in ice, 100 ml. water added, and the solid filtered, washed with water, and recrystallized from water-methanol. Decolorizing charcoal is used if necessary. After drying in a vacuum oven at 60°C. for several hours, the pure product melts at 186.5–188°C. The yield is 48–52 g. (85–91%).

33. Preparation of Poly(3,5-octamethylene-4-amino-1,2,4-triazole) (52)

Twenty grams (0.087 m.) of sebacic dihydrazide and 5.0 g. (0.10 m.) of hydrazine hydrate are placed in a pipe autoclave (11) having an aluminum liner and a pressure gauge. (See Chapter 2) The autoclave is flushed with nitrogen and sealed. The temperature is raised by means of a vapor bath or oil bath to 260°C. for 3 hr., then for 2 hr. further at 270°C. The pressure on the gauge may reach 800–900 p.s.i. It is important for safety reasons to use a pipe autoclave rated for use at these pressures and to have the reaction properly shielded. The pressure is released to about 100 p.s.i. after 3 hr. of the heating cycle. At the end of the polymerization the autoclave is allowed to cool and is cautiously bled to atmospheric pressure. The plug of off-white or light gray polymer has a polymer-melt temperature of around 250°C. and an inherent viscosity in m-cresol (0.5% conc., 25°C.) of 0.6–0.7. The polymer is soluble also in formic and acetic acids, from which the polymer can be spun into filaments or cast into films.

II. Polyureas and Related Polymers

The polyureas may be considered as polyamides derived from the lowest member in the homologous series of dicarboxylic acids, namely carbonic acid, and are therefore like the other polyamides and have a large number of sites available for inter-chain hydrogen bonding. The polyureas are generally higher melting and less soluble than the other polyamides having a similar amount of separation between functional groups. For instance, poly(hexamethyleneurea) has a polymer melt temperature of about 295°C., while that of 6-6 polyamide is about 265°C.

$$\left[-(CH_2)_6-NH\overset{\overset{\displaystyle O}{\|}}{C}NH- \right] \qquad \left[-(CH_2)_6-NH\overset{\overset{\displaystyle O}{\|}}{C}-(CH_2)_4-\overset{\overset{\displaystyle O}{\|}}{C}-NH- \right]$$

PMT 295°C. PMT 265°C.

The greater extent of hydrogen bonding and higher polarity associated with the urea group are thought to account for the difference.

Polyureas can in some cases be made in melt systems, but high polymer-melt temperatures and accompanying thermal instability frequently require solution techniques for preparation. A number of special methods have been developed for the preparation of polyureas.

Polyureas can be prepared in solution **from** the reaction of a **diisocyanate and diamine.** By taking advantage of the far greater reactivity of isocyanates with amines over phenols and alcohols, the polymerization may be conducted in hydroxylic solvents for the polymer (100). Poly(decamethyleneurea) can be prepared by a diisocyanate-diamine reaction carried out in *m*-cresol.

Following polyamide numeral nomenclature, polyureas would be called *n*-1 polyamides; *n* = the number of carbons in the diamine, and 1 = carbonic acid, the one-carbon diacid. The polyurea prepared below is 10-1 polyamide.

34. Preparation of Decamethylenediisocyanate (100)

$$ClH \cdot H_2N(CH_2)_{10}-NH_2 \cdot HCl + COCl_2 \longrightarrow OCN-(CH_2)_{10}-NCO + 4HCl$$

Caution! Run in a Good Hood.

A solution of 86 g. (0.5 *m*.) of decamethylenediamine in 1000 ml. of dry xylene (isomer mixture is satisfactory) is prepared in a 2 l. three-necked flask equipped with gas inlet tube extending nearly to the bottom of the flask, and a condenser having an outlet to a trap or scrubber for the off-gases of the reaction. Dry hydrogen chloride is passed through the diamine solution until no further precipitation occurs and the solution is saturated. The hydrogen chloride source is replaced by a phosgene cylinder and the solution is heated to reflux as a slow stream of phosgene is passed through it. (Phosgene is a highly toxic gas, and the reaction must be run in a good hood.) The gases from the reaction are hydrogen chloride and unreacted phosgene. When almost all the solid has dissolved (a period of about 6 hr. is required), the reaction mixture is cooled and filtered. The xylene is distilled at water aspirator pressure through a 10 in. Vigreux column. The residue is then fractionated through the same column at oil pump pressure to give 70–75 g. (62–67% yield) of decamethylenediisocyanate, boiling at 151–153°C./3.0 mm. The product should be stored under nitrogen in tightly stoppered flasks or in taped, screwcap bottles, preferably in a dry box.

35. Preparation of Poly(decamethyleneurea) (100)

$$H_2N—(CH_2)_{10}—NH_2 + OCN—(CH_2)_{10}—NCO \longrightarrow$$

$$\left[—(CH_2)_{10}NH—\overset{O}{\overset{\|}{C}}—NH \right]_n$$

In a 200 ml. three-necked flask which has been flushed with nitrogen and equipped with stirrer, dropping funnel, and condenser (the latter two protected with drying tubes) is placed a solution of 19.0 g. (0.11 m.) freshly distilled decamethylenediamine (Preparation 15) in 39 ml. of distilled m-cresol. With stirring, 24.8 g. (0.11 m.) decamethylenediisocyanate is added over a 10 min. period. Much heat is evolved and a precipitate forms. The dropping funnel is washed with 10 ml. m-cresol and the temperature is raised to 218°C. for a period of 5 hr. The original precipitate dissolves and the solution becomes viscous. The solution is then permitted to cool and is poured into 1500 ml. methanol with vigorous stirring. The polymer, which separates as a white solid, is filtered and washed several times by stirring (as in a household-type blender) with ethanol. The yield of polymer, when dried at 60°C. in a vacuum oven for 15 hr., is about 38–40 g. (90–95%), and the polymer melt temperature is about 210°C. The inherent viscosity in m-cresol (0.5% conc. at 25°C.) is about 0.3. Despite this low value, films may be melt pressed and drawable fibers melt spun.

Very high melting, soluble polyureas have also been prepared **from all-aromatic reactants** (41) by a solution method similar to that of the preceding example. If the polymer formed is soluble at room temperature in the reaction medium, no heating may be necessary, and a viscous polymer solution may result. The following polymerization, where 4,4'-diaminodiphenylether is added to 2,4-toluenediisocyanate, exemplifies this type of reaction. An alternating copolyurea is formed in this instance.

36. Preparation of Alternating Poly(4,4'-oxydiphenylurea/2,4-tolyleneurea) (41)

For use in the following polymerization, 4,4′-diaminodiphenylether can be purified by recrystallization from ethanol or by vacuum sublimation. Its melting point is 193–195°C. The 2,4-toluenediisocyanate is purified by distillation, b.p. 75–78°C./1 mm. The dimethylformamide should be fractionally distilled (b.p. 154°C.) from 2,4-toluenediisocyanate, which is added to the pot in the amount of 8 g./l.

In a 100 ml. three-necked flask equipped with a stirrer is placed 5.00 g. (0.025 m.) of 4,4′-diaminodiphenylether in 25 ml. of dimethylformamide. To it is added, all at one time, with stirring a solution of 4.35 g. (0.025 m.) 2,4-toluenediisocyanate in 25 ml. dimethylformamide. The diisocyanate solution should be prepared last and added as soon as prepared.

The reaction is stirred for $1/2$ hr., during which time some heat is generated and the solution becomes somewhat viscous. The solution may be cast directly onto glass plates and dried in a vacuum oven at 70–80°C. for about 3 hr. to give clear, flexible films. The polymer may be isolated by pouring into into 400 ml. rapidly stirred water (as in a home blender), washing further with water and drying in vacuum at 70°C. The inherent viscosity in sulfuric acid is 0.4 (0.5% conc., 25°C.); the polymer melt temperature is about 320°C. with decomposition.

For those polyureas that are stable above their melt temperatures the **reaction of a diamine with urea** in a melt-polymerization system with elimination of ammonia can sometimes be used in their preparation (101).

$$H_2N-R-NH_2 + H_2N-\overset{\overset{O}{\|}}{C}-NH_2 \longrightarrow \left[R-NH-\overset{\overset{O}{\|}}{C}-NH \right] + 2NH_3$$

In the following example of this reaction, the diamine is bis (γ-aminopropyl) ether. The resulting polyurea has the relatively low polymer melt temperature of 190°C. due, in part, to the odd number of atoms in the diamine chain.

37. Preparation of Bis(γ-aminopropyl) Ether (88)

$$CH_2{=}CHCN + HOCH_2CH_2CN \longrightarrow NCCH_2CH_2OCH_2CH_2CN$$

$$NCCH_2CH_2OCH_2CH_2CN \xrightarrow{[H]} H_2NCH_2CH_2CH_2OCH_2CH_2CH_2NH_2$$

A. Bis(β-cyanoethyl) Ether (17)

To a stirred mixture of 177 g. (2.5 m.) of ethylene cyanohydrin and 6 g. of a 20% potassium hydroxide solution in a 1 l. three-necked flask equipped with stirrer, dropping funnel and condenser is added dropwise 132 g. (2.5 m.) of acrylonitrile over $2^3/4$ hr. The reaction is maintained at 40°C. during addition. When the addition is complete, the reaction is stirred for 18 hr. further at room temperature. It is neutralized with dilute hydrochloric acid and evaporated to dryness under water aspirator pressure (about 30 mm.) on the steam bath. The residue is fractionally distilled to yield about 266 g. (80%) of bis(β-cyanoethyl) ether, boiling at 159–162°C./5 mm.

B. *Bis(γ-aminopropyl) Ether (88)*

To a solution of 86 g. (0.69 *m*.) bis(β-cyanoethyl)ether in 340 ml. methanol containing 100 g. of anhydrous ammonia in a hydrogenation bomb is added 100 g. of Raney nickel catalyst (54). The dinitrile is hydrogenated at 1500 p.s.i. at 100–110°C. Hydrogen uptake should be complete in about $^1/_2$ hr. Prolonged heating of the reaction mixture reduces the yield of desired product by hydrogenolysis of the ether to γ-aminopropanol. The solution is filtered free of catalyst and the methanol and ammonia removed by distillation on the steam bath at atmospheric pressure. The residue is fractionally distilled through a precision distillation column. Bis(γ-aminopropyl)ether boils at 72–73°C./3 mm. The yield is about 60 g. (65%). The possible by-product, γ-aminopropanol, boils at 60°C./3 mm., and has the same refractive index (n_D^{25} 1.4605) as the desired diamino ether.

38. Preparation of Poly(4-oxaheptamethyleneurea) (101)

$$H_2N(CH_2)_3\!-\!O\!-\!(CH_2)_3NH_2 + H_2N\overset{\overset{\displaystyle O}{\|}}{C}\!-\!NH_2 \longrightarrow$$

$$\left[\!(CH_2)_3\!-\!O\!-\!(CH_2)_3NH\!-\!\overset{\overset{\displaystyle O}{\|}}{C}\!-\!NH\!-\!\right]_n + 2NH_3$$

In a polymer tube with side arm is placed a mixture of 7.5 g. (0.125 *m*.) of urea and 16.5 g. (0.125 *m*.) of bis(γ-aminopropyl) ether.

Nitrogen is passed slowly through a capillary reaching to the bottom of the tube and the temperature is raised to 156°C. for 1 hr. by means of a vapor bath (cyclohexanone), during which time ammonia is evolved. The temperature is raised to 231°C. in a vapor bath for another 1 hr. period, and finally to 255°C. for 1 hr. During the last 20 min. of this part of the heating, an oil pump vacuum is cautiously applied; frothing may be serious if the vacuum is applied suddenly. The polymer is cooled under nitrogen and removed by breaking the tube. The inherent viscosity is about 0.6 in *m*-cresol (0.5% conc., 25°C.) and the polymer melt temperature is around 190°C. Strong films may be melt pressed at or near this temperature.

Polyureas can be prepared also by the **aminolysis of a bisurethane,** with the elimination of an alcohol (102).

$$H_2N\!-\!R\!-\!NH_2 + EtO\overset{\overset{\displaystyle O}{\|}}{C}\!-\!NH\!-\!R\!-\!NH\!-\!\overset{\overset{\displaystyle O}{\|}}{C}OEt \longrightarrow$$

$$\left[\!R\!-\!NH\!-\!\overset{\overset{\displaystyle O}{\|}}{C}\!-\!NH\!\right]_n + 2EtOH$$

Carbonate esters are also reported to form polyureas by reaction with diamines, but the reaction is difficult to control.

The following polymer is a copolyurea of hexamethylene- and decamethylenediamines.

39. Preparation of Poly(hexamethylene-decamethyleneurea) Copolymer (102).

$$H_2N(CH_2)_{10}NH_2 + C_2H_5O\overset{\overset{O}{\|}}{C}-NH(CH_2)_6NH-\overset{\overset{O}{\|}}{C}OC_2H_5 \longrightarrow$$

$$\left[(CH_2)_{10}-NH\overset{\overset{O}{\|}}{C}NH-(CH_2)_6-NH-\overset{\overset{O}{\|}}{C}NH\right]_n + 2C_2H_5OH$$

The hexamethylene bis(ethylurethane) is prepared (25) by the simultaneous addition from separate funnels of 130 g. (1.2 m.) ethyl chlorocarbonate and 48 g. (1.2 m.) sodium hydroxide in 400 ml. water to a rapidly stirred solution of 58 g. (0.5 m.) hexamethylenediamine in 200 ml. ether cooled in an ice bath and maintained at 10°C. or less during the addition. The reaction is stirred for 15 min. after the addition and the solid filtered. It is recrystallized from benzene-petroleum ether. The melting point is 84°C.

A mixture of 12.37 g. (0.072 m.) of decamethylenediamine and 18.70 g. (0.072 m.) of hexamethylene bis(ethylurethane) is placed in a polymer tube which is then purged with nitrogen (Preparation 2) and heated to 202°C. (m-cresol bath) for 3 hr. at atmospheric pressure while a slow stream of nitrogen is passed through the melt. The polymer is cooled under nitrogen and is obtained as a tough plug. It has an inherent viscosity of 0.2–0.4 in m-cresol (0.5% conc., 25°C.) and a polymer melt temperature of about 170°C. It can be pulled into fibers from the melt and melt pressed into films.

A preparation of **aliphatic polyureas from a diamine and carbon oxysulfide** was developed by Van der Kerk (84). This reaction involves, first, the formation of what can be depicted as the thiocarbamate

salt, $\overset{+}{H_3N}-R-NH-\overset{\overset{O}{\|}}{C}-S^-$. The salt is then heated to form polyurea with the loss of hydrogen sulfide. The polymerization is not carried out in the melt, but rather in the form of the solid salt, and is an example of powder polymerization.

Polyureas previously been have prepared in formally similar reactions of diamines with carbon dioxide (18) but these require high temperatures and pressures (100 atm). Carbon disulfide reacts in like manner to give a polythiourea (37), and carbon oxysulfide has been stated to give a polythiourea also. The formation of a normal polyurea from carbon oxysulfide, as in the present case is, therefore, somewhat unusual.

The mechanism of the polymerization involves the formation, first, of low polymer during a mild heating cycle (110°C.), with the loss of some COS and diamine as well as H_2S. The low polymer, on heating at higher temperatures (150–180°C.) splits out more diamine by aminolysis of urea links near the end of a chain by H_2N— ends of another chain, forming higher polymer:

$$H_3\overset{+}{N}-R-NH-\overset{\displaystyle O}{\overset{\|}{C}}-S^- \xrightarrow{110°C.} \left[H_2N-R-NH-\overset{\displaystyle O}{\overset{\|}{C}}-NH\right]_x R-NH_2 + H_2S$$

$$\Bigg\downarrow \text{150–80°C.}$$

$$\left[H_2N-R-NH-\overset{\displaystyle O}{\overset{\|}{C}}-NH\right]_y R-NH_2 + (y-x)H_2N-R-NH_2$$

where y is larger than x. The later stages of the reaction bear a resemblance to the preparation of poly(ethylene terephthalate) from polymerization of bis(hydroxyethyl)terephthalate by elimination of ethylene glycol. The reaction has been used for the preparation of polyureas from the six through ten and the twelve carbon diamines.

40. Preparation of the Thiocarbamate Salt of Decamethylenediamine (84)

$$2KCNS + 3H_2SO_4 + 2H_2O \longrightarrow 2COS + 2KHSO_4 + (NH_4)_2SO_4$$

$$H_2N-(CH_2)_{10}-NH_2 + COS \longrightarrow H_3\overset{+}{N}-(CH_2)_{10}-NH-\overset{\displaystyle O}{\overset{\|}{C}}-S^-$$

A 1 l. three-necked flask is set up as a carbon oxysulfide generator by providing it with a stirrer, dropping funnel, and a short air condenser topped with a gas outlet leading to a purification train. The latter consists, in order, of a U-tube filled with mercuric oxide dispersed on pumice or glass wool to remove hydrogen sulfide, a similarly prepared tube containing phosphorus pentoxide for drying the gas, a soda-lime-packed tube for removing carbon dioxide, and a kerosene bubbler to absorb carbon disulfide.

The generating flask is charged with 520 g. of concentrated sulfuric acid and 400 ml. of water. The purification train is then swept with nitrogen and connected to the gas generator and to the receiver, which is a 1 l. three-necked flask having a gas inlet tube reaching to the bottom of the flask, a stirrer, and an outlet (protected by a calcium chloride drying tube) leading to a solution of strong sodium hydroxide to absorb unreacted carbon oxysulfide. To the receiver is added 5 g. (0.029 m.) of distilled, carbonate-free, decamethylene-diamine and 600 ml. of hexane. (The hexane is purified by shaking with concentrated sulfuric acid, then washing with aqueous sodium hydroxide and water, drying over anhydrous magnesium sulfate, and distilling over sodium.) The receiving flask should be flushed with nitrogen at the same time as the purification trap, and the diamine should be added to the flask under nitrogen.

To the sulfuric acid in the generator is added dropwise a solution of 48.0 g. (0.49 m.) potassium thiocyanate in water to give a total volume of 50 ml., with stirring at a temperature maintained at 30°C. by means of a warm water bath if necessary. The gas is passed into the diamine in the receiving flask with stirring and moderate ice cooling. The decamethylenediamine thiocarbamate precipitates as the reaction proceeds. When no more precipitate forms, the solid product is filtered with suction under a blanket of nitrogen, either in a dry box or under an inverted glass funnel which is attached to a nitrogen line. The salt is washed on the filter with dry hexane and dried in a vacuum desiccator at 0.5 mm. for 24 hr. It is stored under nitrogen in taped bottles, either in a desiccator or a dry box. The latter is preferred, since weighings of the solid can then be readily made under nitrogen.

The salt analyzes for the monothiocarbamate as shown in the equation for this reaction, but it is believed that the amine groups react at random and that various salt compositions are present. The simple equation represents the over-all composition of the salt, however.

41. Preparation of Poly(decamethyleneurea) (84)

$$H_3\overset{+}{N}—(CH_2)_{10}—NH—\overset{\displaystyle O}{\overset{\|}{C}}—S^- \longrightarrow \left[—(CH_2)_{10}—NH—\overset{\displaystyle O}{\overset{\|}{C}}—NH—\right]_n + H_2S$$

A 100 ml. one-necked flask is charged with 10 g. of decamethylenediamine thiocarbamate salt. The flask is fitted with a short bulb condenser, which has a vacuum take-off at the top. The condenser is attached to a vibrator, which is also a solid means of support, to agitate the contents of the flask continually during polymerization. The flask is not clamped, and depends on the application of vacuum to keep it attached to the condenser and its vibrator support. No water is used in the condenser. (Fig. 3.3)

The pressure is reduced to 12 mm. and the flask is heated (with vibration) to about 110°C. for about 5 hr., when the evolution of hydrogen sulfide ceases. Some sublimate collects in the condenser; it should be noted whether the condenser is in danger of plugging. The pressure is reduced now to 1–2 mm. and the temperature raised to 150°C. for 2 hr., then 180°C. for 16 hr. Higher polymer results if an additional 3 hr. heating at 200°C. is used. The reaction mixture is permitted to cool, then opened to the air. The white, free flowing powder weighs 6.6–7.0 g. (90–95% of theory). The inherent viscosity should be at least 0.5 in m-cresol (0.5% at 25°C.). The polymer melt temperature is 210°C.; the polymer is stable enough above its melting temperature to allow fabrication.

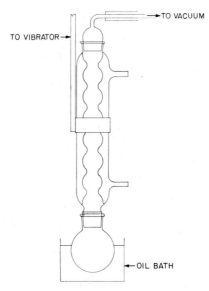

Fig. 3.3. Preparation of a polyurea by powder polymerization.

The highly versatile **interfacial polycondensation** method can be **applied to the preparation of polyureas** also. Phosgene is used as the acid chloride in this instance. In the following preparation of poly(hexamethyleneurea) a definite quantity of phosgene must be used. Bubbling phosgene through the diamine-alkali mixture in unmeasured amount gives lower molecular weights.

42. Preparation of Poly(hexamethyleneurea) (90)

$$H_2N(CH_2)_6NH_2 + COCl_2 \longrightarrow \left[(CH_2)_6-NH\overset{O}{\overset{\|}{C}}NH \right]_n + 2HCl$$

Caution!   Run in a Good Hood.

A solution of 5.8 g. (0.05 *m*.) hexamethylenediamine (Preparation 1) and 4 g. (0.10 *m*.) sodium hydroxide (preferably as an aliquot of a stock solution) in 70 ml. water is added with vigorous manual stirring to a solution of 4.95 g. (0.05 *m*.) phosgene in 200 ml. dry carbon tetrachloride contained in a 500 ml. wide mouth Erlenmeyer flask. The polyurea forms very rapidly and heat is evolved. After the reaction has been stirred briskly for 8–10 min., the carbon tetrachloride is evaporated on the steam bath and the polymer filtered, washed several times with water in a household blender, and air-dried overnight. The weight of polymer obtained is 5 g. (70%), having an inherent viscosity in *m*-

cresol (0.5% conc., 30°C.) of about 0.90. The polymer melt temperature is about 295°C. Films can be melt-pressed.

The solution of phosgene in carbon tetrachloride used in the above polymerization can be prepared by condensing phosgene into dry carbon tetrachloride in a volumetric flask, and adding carbon tetrachloride to complete the volume. The solution is analyzed for g. of phosgene per ml. of solution by shaking thoroughly an aliquot with excess standard sodium hydroxide and titrating the excess sodium hydroxide in the aqueous layer using phenolphthalein indicator. The amount of phosgene, for convenience, should be 0.10–0.20 g./ml.

Certain **polyureas** may be **prepared in dimethyl sulfoxide** as the solvent **using the reaction of a diisocyanate with a monocarboxylic acid.** The solvent participates in the reaction, presumably interacting with the mixed anhydride (I) formed from the addition of the acid to the isocyanate group. As has been shown for the monofunctional reactants, the stoichiometry of the reaction is 2:1:1 for isocyanate:acid:sulfoxide (75).

This reaction is considerably different from the 1:1 reaction of an acid and an isocyanate, alone or in an inert solvent, which leads ultimately to amide formation (see Preparation 28).

43. Preparation of Poly[methylene bis(4-phenylurea)] (75)

This reaction should be carried out in a hood; sulfide odors are formed.

In a 100 ml. three-necked flask fitted with a stirrer and a calcium chloride drying tube is placed 4.84 g. (0.04 m.) dry benzoic acid and 40 ml. dimethyl sulfoxide. (The latter is dried by distillation at reduced pressure with a 20% forerun discarded to insure removal of water; the distillate collected is best stored in a taped, screwcap bottle and opened under nitrogen or in a dry box.) When the benzoic acid has dissolved, 10.0 g. (0.04 m.) methylene bis(4-phenyl isocyanate) is added as a solid all at once to the flask to prevent possible introduction of moisture. (The diisocyanate is purified by distillation, b.p. 142–144°C./0.14 mm., through a short Vigreux column.) As the diisocyanate dissolves, the reaction proceeds exothermically with the evolution of carbon dioxide. When the gas evolution has practically ceased, the reaction is warmed to 50–60°C. for $^1/_2$ hr. in a water bath, then stirred at room temperature until a total of 4 hr. has elapsed since the diisocyanate addition. The solution is now clear, viscous and yellow. Clear, tough films may be cast directly and dried in a vacuum oven at 60–80°C. The polymer may also be isolated from the original solution by precipitation in water, followed by thorough successive washings with water and ethanol in a home blender modified for use with flammable solvents. After drying in a vacuum oven at 60–80°C., the inherent viscosity in dimethyl sulfoxide is about 1.0 (0.5% conc., 25°C.). The polymer melt temperature is around 300°C., and the yield is quantitative (8.8 g.).

Polymer structures **having a high concentration of amide groups** can be made **by the addition of hydrazine or a diacid hydrazide to a diisocyanate.** In many cases, the polymer can be made in solution and cast directly into films or spun into fibers without the need for prior isolation.

The following is an example of **hydrazine-diisocyanate addition to give a polyureylene.** Although anhydrous hydrazine may be used, the hydrate is more convenient.

44. Preparation of Polymer from Methylene bis(4-phenyl isocyanate) and Hydrazine Hydrate: Poly[methylene bis(4-phenylureylene)] (20)

$$OCN-\!\!\left\langle\bigcirc\right\rangle\!-CH_2-\!\!\left\langle\bigcirc\right\rangle\!-NCO + N_2H_4\cdot H_2O \longrightarrow$$

$$\left[-\!\!\left\langle\bigcirc\right\rangle\!-CH_2-\!\!\left\langle\bigcirc\right\rangle\!-NH\overset{O}{\overset{\|}{C}}NHNH\overset{O}{\overset{\|}{C}}NH-\right]_n$$

In a 300 ml. three-necked flask with stirrer, a mixture of 23.0 g. (0.092 m.) of methylene bis(4-phenyl isocyanate), purified as in Preparation 43, and 100 ml. of dry dimethylformamide is treated with a solution of 4.60 g. (0.092 m.) of hydrazine hydrate in 50 ml. of dimethylformamide with stirring. An immediate exothermic reaction occurs, and the solution becomes very viscous.

This solution can be cast to clear, tough film by drying in a vacuum oven at 60°C. in a stream of nitrogen.

The polymer may be precipitated in water, filtered, and washed in a household mixer to cut it up. The yield is quantitative. However, the polymer cannot now be redissolved in dimethylformamide or dimethyl sulfoxide. The polymer decomposes at 300°C. without melting. If dianisidinediisocyanate is used in this preparation, the polymer will redissolve after precipitation.

If **isophthalic dihydrazide** is used in place of hydrazine in the preceding polymerization, the polymer formed is a **poly(isophthaloyl-semicarbazide)**. The structure differs from the preceding example by being less symmetrical and having two less urea-type —NH— groups per chemical repeat unit. The increased solubility in dimethylformamide and related solvents, and lower polymer-melt temperature of the present case reflect this change. The reaction of the diisocyanate with the dihydrazide is initially less vigorous than with hydrazine because of the lower basicity of the hydrazide.

45. Preparation of Isophthalic Dihydrazide (80)

One hundred ninety-four grams (1.0 m.) of dimethyl isophthalate in 500 ml. of methanol is added to 350 g. (7.0 m.) hydrazine hydrate in 2 l. of methanol in a 4 l. Erlenmeyer flask. The solution is allowed to stand overnight. The solid which forms is separated by filtration, washed with methanol on the filter, and dried in a vacuum oven at 70°C. The melting point is 219–220°C. The yield is about 180 g. (93%). The isophthalic dihydrazide may be recrystallized from methanol-water, but this is usually not necessary.

46. Preparation of Polymer from Isophthalic Dihydrazide and Methylene bis(4-phenyl isocyanate) (20)

To a solution of 1.94 g. (0.01 mole) isophthalic dihydrazide in 50 ml. dry dimethyl sulfoxide in a three-necked 100 ml. flask equipped with a stirrer and nitrogen inlet is added at room temperature 2.50 g. (0.01 mole) methylene bis(4-phenyl isocyanate). (Preparation 43). The reaction mixture warms up slightly and becomes viscous very quickly. Stirring at room temperature under nitrogen is continued for 2 hr. The polymer is isolated by pouring the solution into 300 ml. of water, filtered, and is washed twice with water. The solid is dried in air, and has an inherent viscosity in dimethyl sulfoxide of about 1.8. The total yield is 3.5 g. (78%); the polymer melt temperature is 250°C. The polymer is soluble in cold N-methylpyrrolidone, sulfuric acid, dimethyl sulfoxide, dimethylformamide, and in hot hexamethylphosphoramide.

A 20% solution in dimethyl sulfoxide can be prepared and a tough, clear film cast.

Among the more **unusual polymeric products from addition of active hydrogen compounds to diisocyanates** is that from a dioxime (20A). The **reaction of dimethyl glyoxime with hexamethylene diisocyanate** has been given high molecular weight polymer:

$$\underset{\substack{| \\ HON=C}}{\overset{CH_3}{}}\underset{\substack{| \\ C=NOH}}{\overset{CH_3}{}} + OCN{-}(CH_2)_6NCO \longrightarrow$$

$$\left[-ON=\underset{\substack{| \\ C}}{\overset{CH_3}{}}\underset{\substack{| \\ C}}{\overset{CH_3}{}}=NO-\overset{O}{\overset{\|}{C}}NH-(CH_2)_6-NH\overset{O}{\overset{\|}{C}}-\right]_n$$

In the following example, cyclohexanedione dioxime and methylene bis (4-phenyl isocyanate) are the reactants. The products are poly-o-acyloximes. Although they can be fabricated to films and fibers, the polymers degrade at their melting point and in boiling water.

47. Preparation of Cyclohexanedione Dioxime (20A)

A mixture of 39 g. (0.35 m.) of 1,4-cyclohexanedione, 50 g. (0.72 m.) of hydroxylamine hydrochloride, 200 ml. of pyridine, and 200 ml. of absolute alcohol is refluxed for 4 hr. in a 1 l. round-bottom flask equipped with a condenser. The resulting solution is poured into a crystallizing dish and the solvents allowed to evaporate in a stream of air. Four hundred ml. of water is added and the solid is filtered. It is recrystallized from 90% ethanol, giving a white, crystalline solid melting at 201–202°C.

48. Preparation of Polymer from 1,4-cyclohexanedione Dioxime and Biphenylene Diisocyanate (20)

Caution! Biphenylene Diisocyanate Is a Carcinogen.

A solution of 2.93 g. (0.0124 m.) of biphenylene diisocyanate (purified by vaccum sublimation and stored in a freezer) in 15 ml. of dry dimethylformamide is mixed with 1.76 g. (0.0124 m.) of cyclohexanedione dioxime in 10 ml. of dry dimethylformamide at about 80–100°C. in a 100 ml. three-necked flask, equipped with stirrer, condenser, and drying tubes. An immediate reaction is noted and the solution rapidly becomes viscous. After approximately $1/2$ hr., the solution, which has become somewhat cloudy, is poured into water and the polymer is isolated by filtration. It is ground up, washed thoroughly with water, and dried in a high vacuum. The yield is 4.35 g. (94%). The polymer decomposes without melting above 200°C.

The dry polymer is easily soluble in dimethyl sulfoxide. It has an inherent viscosity of 0.81–1.2 (0.5% conc. at 25°C.) in the solvent and can be cast to clear, tough film. A solution of polymer (about 15%) prepared as above can be extruded from a mechanically driven syringe into 50% aqueous dimethylformamide (See Chapter 2) to give fiber which is easily wound up on a mechanical windup.

III. Polyurethanes

The polyurethanes are related in properties to the polyamides because of the similar opportunity for interchain hydrogen bonding. Crystallinity is often easily induced in polyurethanes, or may be present as prepared. They are, however, usually lower melting than the polyamide having the same number of atoms in the chain, for example, as shown in Table 3.4.

TABLE 3.4

Polymer	Polymer-melt temperature, °C.
	180
	240

The most practical methods of preparing polyurethanes in the laboratory are: (a) the reaction of bischloroformates with diamines:

$$Cl-\overset{\overset{\displaystyle O}{\|}}{C}-O-R-O-\overset{\overset{\displaystyle O}{\|}}{C}-Cl + H_2N-R'-NH_2 \longrightarrow$$

$$\left[-\overset{\overset{\displaystyle O}{\|}}{C}-O-R-O-\overset{\overset{\displaystyle O}{\|}}{C}-NH-R'-NH-\right]_n + 2HCl;$$

and (b) the addition of a diol to a diisocyanate:

$$HO-R-OH + OCN-R'-NCO \longrightarrow$$

$$\left[-\overset{\overset{\displaystyle O}{\|}}{C}-O-R-O-\overset{\overset{\displaystyle O}{\|}}{C}-NH-R'-NH-\right]_n$$

Direct melt-polycondensation of a diacid with diol or diamine to form the ester or amide bond, respectively, is impossible in polyurethane preparation because neither the required carbamic acid nor carbonic half-acid ester are stable compounds.

$$HO-\overset{\overset{\displaystyle O}{\|}}{C}-NH-R-NH-\overset{\overset{\displaystyle O}{\|}}{C}OH + HO-R'OH \;-\!/\!-\!/\!\longrightarrow \text{polyurethane}$$

$$HO-\overset{\overset{\displaystyle O}{\|}}{C}-O-R-O-\overset{\overset{\displaystyle O}{\|}}{C}-OH + H_2N-R'-NH_2 \;-\!/\!-\!/\!\longrightarrow \text{polyurethane}$$

Bischloroformates may be prepared from most aliphatic and aromatic diols by reacting them with an excess of phosgene at low temperature (6,62).

$$HO-R-OH + \text{excess } COCl_2 \longrightarrow Cl-\overset{\overset{\displaystyle O}{\|}}{C}-O-R-O-\overset{\overset{\displaystyle O}{\|}}{C}-Cl + 2HCl$$

Chloroformates are less reactive toward amines and alcohols than the comparable carboxylic acid chloride, but more reactive than the sulfonyl chlorides. When they are condensed with diamines, the products are polyurethanes; this type of reaction was the first useage of interfacial polycondensation (7).

The following example is the preparation of a **polyurethane from a cyclic disecondary diamine, piperazine, and ethylene bischloroformate.**

49. Preparation of Ethylene Bischloroformate (62)

$$HOCH_2CH_2OH + COCl_2 \longrightarrow Cl-\overset{\overset{\displaystyle O}{\|}}{C}-O-CH_2CH_2-O-\overset{\overset{\displaystyle O}{\|}}{C}-Cl + 2HCl$$

Carry out in a Good Hood. Phosgene Is Toxic!

About 650 ml. (ca. 900 g., 9 m.) of phosgene is condensed into an ice-cooled, 1-l. three-necked flask equipped with a dry ice condenser, stirrer, and dropping funnel, all suitably protected by drying tubes. To the ice-cooled, stirred liquid is added dropwise 125 g. (2 m.) of ethylene glycol. The reaction is stirred from 3–4 hr. after addition is complete. The excess phosgene is allowed to evaporate or is trapped in aqueous alcohol-caustic if venting through the hood poses a safety hazard. The residue is heated at 40–50°C. at 20 mm. for a short time to remove any volatile material. On distillation at 1–2 mm. through a short path system, 340 g. (91% yield) of ethylene bischloroformate is obtained. It is redistilled through a 10 in. glass helices packed column to give a product boiling at 71–72°C./2.2 mm. If pure ethylene glycol is used, the product obtained after removal of the excess phosgene and other volatiles should be tested in a polymerization before distilling. Polymer grade material may sometimes be gotten without distillation.

50. Preparation of Poly(ethylene N,N'-piperazinedicarboxylate) (89,93)

$$
\text{HN}\begin{array}{c}\diagup CH_2\!-\!CH_2\diagdown\\ \diagdown CH_2\!-\!CH_2\diagup\end{array}\!\!NH + Cl\!-\!\overset{\overset{\displaystyle O}{\|}}{C}\!-\!OCH_2CH_2O\!-\!\overset{\overset{\displaystyle O}{\|}}{C}\!-\!Cl \longrightarrow
$$

$$
\left[\!-\!N\!\!\begin{array}{c}\diagup CH_2\!-\!CH_2\diagdown\\ \diagdown CH_2\!-\!CH_2\diagup\end{array}\!\!N\!-\!\overset{\overset{\displaystyle O}{\|}}{C}\!-\!OCH_2CH_2O\!-\!\overset{\overset{\displaystyle O}{\|}}{C}\!-\!\right]_n + 2HCl
$$

Four and five-tenths g. (0.052 mole) piperazine and 10.6 g. (0.10 mole) sodium carbonate are dissolved in 100 ml. ice cold water. (It is better to use a standardized piperazine stock solution and take aliquots than to weigh piperazine hexahydrate because of its variable moisture content.) The solution is stirred rapidly in a household blender and a solution of 6.4 ml. (9.35 g., 0.050 mole) ethylene bischloroformate in 30 ml. methylene chloride is added all at once. Polymer viscosity will be poorer if the acid chloride solution is added slowly. Using more (50 or 100 ml.) methylene chloride decreases viscosity only slightly.

The reaction mixture thickness rapidly, and in a few minutes it looks like cottage cheese. At that stage it is transferred to a 1-l. beaker with approximately 500 ml. water. The beaker is placed on a hot plate and methylene chloride is partially evaporated while stirring occasionally with a stirring rod. The methylene chloride should not be evaporated completely because then the polymer sets up in extremely tough chunks that can be cut up only with difficulty. As soon as the polymer is solid enough to stick together, it is ready to be chopped up.

The solid polymer is returned to the blender with some water and chopped up into small particles. It is filtered on a Büchner funnel and washed several times with warm water. It is dried in a vacuum oven at 90°C. for 24 hr. The yield is 9.5 g. (95%); the inherent viscosity (m-cresol at 25°C.) may be as high as 4.4 if intermediates are very pure, but 2.5 can easily be obtained. The polymer is soluble in formic acid. The polymer melt temperature is 238°C.

All of the polycondensations involving acid chlorides so far have been between AA and BB type reactants. It is possible, however, to use **AB monomers where one functional group is an acid chloride if the other functional site is blocked by a group, which when removed, permits polymerization** to take place. For instance, an amine group may be blocked by making the hydrochloride or p-toluenesulfonate salt, then freed for reaction by treatment with base:

$$\overset{-}{C}l-H_3\overset{+}{N}-R-\overset{O}{\overset{\|}{C}}-Cl + 2base \longrightarrow \left[-HN-R-\overset{O}{\overset{\|}{C}}-\right]_n + 2base \cdot HCl$$

In the following preparation, pentanolamine is first formed from ω-hydroxyvaleraldehyde and ammonia. The pentanol amine is then converted to the tosylate salt of the amine group, followed by conversion to the chloroformate ester of the hydroxyl group (63). The amine group is then liberated by addition to a potassium carbonate solution and polymerization occurs.

51. Preparation of 5-Aminopentylchloroformate p-Toluenesulfonate (63)

$$HO(CH_2)_4-\overset{O}{\overset{\|}{C}}-H \xrightarrow[NH_3]{[H]} HO(CH_2)_5-NH_2$$

$$HO-(CH_2)_5-NH_2 \xrightarrow{p\text{-}CH_3\text{-}\phi\text{-}SO_3H} HO-(CH_2)_5-\overset{+}{N}H_3\overset{-}{O}_3S-\phi-CH_3-p$$

$$HO-(CH_2)_5-NH_3O_3S-\phi-CH_3-p \xrightarrow{COCl_2}$$

$$Cl-\overset{O}{\overset{\|}{C}}-O-(CH_2)_5-\overset{+}{N}H_3\overset{-}{O}_3S-\phi-CH_3-p$$

A 1 l. hydrogenation bomb (stainless steel) is charged with 102 g. (1.0 m.) hydroxyvaleraldehyde (94B), 300 g. ammonia, and 20 g. Raney nickel (54). The mixture is heated to 110°C. and hydrogenated at 1600 p.s.i. for $3^1/_2$ hr. The product is separated from the catalyst by filtration and distilled through a 10 in. glass helices-packed column. The boiling point of pentanolamine is 95°C./6 mm.; the yield is 57 g. (56%).

The p-toluenesulfonate salt of the pentanolamine is formed by mixing equimolar amounts of pentanolamine and p-toluenesulfonic acid monohydrate in ethyl acetate solution. The precipitated salt is recrystallized from ethyl acetate/ethanol mixture (90/10 by volume) to give 51% yield of the salt melting at 111°C.

One hundred ml. of phosgene (estimated by previously marking the reaction vessel at the desired capacity) is condensed into an ice cooled 250 ml. three-necked flask containing 10 g. (0.41 m.) of the pentanolamine salt, and equipped with stirrer, dry ice condenser protected with drying tube, and a gas inlet tube for admitting phosgene. **(Caution! Phosgene Is Highly Toxic and Should be Used Only in a Properly Functioning Hood.)** The ice bath is removed and the salt suspension in phosgene allowed to stir and reflux at room temperature for $1/2$ hr., after which 50 g. of washed, dry chloroform is added and stirring is continued for another $1/2$ hr. The phosgene is then evaporated by replacing the dry ice condenser with an exit tube protected with a drying tube and placing a bath of warm water (45–50°C.) around the flask. The phosgene may be vented up the hood if the hood exit is sufficiently isolated. In larger runs (or in this one, if conditions require it) the phosgene should be trapped by passing it into an excess of aqueous alcoholic caustic. The chloroform is then evaporated by water aspirator (protect flask with drying tube between it and aspirator) and the solid product recrystallized from dry benzene. The chloroformate salt is obtained as white needles melting at 114–116°C. The weight is 7.5 g. (60%).

52. Preparation of the Polyurethane of ε-Hydroxypentanecarbamic Acid (63)

$$\underset{\substack{\\}}{\overset{\overset{\textstyle O}{\|}}{Cl-C}}-O-(CH_2)_5-\overset{+}{N}H_3\overset{-}{O}_3S-\langle\!=\!\rangle-CH_3 \xrightarrow{K_2CO_3} \left[\overset{\overset{\textstyle O}{\|}}{-C}-O-(CH_2)_5-NH-\right]_n$$

A solution of 1.0 g. of recrystallized 5-aminopentylchloroformate-*p*-toluene-sulfonate in 5 ml. dry chloroform is added to 5 ml. of $4M$ potassium carbonate in an 18 × 150 mm. test tube with vigorous stirring, provided by a motor driven glass rod with a paddle formed at the tip. An ice bath, placed around the tube just before polymerization is removed after 4–5 min. The mixture is stirred vigorously for 30 min., at which point the precipitated polymer is filtered and washed with both cold and hot water by trituration and filtration. It is dried at 60°C. in a vacuum oven. The yield is 0.4 g. (83%) of polymer having a polymer-melt temperature of 150–155°C. and an inherent viscosity of 0.7–0.9 in *m*-cresol (0.5% conc. at 25°C.). It is soluble in chloroform/methanol, (85/15 by volume). It is sufficiently stable to be fabricated from the melt.

Although alcohols do not react with isocyanates as rapidly as do amines, the yield is sufficiently high to permit the formation of **high polymer from diol-diisocyanate reactions** if the proper conditions are used. If the melt stability of the resulting polymer permits, the addition may be carried out without solvent at a sufficiently high temperature to keep the mixture molten. A solvent may be used, providing the polymer is either soluble or is swollen enough to permit reaction of the chain ends to proceed until a high molecular weight is reached.

The diol-diisocyanate addition reaction was used in Germany during World War II for the production on a modest scale of the polyurethane from tetramethylene glycol and hexamethylene diisocyanate (7).

53. Preparation of Poly(tetramethylene hexamethylenedicarbamate) by Melt Methods (7)

$$HO—(CH_2)_4—OH + OCN—(CH_2)_6—NCO \longrightarrow$$

$$\left[—(CH_2)_4—O—\overset{\overset{\displaystyle O}{\|}}{C}—NH(CH_2)_6NH—\overset{\overset{\displaystyle O}{\|}}{C}—O— \right]_n$$

A 250 ml. three-necked flask is fitted with a calcium chloride drying tube and an efficient stirring motor with a metal shaft and paddle. The eventual viscosity of the reaction may break glass stirring equipment. The flask is charged with 45.0 g. (0.500 m.) of tetramethylene glycol and a low pressure nitrogen flow is passed through the flask (above the surface of the liquid) through the third neck to displace the air. The tetramethylene glycol purity must be high; it should be subjected to careful fractional distillation (b.p. 120°C./10 mm.) to give a product melting at 19.7°C.

The nitrogen inlet tube is replaced by a stoppered, pressure-equalizing dropping funnel containing 83.16 g. (0.495 m.) of hexamethylene diisocyanate. The flask is heated to 50°C. in an oil bath and the diisocyanate is added with rapid stirring, over a period of 1 hr., during which time the temperature of the bath is raised to 190–195°C. The reaction is continued at this temperature until no further viscosity increase occurs. Good mixing is required to prevent local hot spots and the possible branched or cross-linked structure that could result. An insoluble, nonfluid product indicates the latter has occurred.

While the mixture is still molten, the stirrer paddle is raised and the mass allowed to cool. The hard, tough polymer is removed by breaking the flask. The polymer is cut up into pieces and ground through a 20 mesh screen in a mill. It is washed with methanol twice in a household blender and dried at 60°C. in a vacuum oven. The yield is essentially quantitative. The polymer melt temperature is about 180°C. and the inherent viscosity is 0.8–1.4 in m-cresol (0.5% conc. at 25°C.). Other solvents are phenol and formamide. The product can be melt-pressed to give films and can be melt spun to fibers, at a temperature of 190–200°C.

As an alternative to the melt-polymerization, one may carry out the **reaction in chlorobenzene/o-dichlorobenzene solution.** The polymer is soluble in the hot solvent mixture, but precipitates on cooling.

54. Preparation of Poly(tetramethylene hexamethylenedicarbamate) in Solution (48)

An 80/20 by volume mixture of chlorobenzene and o-dichlorobenzene, both purified by distillation over calcium hydride, is used as the solvent in the following reaction.

A dry, 1-l. three-necked flask equipped with a stirrer, nitrogen inlet, and reflux condenser with calcium chloride drying tube is flushed out with nitrogen and is then charged with 2.68 g. of pure tetramethylene glycol (Preparation 53) in 100 ml. of solvent. The nitrogen inlet is replaced by a dropping funnel and the solution heated to reflux. From the funnel is added 5.0 g. of hexamethylene diisocyanate in 50 ml. of solvent; about half the diisocyanate is added rapidly with vigorous stirring and the remainder over 3–4 hr. The solution is held at reflux for 1 hr. after addition. When the solution is cooled to room temperature, the polymer precipitates and the solvent is decanted. The polymer is dissolved in 50 ml. of hot dimethylformamide and 50 ml. of methanol is added to the still warm solution. The clear solution is cooled in a refrigerator overnight, and the precipitated polymer separated by filtration and dried at 0.1 mm. pressure in a vacuum desiccator overnight. The inherent viscosity is 0.5–0.7 in m-cresol (0.5% conc., 25°C.). The properties are essentially the same as the melt-prepared polymer.

55. Preparation of Poly(ethylene methylene bis(4-phenylcarbamate) (42b)

$$OCN-\langle\!\!\!\bigcirc\!\!\!\rangle-CH_2-\langle\!\!\!\bigcirc\!\!\!\rangle-NCO + HOCH_2CH_2OH \longrightarrow$$

$$\left[\begin{array}{c} \overset{O}{\underset{\|}{-C}}NH-\langle\!\!\!\bigcirc\!\!\!\rangle-CH_2-\langle\!\!\!\bigcirc\!\!\!\rangle-NH-\overset{O}{\underset{\|}{C}}-OCH_2CH_2O- \end{array}\right]_n$$

The diisocyanate is purified by distillation through a vacuum-jacketed Vigreux column, b.p. 148–150°C./0.12 mm. The ethylene glycol is purified by distillation; b.p. 79°C./4.4 mm., $n_D^{25°C.} = 1.4300$, and % H_2O = 0.05 or less. The solvents are purified by distillation: dimethylsulfoxide, b.p. 66°C./5 mm.; 4-methylpentanone-2, b.p. 115°C.

Forty ml. of 4-methylpentanone-2 and 25.02 g. of methylene bis(4-phenylisocyanate) are placed in a three-neck round bottom flask equipped with stirrer and condenser and protected from moisture. To this rapidly stirred suspension is added 6.20 g. of ethylene glycol in 40 ml. of dimethylsulfoxide. The reaction is heated at 115°C. for $1\frac{1}{2}$ hr. The clear, viscous solution is then poured into water to precipitate the polyurethane. The tough, white polymer is chopped up in a home blender, washed with water, then dried in a vacuum oven at 90°C. Inherent viscosity is 1.0 in N,N-dimethylformamide at room temperature (conc. 0.5%). Films may be dry cast from dimethylformamide or directly from the originally prepared polymerization solution. The polymer-melt temperature is 255°C. and the glass transition temperature is 90°C.

IV. Polyesters

Virtually all the methods of esterification known in organic chemistry have been applied to the preparation of polyesters. Ester exchange, transesterification, and direct reaction of carboxyl or acid chloride groups are commonly used.

It may be necessary to use catalyst to increase the rate of reaction to a reasonable level. Acidic or basic catalysts, or combinations of the two, have been used, and the variety of both types has been great. For reactions involving aliphatic diols, weakly acidic or basic catalysts are usually required in order to prevent dehydration to ether or olefin. Metal oxides of the Group V metals, sodium alkoxytitanates, tetra-alkyltitanate esters, and alkaline earth salts of weak acids are among the catalyst types used (71,86,87,103).

The properties of polyesters vary widely, from the aliphatic esters that are viscous liquids just above room temperature, to the high-melting products from aromatic acids or bisphenols. Lacking the opportunity for interchain hydrogen bonds, the polyesters melt substantially lower than the polyamide of like structure (Table 3.5). Their solubilities differ considerably from polyamides also.

TABLE 3.5

Polymer	Polymer melt temperature, °C.	Solvents
$\left[-O(CH_2)_6O-\overset{\overset{\displaystyle O}{\|\|}}{C}-(CH_2)_4-\overset{\overset{\displaystyle O}{\|\|}}{C}- \right]$	60	Ethyl acetate, benzene
$\left[-NH(CH_2)_6NH-\overset{\overset{\displaystyle O}{\|\|}}{C}-(CH_2)_4-\overset{\overset{\displaystyle O}{\|\|}}{C}- \right]$	265	m-Cresol, formic acid

Unlike polyamidation reactions under melt conditions, the preparation of **polyesters** in the melt **from diols and** the **esters of diacids** does not always require exact reactant balance at the start. An excess of diol leads first to low molecular weight, hydroxy-ended polymer, which then goes over to high polymer by ester exchange reactions and evolution of the excess diol. Ester exchange occurs much more readily than amide exchange. For example, bis(hydroxyethyl)-terephthalate is a suitable monomer for poly(ethylene terephthalate) preparation.

Poly(ethylene terephthalate) is a commercial example of a melt-polymerized polyester.

The following polymerization process is applicable in general to any system in which the monomers and polymers are thermally stable at temperatures above the polymer melting point, and the glycol is sufficiently volatile to permit the excess to be completely removed under vacuum. In this preparation there are two ester exchange reactions. The first forms "monomer," from excess glycol and dimethyl terephthalate, with elimination of methanol. The second eliminates glycol and forms the polymer.

56. Preparation of Poly(ethylene terephthalate) (86,87)

$$CH_3O-\overset{\overset{O}{\|}}{C}-\underset{}{\bigcirc}-\overset{\overset{O}{\|}}{C}-OCH_3 + 2HOCH_2CH_2OH \longrightarrow$$

$$HOCH_2CH_2O-\overset{\overset{O}{\|}}{C}-\underset{}{\bigcirc}-\overset{\overset{O}{\|}}{C}-OCH_2CH_2OH + 2CH_3OH$$

$$HOCH_2CH_2O-\overset{\overset{O}{\|}}{C}-\underset{}{\bigcirc}-\overset{\overset{O}{\|}}{C}-OCH_2CH_2OH \longrightarrow$$

$$\left[-OCH_2CH_2O-\overset{\overset{O}{\|}}{C}-\underset{}{\bigcirc}-\overset{\overset{O}{\|}}{C}-\right]_n + HOCH_2CH_2OH$$

For the following preparation, dimethyl tetrephthalate may be purified by recrystallization from ethanol; the melting point is 141–142°C. The ethylene glycol is purified by dissolving metallic sodium in it (1 g./100 ml.) and refluxing in an atmosphere of nitrogen for 1 hr., followed by distillation (b.p. 196–197°C.)

In a polymer tube bearing a side arm is placed 15.5 g. (0.08 m.) dimethyl terephthalate, 11.8 g. (0.19 m.) ethylene glycol, 0.025 g. calcium acetate dihydrate, and 0.006 g. antimony trioxide (71). The tube is partially immersed in a 197°C. vapor bath to melt the mixture, and a capillary tube is introduced which reaches to the bottom of the tube. A slow stream of nitrogen is passed through the melt. Methanol is distilled from the mixture during the course of 1 hr., after which time the polymer tube is immersed as far as is practical in the vapors of the heating bath. The mixture is heated another 2 hr. at 197°C. Removal of the last trace of methanol is a requisite for high polymer formation. It may become necessary to heat the side arm during this period to prevent clogging from the distillation of some dimethyl terephthalate.

The polymer tube is now heated by means of a 222°C. vapor bath (methyl salicylate) for 20 min., then is transferred to a 283°C. vapor bath (dimethyl phthalate). After 10 min., the pressure is reduced to 0.3 mm., or less, over 15–20 min. Due safety precautions, especially as to adequate shielding, should be observed (see Preparation 2). The polymerization is continued for 3 hr.; the alteration in rate of bubble rise from the capillary indicates the change in viscosity. The polymer tube is wrapped in a towel and is allowed to

cool under nitrogen; shattering of the tube may occur as the polymer con-
tracts. The yield of polymer is quantitative if no dimethyl terephthalate was
distilled in the early phases of the polymerization. The inherent viscosity in
sym-tetrachloroethanol/phenol (40/60 weight) should be about 0.6–0.7 (0.5%
conc., 30°C.). Particularly flexible, tough films may be melt-pressed and
strong, cold-drawable fibers pulled from the melt. The polymer melt temperature is about 270°C. The crystalline melting point is about 260°C.

The polymerization procedure, cited before, may be used to prepare
a wide variety of polyesters. A number of different catalysts have been
used in such reactions. Tetraisopropyl titanate is one of them, and
use is made of it in the following **preparation of a polyester having a
cyclic structure in the glycol as well as the acid portion of the repeating unit,** i.e., poly(1,4-cyclohexanedicarbinyl terephthalate).

57. Preparation of 1,4-Cyclohexanedicarbinol (36,42)

One hundred g. dimethyl terephthalate is hydrogenated in 800 ml. ethanol
over 10 g. Raney nickel at 200°C. and 2000 p.s.i. (36,42). When hydrogen
uptake has ceased, the mixture is filtered, the alcohol distilled at reduced
pressure and the residue fractionally distilled through a 10 in. Vigreux column.
About 95 g. dimethylhexahydroterephthalate, b.p. 124°C./5 mm., is obtained.
This diester is then hydrogenated over 8 g. copper chromite catalyst (42) at
255°C. and 4000 p.s.i. When the hydrogenation is completed, the catalyst is
separated and the residue distilled, first through a 6 in. Vigreux column, then
through a precision distillation column. The boiling point of the diol is 117–
120°C./0.5 mm. It distills at a viscous liquid which partially solidifies on
standing. It is a mixture of cis- and trans-isomers. Chemical reduction of
the hexahydrodiester by means of sodium and alcohol has also been carried
out (45).

58. Preparation of Poly(1,4-cyclohexanedicarbinylterephthalate) (41a)

A mixture of 25.0 g. (0.148 *m.*) 1,4-cyclohexanedicarbinol, 13 g. (0.067 *m.*) dimethyl terephthalate, and 0.02 g. tetraisopropyl titanate is charged to a polymer tube. The mixture is heated in a nitrogen stream at 197°C. in a vapor bath for 3 hr., as described in the preceding preparation. The tube is then heated at 220°C. for 15 min. to remove the last of the methanol and begin the polymerization. Heating is continued at 283°C. as a vacuum is slowly applied over a 15 min. period to bring the pressure to 0.2 mm. The polymerization is complete in about 3 hr. The polymer is removed from the tube after cooling (as in Preparation 56). It has an inherent viscosity of about 0.5–0.6 (0.5% conc., 30°C.) in tetrachloroethane/phenol (40/60 weight) and the polymer melt temperature is about 285–290°C. It is also soluble in sulfuric acid and hot *o*-dichlorobenzene. Films can be melt-pressed at 285°C. and fibers drawn from the molten polymer.

Polyesters from entirely aliphatic reactants are usually low melting even when of high molecular weight. Although these polymeric materials can be crystalline and fiber forming, they are of little utility in unmodified form. Direct esterification or ester interchange are the preparative methods most often used. Various catalysts have been used successfully. One of the most common of such catalysts is litharge, the use of which is demonstrated in the condensation of dimethyl sebacate with tetramethylene glycol. In the following example, equimolar amounts of reactants are used, and only one ester interchange reaction occurs. This is the polymer forming step.

59. Preparation of Poly(tetramethylene sebacate) (48)

$$HO(CH_2)_4OH + CH_3O-\overset{O}{\overset{\|}{C}}(CH_2)_8\overset{O}{\overset{\|}{C}}-OCH_3 \longrightarrow$$

$$\left[-O(CH_2)_4O-\overset{O}{\overset{\|}{C}}(CH_8)\ \overset{O}{\overset{\|}{C}}-\right]_n + 2CH_3OH$$

A mixture of 4.95 g. (0.055 *m.*) of tetramethylene glycol (Preparation 53) 11.50 g. (0.050 m.) of dimethyl sebacate, 0.1 g. litharge, and 0.1 g. di-*t*-butylhydroquinone is placed in a polymer tube having a side arm and nitrogen capillary inlet reaching to the bottom of the tube, as described in Preparation 56. The reaction is heated at about 172°C. in a vapor bath for 2 hr. at atmospheric pressure in a current of nitrogen. Then, the pressure is slowly reduced over a 4 hr. period to 0.05 mm. The temperature is then raised to 215°C. for 4 hr. at the same reduced pressure. The reaction may be heated overnight without harm. The polymer, which is allowed to cool under nitrogen, is obtained as a white solid in nearly quantitative yield (12–13 g.). The inherent viscosity is around 1.0 in chloroform (0.5% conc., 25°C.). Its polymer melt temperature is 60–65°C. Fibers can be pulled from the melt and are cold-drawable.

In many difunctional molecules, the tendency to intramolecular cyclization is so great that intermolecular condensation is suppressed. An example of a hydroxyacid having a great tendency to cyclize to a dimer is glycolic acid. However, **poly(glycollic ester)** can be formed **from glycolic acid** in favorable competition with the reaction leading to cyclic dimer (38).

60. Preparation of Poly(glycollic ester) (38)

$$HO-CH_2-CO_2H \longrightarrow \left[-O-CH_2-\overset{\overset{\textstyle O}{\|}}{C}- \right] + H_2O$$

Fifteen g. (0.197 m.) of hydroxyacetic acid recrystallized from n-butyl alcohol, m.p. 80–80.5°C., is mixed with 0.015 g. triphenylphosphite color stabilizer and 0.001 g. antimony trioxide catalyst in a polymer tube with a nitrogen inlet capillary tube and a side arm. (See Preparations 2 and 56 for general directions on melt-polymerization technique.) The tube is immersed in an ethylene glycol vapor bath at 197°C. for $1/2$–1 hr., during which time the acid melts and water is evolved vigorously. A slow stream of nitrogen is passed through the melted acid by lowering the capillary into the melt. When the reaction has subsided, the pressure is reduced to 1.0 mm. or less as quickly as possible. More water and a small quantity of glycolide (the cyclic dimer) distill during the next 70–80 min. It may be necessary to warm the side arm to prevent glycolide from solidifying. The polymer melt becomes cloudy and begins to crystallize. The polymer tube is quickly shifted to a naphthalene vapor bath (218°C.), previously heated to boiling. The polymer melts once more and is maintained at 218°C. at 1 mm. or less for 3–4 hr. Nitrogen is passed through the melt at the slow rate throughout. During this part of the heating cycle, the polymer may darken to some extent. At the end of this period the melt becomes very viscous and may partially solidify. The tube is removed from the bath and allowed to cool to room temperature under vacuum. The polymer is isolated by breaking the tube after releasing the vacuum.

The polymer plug, freed from any glass chips that might adhere, is ground in a mill to pass a 20 mesh screen. The powder is placed in a 50 ml. round-bottom flask equpped with a glass paddle stirrer, and a vacuum take-off and heated while stirring the solid, at a pressure of 1.0 mm. or lower in the 218°C. vapor bath. The powder polymerization is continued for 8 hr. at least; it may be left overnight (16 hr.).

The operations in the above polymerization cycle must be carried out carefully in order to obtain high polymer. Coloration can be reduced by using a very pure monomer and not exceeding 220°C. in any part of the polymerization.

The polymer removed from the tube may be tan to dark brown in color. It weights 9–11 g. (50–60%), has a polymer melt temperature of 230–235°C., and a crystalline melting point of 230°C. The inherent viscosity is 0.6–1.0, (0.5% conc. at 30°C. in phenol/trichlorophenol (60/40 weight)). The polymer is degraded slowly by contact with this solvent; the determination of inherent viscosity should be made as soon as possible after the solution is prepared. Poly(glycollic ester) can be melt-pressed at 240°C. to give clear, tough films which have a lower inherent viscosity than the original polymer, indicating degradation. However, the films can still be drawn to twice their original length at 50–60°C. with an increase in their toughness. The polymer is degraded severely by prolonged exposure to boiling water.

An unusual and interesting example of a **polyester** prepared **from a hydroxyacid** is that from the condensation product of protocatechuic acid, I, with epichlorohydrin (14). Protocatechuic acid is derived from wood pulp.

The hydroxyacid (II), an AB monomer, is obtained as a mixture of the 6- and 7-carboxy isomers. The polymer from the mixed isomers is stable at its melt temperature of 210°C. and is prepared by melt-polymerization. The polymer prepared from a pure isomer of I (whether the 6- or 7-carboxy was not established) melts above 300°C. with decomposition. Thus, only low polymer can be prepared by melt techniques. The mixture of the two isomers produces a copolymer which melts within the range of its thermal stability. The effect is typical of that usually found in random copolymers.

61. Preparation of 6- (and 7-) Carboxy-2-hydroxymethyl-1,4-benzodioxane (I) (14)

A flask equipped with a mechanical stirrer, gas inlet tube, and dropping funnel is charged with 187 g. (1.21 m.) of protocatechuic acid and flushed with nitrogen. A solution of 100 g. (2.5 m.) of sodium hydroxide in 945 ml. of water is added and the resulting solution cooled to 40–50°C. One hundred twelve g. (1.21 m.) of epichlorohydrin is added over a period of 2 hr. with stirring; the temperature is kept at 40–50°C. and a nitrogen atmosphere is maintained. The reaction is continued under nitrogen for 7 hr. after addition is complete. The mixture is then poured into a cold solution of 240 g. concentrated hydrochloric acid in 240 g. of water with rapid stirring. The oil formed eventually solidifies. This is broken up, filtered, washed with water and dried at 110°C. The yield is 168 g. of crude product (66%). The crude acid is esterified by dissolving in 400 ml. methanol, saturating with dry hydrogen chloride gas, and refluxing 24 hr. After removing the excess methanol and hydrogen chloride at water aspirator pressure, the residual methyl ester is distilled through a 10 in. Vigreux column at 175–196°C./0.4–1.5 mm. The yield of ester is 115 g. (43%). It is saponified by refluxing for 2 hr. under a nitrogen atmosphere in a solution of 60 g. sodium hydroxide in 250 ml. water, followed by acidification with hydrochloric acid. The oily acid solidifies quickly and is recrystallized from a minimum of boiling water, using decolorizing charcoal, and is dried in vacuum at 50–60°C. The melting point after two recrystallizations is 141–168°C.; the yield is 74 g. (35%) of colorless material. The calculated neutral equivalent is 210; the product should have an observed value of about 212. The product is a mixture of the 6- and 7-carboxy isomers.

62. Preparation of the Polyester from 6- (and 7-) Carboxy-2-hydroxymethyl-1,4-benzodioxane (14)

II

Ten g. (0.047 m.) of hydroxyacid(II) is placed in a polymer tube bearing a nitrogen inlet capillary reaching almost to the bottom and a side arm attached to an efficient vacuum pump. (See Preparation 2 and 56 for general instructions on melt-polymerization methods and precautions.) With a slow stream of nitrogen passing through it and under a vacuum of less than 1.0 mm., the tube is heated by the vapors of a 270°C. bath for a period of 17 hr. When cooled under nitrogen the polymer is a clear, glass-like solid, obtained in nearly quantitative yield, about 9 g. It has a polymer melt temperature of 210°C. and an inherent viscosity of 0.6–0.7 in m-cresol (0.5% conc. at 25°C.). Fibers may be melt-spun from the sample. The temperature used is 270°C., and, if provision is made to pass the threadline through an 80°C. water bath while effecting a draw of 140% by varying the speed of the windup rolls, fibers of considerable strength (4 g. per denier) can be obtained.

Unlike polyesters from aliphatic components (discussed in Preparation 59) the **all-aromatic polyesters** are usually high melting materials. They can conveniently be prepared **from the sodium salts of diphenols by interfacial polycondensation** (26). In the following example, a copolyester is prepared which is more soluble and more readily fabricated than either of the corresponding homopolymers. The polymer melt temperature is high, around 280°C., once again pointing up the effect of ring structure on polymer properties.

The following polymerization procedure has been used successfully for preparing high molecular weight polymers from a number of bis-phenols and appears to be generally applicable to the preparation of polyphenyl esters if the sodium salt of the bisphenol is water soluble. It has been very useful for preparing polymers using aromatic acid chlorides in particular, since these are not readily hydrolyzed by the strongly alkaline solution of the salt of the bisphenol.

63. Preparation of Poly[2,2-propane bis(4-phenylisophthalate-co-terephthalate) (50/50)] (26)

A solution of 5.70 g. (0.025 mole) diphenylolpropane (bisphenol A) and 2.0 g. (0.050 mole) sodium hydroxide in 150 ml. water is prepared in a household blender at very low speed stirring. (Bisphenol A is best purified as described in the preparation of its polycarbonate, Preparation 65.) The sodium hydroxide should be added as a standardized carbonate-free solution since this will give a more accurate titre of alkali than weighing out pellets. The speed of the household blender motor can best be regulated by a "Powerstat." A setting of about 20 is adequate for preparing the solution but the maximum setting is used for the polymerization. A second solution of 2.54 g. (0.0125 mole) isophthaloyl chloride and 2.54 g. (0.0125 mole) terephthaloyl chloride in 75 ml. chloroform is prepared in a 150 ml. beaker.

Isophthaloyl chloride can be recrystallized from dry hexane (50 ml. hexane for 100 g. acid chloride) at 21–24°C. Ice cooling should not be used. The melting point is 42–43°C. Terephthaloyl chloride can be purified as described in Preparation 24. The preparation of isophthaloyl chloride is essentially the same as that for terephthaloyl chloride, also given in Preparation 24. Both commercial grade and reagent grade chloroform must be washed with water before use to insure removal of the alcohol added as a stabilizer. The chloroform can then be dried over calcium hydride. To the solution in the blender is now added 15 ml. of a 10% aqueous solution of "Duponol"* ME and the blender is turned to a maximum speed. The chloroform solution of the acid chlorides is added immediately and as rapidly as possible to the well stirred aqueous solution. The rapidly stirred solution has a tendency to foam over. The blender can be covered with aluminum foil, a top with a center hole added, and the acid chloride solution added through a powder funnel inserted through the covers. The emulsion so formed is stirred for 5 min. and the blender is stopped. The thin oil-in-water emulsion is poured into 1 l. of acetone to coagulate the polymer and extract the solvents. The polymer is filtered and washed once on the filter with acetone. The granular polymer is transferred back to the blender jar and washed in 500 ml. water to remove the salt and dispersing agent. The solid polymer is filtered again and washed on the filter with water. The water washing step is repeated twice more and the polymer is given a final wash on the filter with acetone. The polymer is dried 24 hr. in a vacuum oven at 90°C. The dried polymer weighs 8–8.5 g. (90–97%).

Polymer prepared in this way from purified intermediates should have an inherent viscosity in *sym*-tetrachloroethane-phenol (40/60 weight) of 1.8–2.2 (0.5% conc., 30°C.) and a polymer-melt temperature of 280°C. It is very soluble in halogenated hydrocarbons, hot cyclohexanone, pyridine, and phenols and slightly soluble in hot dimethylformamide, dioxane, and tetrahydrofuran. It can be fabricated to films and fibers by casting or spinning from solutions in any of the good solvents listed.

Adipoyl chloride will react at an elevated temperature with **hydroquinone** in a rigorously anhydrous inert solvent such as nitrobenzene to form a high molecular weight **polyphenyl ester** (95). The evolved hydrogen chloride is removed from the refluxing solvent with the aid of an inert gas sweep and no acid acceptor is needed. The reac-

* Trademark for du Pont surface active agent.

tion requires an unusually high degree of purification of reactants and solvents to produce high polymer, and the polymer must be soluble or highly swollen in the hot solvent in which the reaction is run.

64. Preparation of Poly(1,4-phenylene adipate) (95)

$$HO-\left\langle\overline{}\right\rangle-OH + Cl-\overset{O}{\overset{\|}{C}}-(CH_2)_4-\overset{O}{\overset{\|}{C}}-Cl \longrightarrow$$

$$\left[-O-\left\langle\overline{}\right\rangle-O-\overset{O}{\overset{\|}{C}}-(CH_2)_4-\overset{O}{\overset{\|}{C}}-\right]_n + 2HCl$$

For the following polymerization, the hydroquinone is purified by recrystallizing four times from water which has been deoxygenated by boiling and cooled with a stream of nitrogen bubbling through it.   The adipoyl chloride used can be commercially available material which has been fractionally distilled twice at reduced pressure in a nitrogen atmosphere using an oil bath, not in excess of 150°C., as a heat source.   The boiling point at 1 mm. pressure is about 70–72°C.; at 10 mm. it is 112–115°C.   Distillation should be fairly rapid to avoid the decomposition which may result from prolonged heating. The nitrobenzene is purified by washing well with water and drying over calcium chloride.   It is then distilled three times from phosphorus pentoxide at atmospheric pressure, then once from the same material at oil pump pressure. It should be stored under nitrogen under anhydrous conditions.

A mixture of 7.872 g. (0.0232 m.) adipoyl chloride, 4.728 g. (0.0233 m.) of hydroquinone, and 20.0 ml. nitrobenzene is placed in a 100 ml. three-necked flask equipped with a condenser protected with a drying tube.   The flask is flamed out and cooled in a current of nitrogen admitted through a gas inlet tube reaching to the bottom of the flask.

The reaction mixture is heated slowly by means of an oil bath to 140–147°C. over a period of $2^1/_2$ hr., then maintained at that temperature for an additional 6 hr.   A slow stream of nitrogen is passed through the reaction mixture during its course.   Care must be taken to avoid heating above 150°C., since the acid chloride tends to decompose above this temperature.   The nitrobenzene is then distilled at oil pump pressure with an oil bath temperature of about 147°C. The solid remaining is dried 2 hr. further at about 147°C. and 1.0 mm., or less.   The white (or slightly off white) solid obtained has an inherent viscosity of 1.0–1.4 in nitrobenzene/phenol (1:1 by weight, at 0.5% conc., 25°C.). The polymer-melt temperature is about 240°C. and fibers can be pulled from the melt.

Phosgene, the simplest organic diacid chloride, can be used directly in reaction **with bisphenols to produce polycarbonates** (68,69). The reaction can be carried out readily in pyridine solution or in aqueous sodium hydroxide.   Polycarbonates have also been prepared from bisphenols and dialkylcarbonates in ester exchange reactions (96,66).

65. Preparation of Poly[2,2-propanebis (4-phenyl carbonate)] (65,68)

Caution. Phosgene Is Toxic. Run in a Good Hood.

A 1 l. three-necked flask is fitted with an efficient stirrer, a condenser with calcium chloride drying tube, a thermometer capable of being immersed in the reaction mixture and a gas inlet tube reaching as nearly to the bottom of the flask as possible for admitting phosgene. The air is displaced from the flask with nitrogen and the flask charged with 98 g. (0.43 m.) of diphenylolpropane, m.p. 159–160°C., recrystallized from toluene, 80 g./l., and 700 ml. analytical grade pyridine. When the bisphenol has dissolved, phosgene is bubbled through the solution at the rate of about 1 g./min. with stirring. The temperature is maintained at 25–30°C. by means of an ice–water bath, applied as necessary. The phosgene flow may be followed by weighing the cylinder periodically or continuously, or a weighed amount of condensed phosgene may be vaporized into the reaction. The theoretical weight of phosgene is 42.6 g. (0.43 m.), but a 10–15 wt. % excess may be necessary because of loss of unreacted phosgene through the condenser. The exit gases from the reaction should be led to a suitable aqueous alcohol-caustic trap, or to a continuously flowing water scrubber and flushed down a drain with plenty of water. Loss of phosgene can be prevented by moderate stirring to avoid formation of a deep vortex.

At about the midpoint of phosgene consumption, crystals of pyridine hydrochloride begin to form. Toward the end of the reaction, the solution becomes viscous and the rate of phosgene addition is reduced to a very slow flow. At the endpoint of the reaction, a yellow-to-red color develops, and the phosgene flow is stopped. The color may be discharged by the addition of a little bisphenol A in pyridine. The polymer is isolated by pouring the mixture into four times its volume of water with vigorous stirring. The polymer is filtered, washed on the filter with water, and suspended in 1 l. of water at 80°C. for 10 min. with stirring. It is filtered and washed again, and dried in a vacuum oven at 80°C. The inherent viscosity in sym-tetrachloroethane/phenol (40/60 weight) (0.5% conc., 25°C.) is 0.6–0.8. The polymer melt temperature is about 240°C., and strong, flexible films may be melt-pressed at that temperature. The polymer is soluble in chlorinated solvents, such as 1,1,2-trichloroethane.

As an alternate to the above procedure, a method using a methylene chloride–aqueous sodium hydroxide medium is also operable, as follows.

In a 3 l. three-necked flask equipped with stirrer, condenser and gas inlet tube reaching to the bottom of the flask is placed 137 g. (0.6 *m.*) bisphenol A, 60 g. (1.5 *m.*) sodium hydroxide, 10 g. benzyltrimethylammonium chloride, 1 l. distilled water, and 500 ml. methylene chloride. The mixture is stirred rapidly and kept at 20°C. with ice cooling while phosgene is passed in at the rate of 2 g./min. Another 40 g. (1.0 *m.*) of sodium hydroxide is added in portions to keep the mixture strongly alkaline. The polymerization is estimated to be complete when a tough skin of polymer forms when a sample of the methylene chloride phase is evaporated. The methylene chloride is evaporated on a steam bath, finally, and the coarse polymer washed as described above. The polymer is essentially identical to that obtained above. The weight is about 140 g. (86%). The inherent viscosity (as before) is about 0.6.

The **reaction of a dicarboxylic acid chloride and a glycol** in an anhydrous melt system provides a method for preparing polyesters which is much faster than either the glycol-diacid or glycol-diester condensations (32,33). The by-product is hydrogen chloride, which must be removed to prevent alkyl halide formation or etherification. The reaction is applicable in most cases to aliphatic glycols having at least a 3 atom chain between the hydroxyls, and to the aromatic diacid chlorides except for *o*-phthaloyl chloride.

66. Preparation of Poly(tetramethylene isophthalate) (32)

A 100 ml. three-necked flask equipped with a nitrogen inlet tube extending below the surface of the reaction mixture, a mechanical stirrer, and an exit tube for nitrogen and evolved hydrogen chloride (provision should be made for trapping the latter) is flushed with nitrogen and charged first with 40.60 g. (0.20 *m.*) isophthaloyl chloride followed by 18.02 g. (0.20 *m.*) tetramethylene glycol (purification of the acid chloride is given in Preparation 63, the glycol in Preparation 53). The heat of reaction causes the isophthaloyl chloride to melt. The reaction is stirred vigorously and nitrogen is passed through the reaction to avoid accumulation of hydrogen chloride, which may bring about formation of tars. On a larger scale, the initial reaction should be controlled by ice cooling to maintain the temperature at 50°C., or below. In about 1 hr., the evolution of hydrogen chloride slows considerably and the mixture begins to solidify. The temperature of the reaction mixture is then raised to 180°C. by means of an oil bath and held at that temperature for 1 hr. During the last 10 min. of the 180°C. heating cycle, the last of the hydrogen chloride is removed by reducing the pressure to 0.5–1.0 mm.

The polymer is obtained as a white solid having an inherent viscosity of around 0.5 in *sym*-tetrachloroethane/phenol (40/60 weight) (0.5% conc., 25°C.). It is amorphous, as formed, and has a polymer-melt temperature of 100–110°C. It is soluble in 1,1,2-trichloroethane, formic acid, dimethylformamide, and *m*-cresol. When the polyester is crystallized, the polymer-melt temperature is increased to about 140°C., and the polymer is no longer soluble in dimethylformamide and formic acid. Films dry cast from trichloroethane or chloroform are crystalline; such films may be quite brittle because of the high degree of crystallinity. Amorphous films can be obtained by pouring the melted polymer onto plates and spreading with a rod, then crystallizing by heating for 3 hr. at 70°C. Fibers can be pulled from a melt of the polymer with a rod. Amorphous films or fibers can be cold-drawn by hand; the drawn sample then has a tendency to crystallize when held under tension. The amorphous fibers and films are somewhat rubbery.

Polyphosphonate esters can be prepared **from phosphonic acid dihalides and glycols.** Phenylphosphonyl dichloride, for instance, has been condensed with hydroquinone, or di- and tetrachlorohydroquinone to give fiber and film forming products (81,82). The phenylthiophosphonyl polyesters also have been prepared.

67. Preparation of Poly(1,4-phenylene phenylphosphonate) (81)

A polymer tube is charged with 10.2 g. (0.0525 *m*.) of freshly distilled (b.p. 104°C./4 mm.) phenylphosphonyl dichloride (83) and 5.50 g. (0.0500 *m*.) hydroquinone. The tube is filled with nitrogen (Preparation 2) and is heated at atmospheric pressure in a 139°C. vapor bath for 16 hr., during which time a slow stream of nitrogen is passed through the melt by means of a capillary reaching to the bottom of the tube. It is then heated for another 4 hr. in a 218°C. bath. Following this, the tube is heated in a 152°C. bath while the pressure is slowly reduced to 1–2 mm. over a period of 30 min. Heating is continued at this temperature and pressure for 4 hr. The tube is then switched to a 242°C. bath for 17 hr., with a nitrogen flow through the capillary, as in all phases of the polymerization. A final heating stage is carried out at 280–290°C. for 4 hr. at the same reduced pressure. The last heating stage is continued until the viscosity of the melt ceases to increase, as judged by the rate of rise of the nitrogen bubbles. The tube is cooled under nitrogen. The polyphosphonate ester has a polymer melt temperature of around 130°C. Fibers which are cold-drawable may be pulled from the melt. The polymer is soluble in chloroform and ethylene chloride. The inherent viscosity in the latter (0.5% conc., 25°C.) is about 0.4.

In previous preparations (63–65), polyphenyl esters were prepared from diacid chlorides and a bisphenol. **Polyphenyl esters of aliphatic diacids** can also be prepared **by an acidolysis reaction between the free acid and an ester of the bisphenol** (85). In the following example, the polysebacic ester of hydroquinone is prepared. The resorcinol polyester can be prepared by this same technique, as can poly(1,4-phenylene succinate). The latter is an "inverted" poly-(ethylene terephthalate); the structures are formally identical, having a p-benzene ring separated by an ethylene and two carbonyl groups. They are very similar in properties.

poly(ethylene terephthalate)   poly(1,4-phenylene succinate)

68. Preparation of Poly(1,4-phenylene sebacate) (85)

For the following polymerization, p-phenylene diacetate (21) can be prepared by dissolving 11 g. (0.10 m.) hydroquinone in a solution of 9 g. (0.22 m.) sodium hydroxide in 45 ml. water in a 250 ml. Erlenmeyer flask. The mixture is cooled in an ice bath and a small quantity of ice is added to the flask. Then 22.4 g. (0.22 m.) acetic anhydride is added at once and the flask shaken vigorously by hand in the ice bath for 7 or 8 min. The white solid is filtered, washed with water, and recrystallized from ethanol. It can be dried at 60°C. in a vacuum oven to give about 17 g. (88%) of product melting at 123–124°C.

A mixture of 9.70 g. p-phenylene diacetate (0.05 m.), 10.10 g. (0.05 m.) sebacic acid, and 0.03 g. toluenesulfonic acid (monohydrate) is placed in a polymer tube, the tube filled with nitrogen (Preparations 2 and 56) by a capillary inlet reaching to the bottom of the polymer tube. Acetic acid distills as the temperature is slowly raised from 180°C. to 230°C. over a period of at least 30 min. The temperature is then raised over 45 min. to 280°C. while the pressure is slowly reduced (about 10 min.) to about 0.3 mm. The temperature is maintained at 280°C. at this pressure for 45 min. Nitrogen is passed slowly through the melt during the heating. The product is a dark, tough solid, having an inherent viscosity in m-cresol of 0.5–0.6 (0.5% conc., 30°C.) and a polymer melt temperature of around 170°C. It may be melt-pressed to films at this temperature, and drawable fibers may be pulled from the polymer melt.

The **acetates of m- and p-hydroxybenzoic acid** can undergo an **acidolysis reaction** with loss of acetic acid to form high molecular weight **copolymers**. The meta isomer can be homopolymerized successfully, but the para forms an intractable material.

69. Preparation of Poly(m-phenyl carboxylate) (34A)

$$CH_3CO_2\text{—}\bigcirc\text{—}CO_2H \longrightarrow \left[\text{—}O\text{—}\bigcirc\text{—}\overset{\overset{\displaystyle O}{\|}}{C}\text{—} \right]_n + CH_3CO_2H$$

m-Acetoxybenzoic acid is prepared by heating m-hydroxybenzoic acid with excess acetic anhydride for 3 hr., concentrating the mixture under vacuum, and recrystallizing the solid residue from benzene-ligroin. The melting point is 130.5–131.5°C.

Ten g. of m-acetoxybenzoic acid and a small chip of magnesium (ca. 0.01% the weight of monomer) are placed in a polymer tube having a side arm and a nitrogen inlet which can be adjusted to reach the bottom of the tube. The tube is flushed with nitrogen (Preparations 2 and 56) and immersed in a 220°C. vapor bath. A slow stream of nitrogen is continually passed through the melt. The pressure is gradually reduced to 60 mm. Acetic acid acid distills from the tube. After 2 hr., the tube is immersed in a 300°C. vapor bath and the pressure brought to about 0.2 mm. This temperature is maintained until a maximum melt viscosity has been reached, as judged by the rate of bubble rise. The polymer is allowed to cool under nitrogen. The inherent viscosity is about 0.5 in sym-tetrachloroethane/phenol (40/60, weight) at 0.23% conc., 30°C. The polymer melts at 185–205°C., and is soluble in 1,1,2-trichloroethane, m-cresol, and N,N-dimethylaniline.

As an alternative to the above procedure, the polymerization can be carried out in a 100 ml. flask equipped with a nitrogen inlet, vacuum outlet, and a glass stirrer, using about 10–15 g. of o-terphenyl or a mixture of ditolyl sulfone isomers as a diluent to reduce the melt viscosity. Here, the temperature of reaction is 220–250°C. at a pressure which permits the solvent to reflux but not distill. The diluent is extracted from the final polymer with acetone.

In either case, the polymer, so obtained, can be further powder polymerized by grinding to a fine particle size (0.8 mm. or less) and heating at 160–170°C. under high vacuum.   Inherent viscosities as high as 0.9 may be obtained.

Preparations of various other polyesters will be found elsewhere. In this chapter, polyesters modified with diisocyanates are to be found in Section V, which follows.   Cross-linked polyester resins are discussed in Chapter 7.   The entire polyester field has been extensively treated in book form in terms of intermediates, processes, properties and uses (13).

V. Miscellaneous Condensation Polymers

Dithiols add to nonconjugated diolefins in solution or in emulsion using a free radical catalyst **to give a polythioether** (47).   The course of the reaction in all likelihood involves a radical initiated anti-Markownikoff addition of the sulfhydryl to the olefin:

$$R \cdot + -CH_2-SH \longrightarrow -CH_2-S \cdot + RH$$

$$-CH_2-S \cdot + CH_2{=}CH-CH_2- \longrightarrow -CH_2S-CH_2-\overset{\cdot}{C}H-CH_2-$$

$$-CH_2-S-CH_2-\overset{\cdot}{C}H-CH_2- + -CH_2SH \longrightarrow$$

$$-CH_2-S-CH_2-CH_2-CH_2- + -CH_2-S \cdot$$

The polythioethers are usually low melting (100°C.), but are fiber forming when of high molecular weight.   They show some crystallinity as well.

70. Preparation of Poly(hexamethylene thioether) (47)

$$CH_2{=}CH-CH_2-CH_2-CH{=}CH_2 + HS-(CH_2)_6-SH \longrightarrow$$

$$[-(CH_2)_6-S-]_n$$

Caution.   Dithiols may cause dermatitis, especially on prolonged exposure. Use care in handling.

A mixture of 12.30 g. (0.0819 *m.*) hexamethylenedithiol and 6.72 g. (0.0819 *m.*) biallyl, both freshly distilled, is prepared and stored in a nitrogen-filled, 10 oz. screw cap bottle.   One hundred twenty-five ml. of an emulsifier solution prepared from 5 g. emulsifier (as, MP-189-EF, a sodium salt of a hydrocarbon sulfonate—see Chemicals Appendix) in 500 ml. distilled water is added to the mixture of monomers, using a nitrogen line at the mouth of the bottle to keep air out.   The bottle is capped and cooled to about 5°C. in an ice bath.

A catalyst solution is prepared no more than 5 hr. before the polymerization from the following, using 2.5 ml. of each solution: 1.46 g. ammonium persulfate in 20 ml. distilled water; 0.37 g. sodium metabisulfite in 10 ml. distilled water; 0.37 g. copper sulfate (hydrate) in 100 ml. distilled water.   The catalyst mixture is added, again using a nitrogen line for exclusion of air, and the bottle is capped tightly and put on a tumbler at 30°C. in a constant temperature bath.   This may be accomplished by wiring the bottle very firmly to the end of a metal stirrer shaft which is then placed in the bath at an acute angle so that the bottle is turned mainly end-over-end.

After 24 hr. the polymer is precipitated by adding 35 ml. of a 10% solution of potassium aluminum sulfate to which is added 4 ml. of concentrated hydrochloric acid.   The polymer is filtered and dissolved in 250 ml. benzene.   The wet benzene solution is filtered into 500 ml. methanol with stirring and the precipitated polymer filtered.   It is washed with methanol and dried in a vacuum desiccator at 1 mm. pressure.   The yield of white, solid polymer is 17 g. (95%).   The polymer melt temperature is 70–75°C., and the inherent viscosity is 0.5–0.7 in benzene (0.5% conc. at 25°C.).   If the inherent viscosity is above about 0.45, it should be possible to pull cold-drawable fibers from the melt.

Polythioethers may also be prepared **by the condensation of the disodium salt of a dithiol with an alkylene dihalide** (49,56).

$$NaS{-}R{-}SNa + X{-}R'{-}X \longrightarrow [{-}S{-}R{-}S{-}R'{-}]_n + 2NaX$$

The following is an example of such a reaction.

71. Preparation of Alternating Poly(hexamethylene tetramethylene thioether) (49)

$$NaS(CH_2)_6SNa + Br(CH_2)_4Br \longrightarrow [{-}S{-}(CH_2)_6{-}S{-}(CH_2)_4{-}]_n + 2NaBr$$

Into a 200 ml. three-necked flask equipped with dropping funnel and condenser with drying tube is distilled 30 ml. of absolute ethanol (30).   To it is added 0.92 g. (0.04 m.) of sodium.   When the sodium has dissolved, 3.0 g. (0.02 m.) distilled hexamethylenedithiol is added.   The salt of the dithiol precipitates, but redissolves on heating the solution to reflux.   To this boiling solution is added first 40 ml. of dry benzene (thiophene free), followed by 4.30 g. (0.02 m.) of distilled tetramethylene bromide in 10 ml. of benzene as rapidly as possible.   A vigorous reaction results.   When it subsides, another 25 ml. of benzene is added to the solution and the mixture is refluxed overnight, then cooled to room temperature.   Some polymer separates and is removed by filtration.   This collected polymer is freed of inorganic solids, by stirring with three successive 100 ml. portions of water and filtering.   Only about 0.5 g. of polymer is recovered in this way, having an inherent viscosity of about 0.5–0.6 in benzene (0.5% conc., 25°C.), after drying at 0.01 mm. in a vacuum desiccator over phosphorus pentoxide.   The polymer melt temperature is around 65°C.

Additional polymer can be recovered by pouring the filtrate from the original reaction into 500 ml. methanol with stirring.   The precipitated polymer is removed by filtration, washed well with methanol and dried under vacuum. The inherent viscosity, as above, is about 0.3, and the polymer weighs about 2.1 g.

Polythioethers have been quantitatively **oxidized to** the corresponding **polysulfone** without degradation in a mixture of formic acid–
hydrogen peroxide (56,57). The polymer melt temperatures of the
polysulfones are much higher than the precursor polymer. Where
the hydrocarbon unit is hexamethylene, the sulfone has a polymer
melt temperature of about 212°C., as compared to 75°C. for the
thioether. The melt temperature increases linearly in the polysulfones
as the hydrocarbon portion decreases in length. A number of polysulfones have been prepared and melt-spun into fibers which were cold
drawable and of good tensile properties (57). The alkylene portions
of the chain had at least 4 carbons. In contrast, the polysulfone from
propylene and sulfur dioxide (prepared in Chapter 4), having only 2
carbons in the chain unit, decomposes before it melts.

72. Preparation of Poly(hexamethylene sulfone) (57)

$$\text{--}[(CH_2)_6\text{---}S]_n \xrightarrow{H_2O_2} [(CH_2)_6\text{---}SO_2]_n$$

Ten g. (0.067 m. of repeat unit) of finely divided poly(hexamethylene thioether) with an inherent viscosity of at least 0.5 (see Preparation 70) is suspended
in 400 ml. of 90% formic acid in a 1 l. three-necked flask fitted with condenser,
dropping funnel, thermometer, and stirrer. The reaction is heated to 50°C.
with stirring and 40 g. of 30% hydrogen peroxide (0.35 m.) is added dropwise
at such a rate that the temperature of reaction does not materially change.
Slightly over halfway through this addition, the suspended polymer goes
into solution, then shortly begins to separate again. Presumably, the sulfoxide polymer is the soluble intermediate form. The solution is stirred and
heated 1 hr. after the addition is complete. The mixture is then poured with
stirring into 4 l. of water, the polymer filtered and washed thoroughly with
water and dried at 60°C. in a vacuum oven. The polymer melt temperature
is about 212°C. and the yield should be 12–12.5 g. (95–100%). The polysulfone has about the same inherent viscosity (m-cresol, 0.5% at 30°C.) as
the original polymer.

Unlike the alkylene polythioethers and sulfones which have found
no industrial application, the **alkylene polysulfides** (29) are the basis
of the Thiokol-type rubbers, noted for their resistance to solvents, oils,
oxidation and light. These polymers are prepared by the **condensation of an alkylene dihalide,** usually the chloride, **with a sodium polysulfide.**

$$Cl\text{---}R\text{---}Cl + Na_2S_x \longrightarrow [R\text{---}S_x]_n + NaCl$$

R may be almost any aliphatic grouping, while the value of x,
called the "rank," is usually from 2 to 4, although it may be higher.

Ethylene dichloride and dichloroethyl formal have been the most generally used dihalides in commercial practice. The polymers so formed are linear. To obtain cross-linked products, about 2 mol. % of the dihalide used is replaced by a trihalide, such as 1,2,3-trichloropropane. The following preparations of a polysulfide polymer may be so modified. The cross-linked polymers are resistant to cold flow, but are more difficult to process in latex compounding operations. The polymerization in either event, may be carried out simply by mixing the reactants in water and heating, either alone or in the presence of a dispersing agent. In the first case, bulk polymer is obtained, while a polymer dispersion results in the second.

73. Preparation of Poly(ethylene tetrasulfide) (59)

$$Na_2S + S \longrightarrow Na_2S_4$$
$$Na_2S_4 + Cl\!-\!CH_2CH_2\!-\!Cl \longrightarrow \{\!-\!CH_2CH_2\!-\!SSSS\!-\!\}_n$$

A. In a 500 ml. three-necked flask equipped with stirrer, condenser, thermometer, and dropping funnel, 38.4 g. (0.40 m.) of sodium sulfide monohydrate is dissolved in 150 ml. water. To this is added 37.5 g. (1.17 m.) of sulfur and the mixture heated to reflux for 1 hr. with stirring. To this solution at 70°C. is added 40 g. (0.40 m.) of ethylene dichloride with stirring over a period of 1 hr. The dark red color of the polysulfide solution disappears by the time the last of the dichloride is added. The reaction is heated at 70°C. for another hour after addition. The reaction is cooled and the supernatant liquid decanted from the yellow, rubbery solid. The solid in the flask is washed three times by boiling with water and decanting. The polymeric product is dried over phosphorus pentoxide in a vacuum desiccator to give 50–54 g. (79–86%) of polymer. The offensive odor of the product is thought to be due to low molecular weight dithiols or cyclic disulfides. Carbon disulfide swells and partially dissolves the polymer; carbon tetrachloride and benzene swell the polymer to some extent also. On a hot bar, the polymer melt temperature is about 130°C.

B. To prepare the above polymer in a more easily handled, dispensed form, the polymerization is conducted in the presence of a magnesium hydroxide suspension (60). The reaction sequence in A is modified by addition of 8.5 g. (0.04 m.) magnesium chloride hexahydrate and 3.6 g. sodium hydroxide to the sodium tetrasulfide solution just before the addition of the ethylene dichloride. The addition of 5 g. of a dispersing agent such as a sodium alkylnaphthalene sulfonate will facilitate reaction of the water-insoluble dichloride. The polymerization is carried out as in A with vigorous stirring. When the reaction is completed, the polymer particles are allowed to settle for 2 hr., and the supernatant liquid decanted. The polymer is redispersed in 600 ml. water, stirred, and once again separated from the wash liquid. This is repeated twice to remove inorganic salts. Centrifugation hastens the washing process. For some uses, a polymer suspension in water is a preferred form for handling. To coagulate to a bulk rubber, 10 ml. of concentrated hydro-chloric acid is added with stirring. The spongy, rubbery polymer is yellowish to white in color; it is removed and dried in a vacuum desiccator as above.

An interesting, linear, high molecular weight **polysiloxane** has been prepared **by the condensation of p-phenylene bis(dimethylsilanol)** under melt-polymerization conditions with water as the molecule eliminated (79).

$$\underset{\underset{CH_3}{|}}{\overset{\overset{CH_3}{|}}{HO-Si}}-R-\underset{\underset{CH_3}{|}}{\overset{\overset{CH_3}{|}}{Si}}-OH \longrightarrow \left[O-\underset{\underset{CH_3}{|}}{\overset{\overset{CH_3}{|}}{Si}}-R-\underset{\underset{CH_3}{|}}{\overset{\overset{CH_3}{|}}{Si}} \right] + H_2O$$

$$R = -\!\!\!\left\langle\!\!\!\bigcirc\!\!\!\right\rangle\!\!\!-$$

The polymer is a solid melting around 130°C., in sharp contrast to the elastomeric poly(dimethylsiloxane) which is described in Chapter 5.

74. Preparation of p-Phenylene Bis(dimethylsilanol) (79)

$$Br-\!\!\!\left\langle\!\!\!\bigcirc\!\!\!\right\rangle\!\!\!-Br + (CH_3)_2SiCl_2 \xrightarrow[\text{2) H}_2\text{O}]{\text{1) Mg}} \underset{\underset{CH_3}{|}}{\overset{\overset{CH_3}{|}}{HO-Si}}-\!\!\!\left\langle\!\!\!\bigcirc\!\!\!\right\rangle\!\!\!-\underset{\underset{CH_3}{|}}{\overset{\overset{CH_3}{|}}{Si}}-OH$$

In a 3 l. three-necked flask equipped with stirrer, condenser with drying tube, and 1 l. dropping funnel is placed 656 g. (5.09 m.) dimethyldichlorosilane, 124 g. (5.09 g.a.) magnesium turnings, and 500 ml. dry ether. To the stirred mixture is added 400 g. (1.69 m.) p-dibromobenzene in 1100 ml. dry ether over a period of hours. The rate of addition is governed by the refluxing of the ether from the heat of reaction. A precipitate forms about halfway through the addition. The mixture is stirred and heated to reflux for a period of 12 hr. after addition is complete.

The mixture is then filtered under anhydrous conditions to remove mag-nesium halides, and the salts are washed on the filter with 600 ml. dry benzene. The ether filtrate and benzene washings are combined and these solvents removed by distillation on the steam bath. More magnesium halides separate during this distillation. They are filtered and washed with dry benzene, and the distillation of solvents is continued. The final residue is fractionally distilled. The desired p-phenylene bis(dimethylchlorosilane) is obtained as a solid boiling at 108–110°C./1.5 mm., m.p. 87°C., in a yield of about 160 g. (36%).

An ice-cooled, 500 ml. three-necked flask equipped with stirrer and dropping funnel is convenient for the following phase of the preparation. The bis(di-methylchlorosilane) is hydrolyzed by adding 13.6 g. (0.052 m.) of the compound dissolved in 200 ml. anhydrous ether to 70 ml. of 1.5 N sodium hydroxide over a period of 10 min.   The caustic solution should be maintained at 0°C., and addition of the ether solution should be with vigorous stirring.

After the addition is complete, the ether layer is immediately separated, the aqueous layer extracted with another 100 ml. of ether, and the combined ether layers dried at once over 20 g. anhydrous potassium carbonate.   The drying agent is separated by filtration and the ether solution concentrated under water aspirator pressure until crystals of the desired product begin to form.   These are removed by filtration.   Additional product can be recovered from the mother liquor by addition of benzene.   The product may be recrystallized from ether-benzene as above.   The p-phenylene bis(dimethylsilanol) melts at 135°C. after drying in a vacuum desiccator over calcium chloride.   The yield is about 7 g. (58%).

75. Preparation of Poly[p-phenylene bis(dimethylsiloxane)] (79)

$$HO-\underset{\underset{CH_3}{|}}{\overset{\overset{CH_3}{|}}{Si}}-\hspace{-2pt}\langle\bigcirc\rangle\hspace{-2pt}-\underset{\underset{CH_3}{|}}{\overset{\overset{CH_3}{|}}{Si}}-OH \longrightarrow \left[\underset{\underset{CH_3}{|}}{\overset{\overset{CH_3}{|}}{Si}}-\hspace{-2pt}\langle\bigcirc\rangle\hspace{-2pt}-\underset{\underset{CH_3}{|}}{\overset{\overset{CH_3}{|}}{Si}}-O\right]_n + H_2O$$

Four g. (0.177 m.) of p-phenylene bis(dimethylsilanol) and a small boiling chip are placed in a polymer tube with a side arm.   Four ml. of a 0.02% aqueous sodium hydroxide solution is added, and the tube is flushed with nitrogen by alternate application of vacuum and admission of nitrogen (Preparation 2).   The tube is then immersed at atmospheric pressure in a 143°C. vapor bath for 30 min., taking care that water is not evolved too rapidly, or some loss of monomer will occur.   The tube is then transferred to a 200°C. vapor bath for another 30 min., followed by 1 hr. at 259°C.

The tube is now transferred to a 273°C. vapor bath and fitted with a capillary reaching to the bottom of the tube.   A vacuum of 1–2 mm. is then applied and nitrogen passed through the melt for 1–2 hr., or until melt viscosity is judged to have reached a maximum.   The polymer is then cooled under nitrogen.   The yield is quantitative (3.6 g.).   The polymer melt temperature is about 130°C., and the inherent viscosity in toluene (0.5% conc., 25°C.) is 0.7–1.0.   A value of 0.95 corresponds to a molecular weight of about 135,000. The polymer is crystalline as prepared.   Fibers may be pulled from a melt of the polysiloxane.   These are drawable at room temperature; greater drawability is obtainable, however, by passing them over a 50°C. surface while they are undergoing extension.

A class of **synthetic elastomers** has been developed from copolymer formulations **based on low molecular weight aliphatic polyesters or polyethers having terminal hydroxyl and/or carboxyl groups which are capable of further reaction with diisocyanates.**   This latter reaction can be used to couple the lower molecular weight polyester or polyether via urethane links (50), or the diisocyanate may be used in excess so that it becomes a terminal group (15,64).   In the latter case, these macrodiisocyanates may be coupled by means of still another reagent, such as water, diols, aminoalcohols, or diamines (15), with the subsequent formation of high polymer. Such elastomeric products are complex **block copolymers.** The formulas written for these materials are approximations of the actual structure rather than precise representations, because of the complex nature of the starting materials.

In the following example an aliphatic copolyester of low molecular weight is prepared having terminal hydroxyl groups. It is coupled by reaction with an equivalent of a diisocyanate. The resulting polymer is of high molecular weight and is linear. It is easy to see, however, that excess diisocyanate in this reaction can cause cross-linking by reaction with the —NH— of urethane linkages that are formed. In fact, this is the reaction used to produce the cross-links which may be desired in the elastomer at a later stage.

76. Chain Extension of Poly(ethylene-co-propylene adipate) with Methylene Bis(4-phenylisocyanate) (50)

A. Preparation of the Polyester:

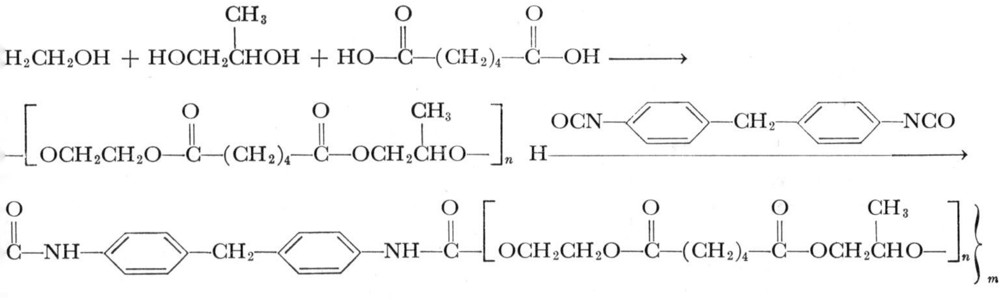

In a 500 ml. three-necked flask equipped with stirrer, nitrogen inlet tube below the level of the reaction mixture, and a straight distilling head and condenser is placed 351.5 g. (2.40 $m.$) adipic acid, 106.4 g. (1.71 $m.$) distilled ethylene glycol, and 86.9 g. (1.14 $m.$) distilled 1,2-propylene glycol. The reaction mixture is heated to 140°C. by means of an oil bath, with stirring, and nitrogen is passed slowly through the mixture until the distillation of water ceases. This may require 10–15 hr. The temperature is then raised to 200°C. and the pressure gradually reduced to about 20 mm. by means of a water aspirator. The reaction mixture is stirred and the slow passage of nitrogen is continued. Part of the excess glycols are removed during this step, and the molecular weight is determined by this heating and vacuum cycle. After a period of 23 hr. total, the mixture is cooled under nitrogen to give a white, waxy solid. A viscous syrup may result if insufficient glycol is removed, and the resulting polyester is of very low molecular weight.

A sample of the polyester is removed and analyzed for hydroxyl and carboxyl ends in the following manner (46,58). About 2 g. of polyester is weighed to the nearest miligram into a 100 ml. round bottom flask. To dissolve the sample, 25.0 ml. of a mixture of 12.0 ml. acetic anhydride and 500 ml. dry pyridine is added by pipet. The solution is refluxed for 1 hr. The condenser is then washed out by the addition of about 5 ml. water through the top, and the heating is continued for 5 min. The heat is then removed and the condenser tube and tip washed with 25 ml. methanol. When the mixture has cooled to room temperature, it is titrated with approximately 0.5 N standard potassium hydroxide solution to a phenolphthalein endpoint. This is a value A, taken as mg. KOH per g. polymer. Value A should never be less than 65% of value B. If it is, insufficient acetic anhydride was added for complete acetylation.

A blank is then run on a mixture of the same volumes used above of acetic anhydride–pyridine reagent and water, which has been allowed to stand for 15 min. Methanol is added in the same amount, as in the preceding case, just before titrating. This value, in mg. KOH per g. polymer, is blank value B.

Another titration is carried out on a sample of polymer of about the same size as the first dissolved in 25 ml. pyridine, again with 0.5 N KOH, to a phenolphthalein endpoint. Here, the number of mg. KOH per g. polymer, value C, gives the acid number of the polyester. The hydroxyl number of the polyester is obtained from value C + value B − value A, all as mg. KOH per g. sample.

[The method for hydroxyl number depends on a quantitative acetylation of —OH groups followed by titration of the acetic acid from the hydrolyzed, unreacted acetic anhydride, plus any carboxyls in the polymer. The latter are determined separately by titration as described. Other active hydrogen compounds, such as amines, interfere with —OH determination.

The sum of the acid and hydroxyl numbers permits a calculation of number average molecular weight:

$$(\text{Acid No.} + \text{Hydroxyl No.})/(2 \times 56.1 \times 1000) =$$

$$\text{moles of polymer per gram}$$

$$\text{MW} = 1/\text{moles of polymer per gram}$$

Because there are two ends per polymer molecule, the total of hydroxyl and carboxyl ends equals twice the number of polymer molecules.

In polyester prepared as previously described, the hydroxyl number will be about 58–59 and the carboxyl number about 3–4.]

B. Chain Extension of the Polyester with Diisocyanate:

In a 500 ml. flask equipped with stirrer and nitrogen inlet tube reaching to the bottom of the flask is placed about 200 g. of the polyester prepared above. The polymer should have a molecular weight of around 2000–3000 and a ratio of hydroxyl to carboxyl numbers of at least 12. The polyester may be washed into the flask with a small quantity of methylene chloride. The temperature is raised to 120°C. by means of an oil bath, with stirring and passage of a slow stream of nitrogen over the liquid ester. A quantity of solid methylene bis(4-phenylisocyanate) (Preparation 43) is added corresponding to 96% of the theoretical amount based on the number of moles of polyester used, as determined by the end group analysis above. The mixture is stirred vigorously at 120°C. for 40 min. After cooling under nitrogen, the polymer obtained is a white or off-white solid. The inherent viscosity of the polymer is about 1.0–1.5 in dimethylformamide (0.5% conc., 30°C.). Films dry-cast from dimethylformamide are elastomeric.

A curable polyester-urethane can be prepared by thorough mixing with additional diisocyanate, e.g., on a rubber mill. When the polyester used has a molecular weight of 2000 and 96% of the theoretical diisocyanate is used in the chain extending reaction, 100 g. of the final polymer can be mixed with 5.5 g. of diisocyanate, molded or pressed into a desired shape, and cured at 150°C. for 70 min. to give a strong, useful elastomer.

As an alternative to chain-extending a hydroxy-ended polyester segment with a diisocyanate, the **initial low polymer** may be **terminated with a diisocyanate at each end** of the molecule (15,64). A **second difunctional molecule** is then **used for the chain-extending** step. The general reaction is:

$$HO\text{-[polyester]-}OH + 2\ R(NCO)_2 \longrightarrow$$

$$OCN\text{—}R\text{—}NH\overset{O}{\underset{\|}{C}}\text{—}O\text{-[polyester]-}O\overset{O}{\underset{\|}{C}}\text{—}NH\text{—}R\text{—}NCO \xrightarrow{\ H\text{—}X\text{—}H\ }$$

$$\left\{ \overset{O}{\underset{\|}{\text{—}C}}\text{—}NH\text{—}R\text{—}NH\overset{O}{\underset{\|}{C}}\text{—}O\text{-[polyester]-}O\overset{O}{\underset{\|}{C}}\text{—}NH\text{—}R\text{—}NH\overset{O}{\underset{\|}{C}}\text{—}X\text{—} \right\}_n$$

H-X-H is a difunctional, active hydrogen compound, such as a glycol, diamine, or water. When water is used, carbon dioxide is evolved and a urea is the connecting linkage of the final product, as shown:

$$OCN\text{ww}NCO + H_2O \longrightarrow OCN\text{ww}NH\text{—}CO_2H \longrightarrow OCN\text{ww}NH_2 + CO_2$$

77. Chain Extension of Isocyanate-Terminated Poly(ethylene-co-propylene adipate) with water (15)

$$HO\left[CH_2CH_2OC(CH_2)_4COCH_2CHO\right]_n H + 2OCN\!\!-\!\!\bigcirc\!\!-\!\!CH_2\!\!-\!\!\bigcirc\!\!-\!\!NCO \longrightarrow$$

$$OCN\!\!-\!\!\bigcirc\!\!-\!\!CH_2\!\!-\!\!\bigcirc\!\!-\!\!NHCO\left[CH_2CH_2OC(CH_2)_4COCH_2CHO\right]_n CNH\!\!-\!\!\bigcirc\!\!-\!\!CH_2\!\!-\!\!\bigcirc\!\!-\!\!NCO \xrightarrow{H_2O}$$

$$\left\{-\!\!\bigcirc\!\!-\!\!CH_2\!\!-\!\!\bigcirc\!\!-\!\!NHCO\left[CH_2CH_2OC(CH_2)_4COCH_2CHO\right]_n CNH\!\!-\!\!\bigcirc\!\!-\!\!CH_2\!\!-\!\!\bigcirc\!\!-\!\!NHCNH\right\}_m + CO_2 \quad (A)$$

$$HO(CH_2CHO)_n H + OCNRNCO \xrightarrow[H_2O]{trace} OCNRNHCO(CH_2CHO)_n CNHRNCNHRNCO \xrightarrow{H_2O}$$

$$\left[-NHCNHRNHCO(CH_2CHO)_n NHRNCNHRNHCNH-\right]_m + CO_2 \quad (B)$$

$$R = \bigcirc$$

A sample of poly(ethylene-propylene adipate) prepared as described (in the preceding preparation) is analyzed for the number of hydroxyl end groups. The following directions are for use with a copolyester having an average molecular weight of 2000–3000 and a hydroxyl number of 55–60. Two hundred g. of the polyester is placed in a 1 l. three-necked flask equipped with stirrer, condenser with drying tube, and nitrogen inlet. To the flask, flushed with nitrogen, is added two molar equivalents of methylene bis(4-phenylisocyanate) (Preparation 43), based on the number of moles of polyester used as derived from its observed molecular weight. The mixture is stirred vigorously at 80°C. under nitrogen for 3 hr. It is then cooled to room temperature and 500 ml. of dry dimethylformamide is added. The mixture is brought into solution as rapidly as possible by stirring at room temperature. Another 100 ml. of dimethylformamide, containing a quantity of water equivalent in moles to one-half the number of moles of diisocyanate used, is added. The over-all stoichiometry is: 1 mole polyester + 2 moles diisocyanate + 1 mole water. The resulting viscous solution may be cast and dried in a vacuum oven at 50°C. to give elastomeric films, which may be somewhat tacky. The final film also may become insoluble after heating.

A low molecular weight **poly(propylene oxide) terminated with hydroxyls may be used to prepare foamed polymers** by reactions related to those of the two preceding examples. The polyether glycol is caused to react with excess diisocyanate, then treated with water. The foaming agent is the carbon dioxide liberated when water reacts with the free isocyanate groups in the prepolymer mixture (39). The foam effect is caused by the trapping of the gas in the polymeric mass. Polymerization reactions of this variety are used to make some of the widely employed urethane foam products.

78. Preparation of a Resilient Polyurethane Foam from Poly(propylene oxide) Glycol and 2,4-Tolylenediisocyanate (10A)

In the following preparation, amounts specified correspond to the use of a poly(propylene oxide) glycol of molecular weight 2000, a hydroxyl number of 56.1 (see Preparation 76 for determination of hydroxyl number), and an equivalent weight of 1000. If the poly(propylene oxide) glycol actually used has a different hydroxyl number of molecular weight, suitable corrections must be made in the amounts of reactants that follow.

A 500 ml. resin kettle equipped with stirrer, condenser with drying tube, thermometer and gas inlet is flushed with nitrogen, and in it is placed 200 g. of poly(propylene oxide) glycol. Water is added, if necessary, to bring the total water content to 0.8 g. If the original water content of the polyether glycol is not known, and a water analysis cannot be conveniently carried out, the polyether glycol can be dried by heating to 160°C. under nitrogen at a pressure of 1 mm. or less for a period of 3–4 hr. To the dried macroglycol is then added 0.8 g. water. The macroglycol–water mixture is stirred and

heated for 30 min. at 30–35°C. with a heating mantle. This and all subsequent operations must be carried out under nitrogen.

With continued stirring, but with removal of the heat source, 29.4 g. of
2,4-tolylenediisocyanate is added. This is an amount calculated to give an
NCO/OH ratio of 1.25 and an NCO/H_2O ratio of 1.00. The reaction which
occurs is slightly exothermic. After 30 min., the temperature is raised at the
rate of about 2°C./min. to 120°C. ± 3°C., where it is maintained for 90 min.
The mixture is then cooled to 80°C. If the molecular weight and hydroxyl
number of the macroglycol used are not as stated for this preparation, the
calculations for the amount of diisocyanate used are given by:

A. Wt. of diisocyanate (DI) for OH reaction = [(wt. of diol)/(equiv. wt.
of diol)] × equiv. wt. of DI × 1.25.

B. Wt. of DI for reaction with H_2O present = [(wt. of water)/(equiv. wt.
of H_2O)] × equiv. wt. of DI.

The sum of A and B is the required amount of diisocyanate. For the macro-
diol stipulated above, this is 29.4 g. (The equivalent weight of the diisocyanate is 87; of water, 9.) At this point, a second addition of 2,4-tolylenedi-
isocyanate is necessary to bring the total isocyanate content of the mixture to
the desired level of 9.5%. In order to do this, the isocyanate content of the
first reaction product must be determined, as follows.

Weigh about 0.5 g. of polymer from the resin kettle to the nearest milligram
and transfer to a dry 250 ml. Erlenmeyer flask. Add 25 ml. dry toluene and
stir magnetically for 5 min. to dissolve the polymer. Add 25.0 ml. of 0.1 N
butylamine in toluene (prepared as a primary standard from distilled butylamine and dry toluene) and continue stirring for 15 min. Add 100 ml. isopropyl alcohol and 4–6 drops of bromophenol blue indicator solution. Titrate
with 0.1 N HCl to a yellow-green endpoint. Run a blank including all
reagents, but omitting the sample.

% NCO = [(ml. HCl for blank—ml. HCl for sample) ×

(normality of HCl) × 4.202]/[weight of sample]

In the present example, the NCO content of the polymer at the present stage
should be about 1.5–1.8%. The amount of diisocyanate needed to bring the
total isocyanate content to 9.5% would be about 45 g., and is obtained from
the expression:

Wt. of diisocyanate to be added =

[(z − y)/(48.3 − z)] × (wt. of polymer)

where z = % NCO desired (9.5 in this experiment); and y = % NCO in
polymer, determined as above.

Weight of polymer in this experiment, at the end of the reaction of the
first amount of diisocyanate added, is about 229.4 g.

The amount of diisocyanate so determined is added to the reaction mixture
at 80°C. Stirring is continued for 30 min. while the temperature is allowed

to fall to 40°C. The product at this point, usually termed the prepolymer, is ready for the subsequent foaming step. The prepolymer may be safely stored under nitrogen at room temperature for six months or more.

Foaming can be carried out in a large beaker or other suitable container. It is suggested that a small amount be tried initially to estimate the volume of the vessel needed to contain the foamed product. A blend of the following relative amounts is made at room temperature under nitrogen:

100 Parts prepolymer having 9.5% NCO.
0.5 Part silicone oil, 50 centistokes (as Dow Corning DC-200).
1.0 Part N-methylmorpholine.
0.3 Part triethylamine.

To this mixture is added 2.25 parts of water (110% of theory). A foam results having a density of about 2.5 lbs./cu. ft.

The **elimination of water between carboxyl groups can give rise to polyanhydrides** when a dicarboxylic acid is used, which has the spatial requirements that favor the formation of linear, rather than cyclic, anhydride molecules. The behavior of diacids toward anhydride formation was studied by Carothers (4). Malonic acid forms only a polymeric anhydride, while succinic and glutaric acids form only the cyclic anhydrides. Adipic acid forms both a monomeric and polymeric anhydride, but higher diacids yield only linear products. Carothers investigated a large number of diacids and found that from sebacic acid a linear polyanhydride was first formed with a molecular weight of about 5000. When this polyanhydride (which was called α-anhydride) was subjected to molecular distillation, a cyclic dimer (β-anhydride) distilled and a much higher molecular weight (ca. 20,000) ω-polyanhydride residue remained. The β-anhydride was converted to γ-anhydride on standing or remelting. The latter was practically identical with α-anhydride, and was thought to contain very large ring structures while the α-form was linear.

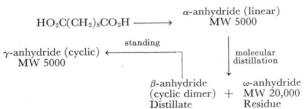

$$HO_2C(CH_2)_8CO_2H \longrightarrow \quad \begin{array}{c} \alpha\text{-anhydride (linear)} \\ \text{MW 5000} \end{array}$$

The ω-anhydride polymers are melt-spinnable to strong, lustrous, crystalline fibers. However, the aliphatic polyanhydrides are all so hydrolytically unstable that the polymers and fibers degrade rapidly on standing.

79. Preparation of Poly(sebacic anhydride) (4)

$$HO-\overset{O}{\underset{||}{C}}(CH_2)_8\overset{O}{\underset{||}{C}}OH \xrightarrow{(CH_3CO)_2O} \left[(CH_2)_8\overset{O}{\underset{||}{C}}-O-\overset{O}{\underset{||}{C}}\right]_n + H_2O$$

A solution of 20 g. sebacic acid in 100 ml. acetic anhydride in a 200 ml. flask equipped with a reflux condenser protected by a drying tube, is refluxed for 6 hr. The solvent is removed by warming on the steam bath under water aspirator vacuum. The crude anhydride is dissolved in 200 ml. of hot, dry benzene, and filtered through a fluted filter. Dry petroleum ether is added to precipitate the polymer (α-anhydride) which is stored over phosphorus pentoxide in a desiccator. This product melts at 75–80°C. to give a viscous liquid.

The polyanhydride prepared as before (α-polyanhydride) is placed in a flat, or slightly round bottomed, sublimation apparatus to form a thin layer of solid. The water-cooled condensing bulb or finger of the sublimator is adjusted to be about 2–3 cm. from the bottom of the heated portion of the apparatus. The pressure is reduced to at least 0.01 mm. by use of a mercury diffusion pump backed by an oil pump. The sublimator, which functions as a molecular still in this case, is then heated by means of a Wood's metal bath to 200°C. A crystalline distillate gradually accumulates on the condenser. The amount of distillate collected in a given time depends on the surface area of the anhydride being heated and the pressure. When an amount estimated to be about one-eighth the original anhydride used has collected, the distillation is stopped. The solid which has collected on the condenser is cyclic, dimeric sebacic anhydride (β-anhydride), which melts at 68°C. When cooled and remelted, it melts at about 82°C. and is now very viscous in the liquid form. This change represents the repolymerization of the cyclic dimer (β) to cyclic polyanhydride (γ). The residue from the distillation (high molecular weight ω-anhydride) melts at about 83°C. and is then extremely viscous. If it is heated to 130°C. strong filaments may be pulled from the melt; these can be cold drawn. They are rapidly degraded on standing at normal room humidity. Inherent viscosity determinations on solutions of the polymer are unreliable because of trace moisture pick-up even in hydrocarbons.

A series of **polyanhydrides based on aromatic diacids** of the type

$$HO-\overset{O}{\underset{||}{C}}-\langle\!\!\!\!\bigcirc\!\!\!\!\rangle-O(CH_2)_n-O-\langle\!\!\!\!\bigcirc\!\!\!\!\rangle-\overset{O}{\underset{||}{C}}-OH \quad n = 1\text{--}4$$

has been prepared by Conix (23). These polymers are much more stable to hydrolysis than their aliphatic counterparts. Preparation is best accomplished by forming the mixed anhydride of the diacid with acetic acid and heating that intermediate under vacuum to eliminate acetic anhydride.

The products are crystalline, high melting and thermally stable enough to permit fibers to be melt spun.   Polyanhydrides from related diacids have been reported by Yoda (95A), using essentially the same reaction described above.

80. Preparation of 1,3-Bis(p-carboxyphenoxy)propane*

One hundred thirty-eight g. (1.0 m.) of p-hydroxybenzoic acid is dissolved in a solution of 80 g. (2.0 m.) sodium hydroxide in 400 ml. water in a 1 l. three-necked flask, fitted with a reflux condenser, stirrer, and dropping funnel. Through the funnel, 102 g. (0.5 m.) 1,3-dibromopropane is added over a period of 1 hr. while the contents of the flask are stirred and kept at reflux temperature. After this addition, the reaction mixture is heated under reflux for $3^1/_2$ hr. At this time, 20 g. (0.5 m.) solid sodium hydroxide is added to the mixture, which is further heated for 2 hr. at reflux. Heating is discontinued, and the reaction mixture is left standing overnight. The fine, powdery, white precipitate of the disodium salt is filtered and washed with 200 ml. of methanol. The wet precipitate is dissolved in 1 l. of distilled water and acidified with 6 N sulfuric acid. The dibasic acid is isolated by filtration and dried in a vacuum oven at 80°C. The yield is 79 g. (50%). The neutralization equivalent is 157; calculated, 158. The 1,3-dibromopropane can be replaced by 1,3-dichloropropane using the same procedure but a longer reaction time (6 hr.). The yield is unchanged.

* We wish to thank Dr. Andre Conix and Photo-Produits Gevaert, S. A., Mortsel, Belgium, for making available to us the detailed preparation of this material.

81. Preparation of the Mixed Anhydride of 1,3-Bis(*p*-carboxyphenoxy) propane and Acetic Acid*

$$
HO\overset{O}{\overset{\|}{C}}-\hspace{-2pt}\bigcirc\hspace{-2pt}-O(CH_2)_3O-\hspace{-2pt}\bigcirc\hspace{-2pt}-\overset{O}{\overset{\|}{C}}O-H\ +\ 2(CH_3C)_2O\ \longrightarrow
$$

$$
CH_3O-O-\overset{C}{\overset{\ }{\underset{\|}{O}}}-\hspace{-2pt}\bigcirc\hspace{-2pt}-O(CH_2)_3O-\hspace{-2pt}\bigcirc\hspace{-2pt}-\overset{O}{\overset{\|}{C}}-O-\overset{O}{\overset{\|}{C}}-CH_3
$$

$$
+\ 2CH_3\overset{O}{\overset{\|}{C}}-OH
$$

Sixty g. (0.19 *m*.) of 1,3-bis(*p*-carboxyphenoxy)propane is refluxed with 650 ml. of acetic anhdride while a slow stream of dry nitrogen is bubbled through the solution.   After 30 min. almost all the dibasic acid is dissolved.   The mixture is filtered while still hot.   The filtrate, which is colored slightly yellow, is concentrated to a volume of about 60 ml. by distilling acetic anhydride (contaminated with acetic acid) under vacuum at a temperature of 65°C. The concentrated reaction mixture is stored in a refrigerator overnight.   The white, needle-like crystals which are formed are separated by filtration and washed with dry ether.   The yield is 66 g. (87%), and the melting point is 102–103°C.

82. Preparation of Poly(1,3-bis(*p*-carboxyphenoxy)propane anhydride)*

$$
CH_3\overset{O}{\overset{\|}{C}}-O-\overset{O}{\overset{\|}{C}}-\hspace{-2pt}\bigcirc\hspace{-2pt}-O(CH_2)_3O-\hspace{-2pt}\bigcirc\hspace{-2pt}-\overset{O}{\overset{\|}{C}}-O-\overset{O}{\overset{\|}{C}}-CH_3\ \longrightarrow
$$

$$
\left[\overset{O}{\overset{\|}{C}}-\hspace{-2pt}\bigcirc\hspace{-2pt}-O(CH_2)_3O-\hspace{-2pt}\bigcirc\hspace{-2pt}-\overset{O}{\overset{\|}{C}}-O\right]_n\ +\ (CH_3\overset{O}{\overset{\|}{C}})_2O
$$

In a polymer tube equipped with a side arm leading to a receiving flask is placed 20 g. of the mixed anhydride of 1,3-bis(*p*-carboxyphenoxy)propane with acetic acid.   A capillary reaching to the bottom of the tube is inserted.   The polymer tube is heated in a 280°C. (dimethyl phthalate) vapor bath which is brought to that temperature after the tube is in position.   Nitrogen is passed through the mixture and acetic anhydride distills.   After 30 min. at 280°C., a vacuum of about 1 mm., or less, is applied.   A stream of nitrogen is continually passed through the increasingly viscous melt.   Periodically, the vacuum may be released and a strong current of nitrogen flushed through the viscous melt for additional mixing.   At the end of 30 min., the polycondensation is terminated.

On cooling the tube, adhesion of the polymer to the walls of the vessel and shrinkage during crystallization may cause the tube to shatter.

The polymer is obtained in the form of a yellowish, opaque, hard block, which can be crystallized further by annealing at 130°C. in an oven for about 30 min. The crystalline melting point is about 267°C. From the melt, yellowish, lustrous fibers can be drawn which show the typical phenomenon of cold drawing.

When potassium dihydrogenphosphate is heated to an elevated temperature, water is eliminated and an essentially linear inorganic polymer is formed which is a **polyanhydride of phosphoric acid** (61).

$$
\underset{\underset{K}{\overset{\displaystyle O}{\underset{|}{\overset{\parallel}{HO-P-OH}}}}}{} \longrightarrow \underset{\underset{K}{\overset{\displaystyle O}{\underset{|}{\overset{\parallel}{\left[P-O\right]}}}}}{}_n + H_2O
$$

The chemical repeat unit has the composition of potassium metaphosphate, KPO_3. Molecular weights of 100,000 or more have been obtained. However, the polymer is very readily hydrolyzed in water, particularly under acidic conditions.

In order to obtain linear polymer, a potassium-to-phosphorus atomic ration of 1.0 or slightly greater is necessary in the starting material (K/P ≧ 1.0). At K/P of 0.98, a completely insoluble, cross-linked polymer results. At a K/P ratio of 0.9996 ± 0.0002, an appreciable

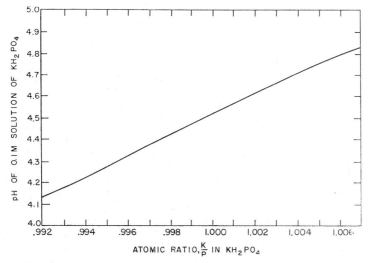

Fig. 3.4. pH of KH_2PO_4 solution as function of K:P.

amount of cross-linking occurs.   In such cases, the small amount of trifunctional $O = P(OH)_3$ present accounts for the cross-linking.

The K/P atomic ratio is determined by measuring the pH of a 0.1 M solution of potassium dihydrogenphosphate in carbon dioxide-free water.   From Fig. 3.4, which relates pH and K/P atomic ratio, the latter may be obtained directly.   In practice, most samples of KH_2PO_4 have a K/P ratio slightly less than one, in which case the ratio is adjusted to 1.00, or slightly greater, by the addition of potassium hydroxide.   Addition of phosphoric acid is used to lower a K/P ratio which is substantially greater than 1.00.   In the following example, directions are given for adjusting a KH_2PO_4 sample of K/P = 0.9996 to K/P = 1.001.   The K/P ratio of the adjusted sample should be checked to verify that the desired ratio was achieved.

83. Preparation of Potassium polymetaphosphate (61)

$$HO-\underset{\underset{K}{\overset{\displaystyle O}{|}}}{\overset{\displaystyle \overset{O}{\|}}{P}}-OH \longrightarrow \left[\underset{\underset{K}{\overset{\displaystyle O}{|}}}{\overset{\displaystyle \overset{O}{\|}}{P}}-O\right]_n + H_2O$$

To 188 g. of potassium dihydrogenphosphate (K/P ratio = 0.9996) in a 500 ml. stainless steel beaker is added enough 95% ethyl alcohol to just cover the crystals.   Then 0.18 g. of potassium hydroxide, dissolved in a mixture 1 ml. of water and 10 ml. of ethyl alcohol, is slowly added to the mixture in the beaker with continuous stirring.

The alcohol is then evaporated on the steam bath with continuous stirring. A 3 in. diameter platinum dish containing 100 g. of the treated potassium dihydrogenphosphate (K/P ratio 1.001) is then placed in a furnace at 850°C. After 30 min., the molten material is cooled to 800°C., which is just below its melting point, then gradually lowered over a 4 hr. period to 775°C.   The temperature is maintained at 775°C. for 40 min.   The sample is then removed from the furnace and chilled by holding the lower part of the dish in water. The polymer is obtained as a transparent crystalline product.   It is less than 0.004% soluble in water, but dissolves readily in an aqueous solution of a sodium salt, as sodium chloride.

After grinding to a powder in a laboratory mill, the polymer may be dissolved in water for a viscosity determination in the following way.   A 1% slurry of polymer in boiled distilled water is placed in a three-necked flask equipped with stirrer and pH electrodes.   With vigorous stirring, the pH is brought to 8.0 with 0.1 N sodium hydroxide.   Freshly washed sodium salt of Nalcite HCR ion exchange resin is then added, in the ratio of 6 g. air-dried resin per gram of polymer.   The polymer begins to swell immediately.   The pH tends to drop slightly, but is maintained between 7.5 and 8.5 by the addition of more alkali.   Vigorous stirring is continued for 40 min. to disperse any lumps and the temperature is kept at 25–30°C. The resulting solution at pH 8.0–8.5 is filtered under slight vacuum through a mat of glass wool to remove the ion exchange resin. The filtrate is then a solution of poly-(sodium–potassium metaphosphate) in water at a concentration of 1%. The specific viscosity (see Chapter 2) of the solution is determined at 25°C., using water as the reference liquid. Determinations must be made within 2 hr. after preparing the solution or degradation will be significant; molecular weight, estimated by means of end group determinations, has been correlated with specific viscosity measurements on 1% solutions of the mixed sodium-potassium salt of the polymer.

The following emperical relationship has been derived,

$$y = 0.61x + 2.12$$

where $y = \log_{10}$ (degree of polymerization); and $x = \log_{10}$ (specific viscosity).

From the above preparation, specific viscosities of 30–100 may be obtained. Films may be cast from freshly prepared solutions of the mixed sodium-potassium salt at about 11% solids concentration and pH 7.5–8.0 by drying in a stream of air. The film is too brittle, when dry, to be removed from the glass casting plate.

REFERENCES

The first four references relate to books on the subject of condensation polymers in general.

1. Billmeyer, F. W., *Textbook of Polymer Chemistry*, Interscience Publishers, New York, 1957.
2. Flory, P. J., *Principles of Polymer Chemistry*, Cornell University Press, Ithica, N. Y., 1953.
3. Hill, R., *Fibers from Synthetic Polymers*, Elsevier, New York, 1953.
4. Mark, H., and S. B. Whitby, ed., *Collected Papers of Wallace Hume Carothers*, Interscience Publishers, New York, 1940.

The following references relate to specific topics mentioned in this chapter.
5. Aelion, R., *Ann. chim.*, **3**, 5 (1948).
6. Broker, W., R. E. Oesper, and W. A. Cook, *J. Am. Chem. Soc.*, **47**, 2609 (1925).
7. Alexander, P., and C. S. Whewell, *Some Aspects of Textile Research in Germany*, H. M. Stationery Office, London, 1947. BIOS Report No. 1472.
8. Allen, S. J., and J. G. N. Drewitt, British Pat. 610,304, (October 14, 1948).
9. Allen, S. J., and J. G. N. Drewitt, U. S. Pat. 2,558,031, (June 26, 1951).
10. Allen, S. J., and J. G. N. Drewitt, U. S. Pat. 2,483,514, (October 4, 1949).
10A. Barringer, C. M., HR-26, Elastomer Chemicals Dept. Bulletin, April 1958, E. I. du Pont de Nemours & Co., Inc.
11. Beaman, R. G., and F. B. Cramer, *J. Polymer Sci.*, **21**, 223 (1956).
12. Beste, L. F., and R. C. Houtz, *J. Polymer Sci.*, **8**, 395 (1952).
13. Bjorksten Research Laboratories, Inc., *Polyesters and Their Applications*, Reinhold, New York, 1956.

14. Bock, L. H., and J. K. Anderson, *J. Polymer Sci.*, **28,** 121 (1958).
15. Brenschede, W., U. S. Pat. 2,755,266, (July 17, 1956).
16. Brinker, K. C., and I. M. Robinson, German Pat. 1,038,280, (September 4, 1958); Can. Pat. 575,411, (May 5, 1959); U. S. Pat. 2,895,948 (July 21, 1959).
17. Bruson, H. A., and T. W. Riener, *J. Am. Chem. Soc.*, **65,** 23 (1943).
18. Buckley, G. D., and N. H. Ray, U. S. Pat. 2,550,767, (May 1, 1951).
19. Cairns, T. L., H. D. Foster, A. W. Larchar, A. K. Schneider, and R. S. Schreiber, *J. Am. Chem. Soc.*, **71,** 651 (1949).
20. Campbell, T. W., V. S. Foldi, and J. Farago, *J. Appl. Polymer Sci.*, **2,** 155 (1959).
20A. Campbell, T. W., V. S. Foldi, and R. G. Parrish, *J. Appl. Polymer Sci.*, **2,** 81 (1959).
21. Chattaway, F. D., *J. Chem. Soc.*, **1931,** 2495.
22. Coffman, D. D., G. J. Berchet, W. R. Peterson, and E. W. Spanagel, *J. Polymer Sci.*, **2,** 306 (1947).
23. Conix, A., *J. Polymer Sci.*, **29,** 343 (1958).
24. Cramer, F. B., and R. G. Beaman, *J. Polymer Sci.*, **21,** 237 (1956).
25. Curtius, T., and H. Clemm, *J. prakt. Chem.*, (2) **62,** 202 (1900).
26. Eareckson, W. M., *J. Polymer Sci.*, **40,** 399 (1959); see also Conix, A., *Ind. Eng. Chem.*, **51,** 147 (1959).
27. Edwards, W. M., and I. M. Robinson, U. S. Pat. 2,710,853, (June 14, 1955).
28. Farago, J., private communication.
29. Fettes, E. M., and J. S. Jorczak in C. E. Schildknecht, ed., *Polymer Processes*, Interscience Publishers, New York, 1956.
30. Fieser, L. F., *Experiments in Organic Chemistry*, 3rd ed., Heath, New York, 1957, p. 285.
31. Fisher, J. W., *Chem. and Ind.*, **71,** 244 (1952).
32. Flory, P. J., and F. S. Leutner, U. S. Pat. 2,623,034, (December 23, 1952).
33. Flory, P. J., and F. S. Leutner, U. S. Pat. 2,589,688 (March 18, 1952).
34. Frosch, C. J., U. S. Pat. 2,421,024, (May 27, 1947).
34A. Gilkey, R., and J. R. Caldwell, *J. Appl. Polymer Sci.*, **2,** 198 (1959).
35. Haas, H. C., S. G. Cohen, A. C. Oglesby, and E. R. Karlin, *J. Polymer Sci.*, **15,** 427 (1955).
36. Haggis, G. A., and L. N. Owen, *J. Chem. Soc.*, **1953,** 404.
37. Hanford, W. E., and P. L. Salzburg, U. S. Pat. 2,313,871, (March 16, 1943).
38. Higgins, N. A., U. S. Pat. 2,676,945, (April 27, 1954).
39. Hill, F. B., U. S. Pat. 2,929,800, (March 22, 1960).
40. Katz, M., *J. Polymer Sci.*, **40,** 237 (1959).
41. Katz, M., U. S. Pat. 2,888,438, (May 26, 1959).
41A. Kibler, C. J., A. Bell, and J. G. Smith, U. S. Pat. 2,901,466 (Aug. 25, 1959).
42. Lazier, W. A., and H. R. Arnold, *Organic Synthesis*, coll. vol. II, A. H. Blatt, ed., Wiley, New York, p. 144.

42A. Lyman, D. J., and S. L. Jung, *J. Polymer Sci.*, **40**, 407 (1959).
42B. Lyman, D. J., *J. Polymer Sci.*, 1960, in press.
43. Magat, E. E., U. S. Pat. 2,831,834, (April 22, 1958).
44. Magat, E. E., and D. R. Strachan, U. S. Pat. 2,708,617, (May 17, 1955).
45. Malachowski, R., J. J. Wasowska, and S. Jozkiewicz, *Ber.*, **71**, 759 (1938).
46. Mackay, T. E., private communication.
47. Marvel, C. S., and P. H. Aldrich, *J. Am. Chem. Soc.*, **72**, 1978 (1950).
48. Marvel, C. S., and J. H. Johnson, *J. Am. Chem. Soc.*, **72**, 1674 (1950).
49. Marvel, C. S., and A. Kotch, *J. Am. Chem. Soc.*, **73**, 481 (1951).
50. Mastin, T. G., and N. V. Seeger, U. S. Pat. 2,625,535, (January 13, 1953).
51. Matlack, A. S., U. S. Pat. 2,672,480, (March 16, 1954).
52. Moncrieff, R. C., U. S. Pat. 2,512,667, (June 27, 1950).
52A. Morgan, P. W., *Soc. Plastics Eng. J.*, **15**, 485 (1959).
53. Morgan, P. W., and S. L. Kwolek, *J. Chem. Ed.*, **36**, 182 (1959).
54. Mozingo, R., *Organic Synthesis*, vol. 21, Wiley, New York, 1941, p. 15.
55. Naegli, C., and A. Tyabji, *Helv. Chim. Acta,* **17**, 931 (1934); **18**, 142 (1935).
56. Noether, H. D., *Textile Res. J.*, **28**, 533 (1958).
57. Noether, H. D., U. S. Pat. 2,534,366, (December 19, 1950).
58. Ogg, C. L., W. L. Porter, and C. O. Willits, *Ind. Eng. Chem., Anal. Ed.*, **17**, 394 (1945).
59. Patrick, J. C., U. S. Pat. 1,890,191, (December 6, 1933).
60. Patrick, J. C., U. S. Pat. 1,950,744, (March 13, 1934).
61. Pfanstiel, R., and R. K. Iler, *J. Am. Chem. Soc.*, **74**, 6059 (1952).
62. Rabjohn, N., *J. Am. Chem. Soc.*, **70**, 1181 (1948).
63. Schaefgen, J. R., F. H. Koontz, and R. F. Tietz, *J. Polymer Sci.*, **40**, 377 (1959).
64. Schmidt, F. W., U. S. Pat. 2,621,166, (December 9, 1952).
65. Schnell, H., *Ind. and Eng. Chem.*, **51**, 157 (1959).
66. Schnell, H., and G. Fritz, German Pat. 1,031,512, (June 4, 1958).
68. Schnell, H., *Angew. Chem.*, **68**, 633 (1956).
69. Schnell, H., and L. Bottenburch, German Pat. 1,046,311 (Dec. 11, 1958).
70. Shashoua, V. E., and W. M. Eareckson, *J. Polymer Sci.*, **40**, 343 (1959).
71. Shivers, J. C., Canadian Pat. 563,070, (September 9, 1958).
72. Siggia, S., *Quantitative Organic Analyses via Functional Groups*, Wiley, New York, 1954, p. 21.
73. Signaigo, F. K., U. S. Pat. 2,166,183, (July 18, 1939).
74. Somers, J. A., *Man-Made Textiles*, **32**, No. 381, 60 (1956).
75. Sorenson, W. R., *J. Org. Chem.*, **24**, 978 (1959).
76. Speck, S. B., *J. Am. Chem. Soc.*, **74**, 2876 (1952).
77. Stamatoff, G. S., U. S. Pat. 2,704,282, (March 15, 1955).
78. Sundet, S. A., W. A. Murphey, and S. B. Speck, *J. Polymer Sci.*, **40**, 389 (1959).
79. Sveda, M., U. S. Pat. 2,562,000, (July 24, 1951).
80. Sweeny, W., private communication.
81. Toy, A. D. F., U. S. Pat. 2,435,252, (February 3, 1948).

82. Toy, A. D. F., U. S. Pat. 2,572,076, (October 23, 1951).
83. Toy, A. D. F., *J. Am. Chem. Soc.*, **70**, 186 (1948).
84. Van Der Kerk, G. J. M., H. G. J. Overmars, and G. M. Van Der Want, *Rec. trav. chim.*, **74**, 1301 (1955).
85. Walsgrove, E. R., and F. Reeder, British Pat. 636,429, (April 26, 1950).
86. Whinfield, J. R., *Nature*, **158**, 930 (1946).
87. Whinfield, J. R., and J. T. Dickson, British Pat. 578,079, (June 14, 1946).
88. Wiley, P. F., *J. Am. Chem. Soc.*, **68**, 1867 (1946).
89. Wittbecker, E. L., U. S. Pat. 2,731,446, (January 17, 1956).
90. Wittbecker, E. L., U. S. Pat. 2,816,879, (December 17, 1957).
91. Wittbecker, E. L., R. C. Houtz, and W. W. Watkins, *J. Am. Chem. Soc.*, **69**, 579 (1947).
92. Wittbecker, E. L., W. W. Watkins, and R. C. Houtz, *Ind. Eng. Chem.*, **40**, 875 (1948).
93. Wittbecker, E. L., and M. Katz, *J. Polymer Sci.*, **40**, 367 (1959).
94. Wittbecker, E. L., and P. W. Morgan, *J. Polymer Sci.*, **40**, 289 (1960).
94A. Woods, G. F., and H. Saunders, *J. Am. Chem. Soc.*, **68**, 2111 (1946).
95. Yamaguchi, K., M. Takayanagi, and S. Kuriyama, *J. Chem. Soc.* (*Japan*), Ind. Chem. Sec., **58**, 358 (1955); *C. A.* **49**, 14373g (1955).
95A. Yoda, N., *Makromol. Chem.*, **32**, 1 (1959).
96. Belgian Pats. 546,376 and 546,377, (March 23, 1956).
97. British Pat. 591,027, (August 5, 1947).
98. British Pat. 737,939, (October 5, 1955).
99. British Pat. 543,297, (February 18, 1942).
100. British Pat. 535,139, (March 31, 1941).
101. British Pat. 530,267, (December 9, 1940).
102. British Pat. 528,437, (October 29, 1940).
103. French Pat. 1,158,755, (June 19, 1958); *Jap. Pat. Publn.*, 2,595, (1959).
104. Schröter, R., in *Newer Methods of Preparative Organic Chemistry*, Interscience Publishers, New York, 1948, p. 76.

CHAPTER 4

Addition Polymers from Unsaturated Monomers

I. General Considerations

An ethylenic monomer is a substance with the general formula

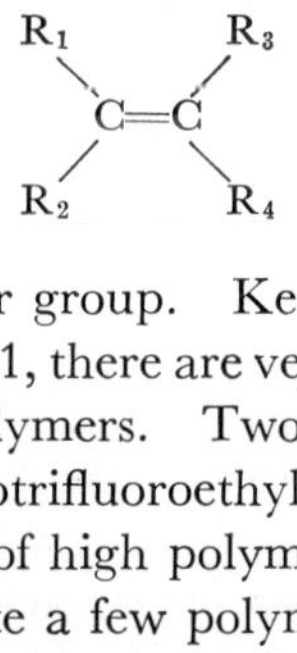

$$R_1 \diagdown R_3 \diagup$$
$$C = C$$
$$R_2 \diagup R_4 \diagdown$$

where R is H or some other group. Keeping in mind the definition of polymer given in Chapter 1, there are very few tetrasubstituted monomers which gave high polymers. Two important ones are tetrafluoroethylene and chlorotrifluoroethylene. Larger groups than fluorine inhibit the growth of high polymer by known polymerization techniques. There are quite a few polymerizable monomers in which $R_1 = R_2 = H$, and R_3 and R_4 are other groups, and a few where $R_1 = R_3 = H$, with R_2 and R_4 other groups. The largest group of polymerizable vinyl compounds are those in which $R_1 = R_2 = R_3 = H$ with R_4 the only disimilar group.

1. MECHANISM

The polymerization of a typical vinyl monomer may be represented simply as follows:

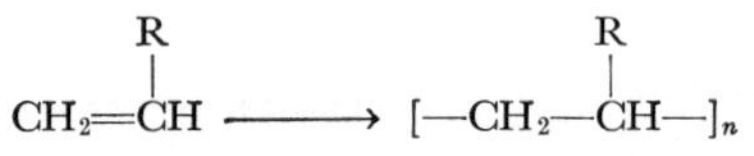

$$\underset{\displaystyle CH_2 = CH}{\overset{\displaystyle R}{|}} \longrightarrow [-CH_2 - \underset{\displaystyle}{\overset{\displaystyle R}{|}}CH-]_n$$

The mechanism of vinyl polymerization is far more complex than is indicated by this oversimplified equation. This subject is treated

149

at great length in the references listed at the end of this section, so no attempt will be made to discuss the various mechanisms rigorously. Vinyl polymerization is basically a three-step process.* (1) initiation by appropriate initiator; (2) propagation; and (3) chain termination.

In the initiation step, the monomer reacts with an initiator fragment to give an activated species

$$X^* + CH_2{=}\overset{R}{C}H \longrightarrow X{-}CH_2{-}\overset{R}{C}H^*$$

transferring the active center from the initiator to a monomer unit. The chain then propagates, or grows, by a rapid addition of the new activated species to a new monomer unit, a step which may be repeated many thousand times:

$$XCH_2\overset{R}{C}H^* + CH_2{=}\overset{R}{C}H \longrightarrow XCH_2\overset{R}{C}H{-}CH_2\overset{R}{C}H^*$$

$$XCH_2\overset{R}{C}H{-}CH_2{-}\overset{R}{C}H^* + CH_2{=}\overset{R}{C}H \longrightarrow XCH_2\overset{R}{C}H{-}CH_2\overset{R}{C}H{-}CH_2{-}\overset{R}{C}H^*$$

$$\vdots$$

$$XCH_2\overset{R}{C}H{-}(CH_2{-}\overset{R}{C}H)_{n-1}{-}CH_2\overset{R}{C}H^* \longrightarrow \text{dead polymer.}$$

Chain termination may occur by a variety of mechanisms, such as disproportionation, combination, elimination, reaction with an impurity, or chain transfer. A discussion of termination mechanisms will be found in any standard polymer text, hence will not be treated here. It is interesting to note, however, one reason for temporary cessation of growth, that is disappearance of monomer units. In this specialized case, the activated ends (usually anions) remain in an activated state for relatively long periods, and polymerization may continue if more monomer is added. Polymers of this type are known as "living polymers" and have been studied extensively by Szwarc (41,177,178).

* The mechanism of coordination polymerization is not clear, but may not be correctly described by this oversimplified scheme. It is, however, satisfactory for free radical cationic, and certain types of anionic systems. In some anionic systems there is apparently no termination.

2. INITIATION

Vinyl monomers respond to four types of initiators: (1) free radical; (2) cationic; (3) anionic; and (4) coordination. The coordination catalysts undoubtedly have some of the character of one or more of the first three, but the mechanisms are as yet unclear. For this reason they will be treated separately.

The nature of the activated center will depend on the nature of the initiator. Thus, in a polymer chain initiated by a free radical, the growing chain will be terminated by a free radical, while with a cationic or anionic initiator the active center will be a carbonium ion, or a carbanion. As will be seen from subsequent experiments, the type of initiator used will depend on the monomer, since not all monomers will respond to all types of initiators. Discussions of the relationships between initiator type and monomer structure will be found in Flory (6), Billmeyer (3), Schildknecht (16), and elsewhere. Polymerization by ionizing radiation may occur by either radical or ionic mechanisms (196).

3. CONJUGATED DIENES

Another aspect of vinyl polymerization of much industrial significance is the polymerization or copolymerization of a monomer containing two vinyl groups. At first glance, one might expect that each vinyl group would polymerize independently to give a highly branched, three-dimensional polymer. In some cases this does occur, but with the technically important conjugated dienes, essentially linear polymer is formed. The structure of the polymer varies greatly with the initiator. Thus polymerization of butadiene may give the following structural units:

(1) 1,4-*Polymerization*

$$CH_2{=}CH{-}CH{=}CH_2 + X^* \longrightarrow X{-}CH_2{-}CH{=}CH{-}CH_2^*$$

$$\longrightarrow X(CH_2{-}CH{=}CH{-}CH_2)_r$$

The product may be cis or trans, or a mixture.

(2) 1,2-*Polymerization*

$$CH_2{=}CH \quad CH{=}CH_2 + X^* \longrightarrow X{-}CH_2\overset{\displaystyle CH{=}CH_2}{\underset{\displaystyle |}{CH}}{}^*$$

$$\longrightarrow X(CH_2{-}\overset{\displaystyle CH{=}CH_2}{\underset{\displaystyle |}{CH}}{-})_n$$

With substituted butadienes, such as isoprene (2-methyl butadiene), additional structural variations are possible. Natural rubber (Hevea) is a polymer of isoprene which is predominately cis-1,4. Catalysts have been developed recently which will polymerize isoprene to a product identical in all respects to natural rubber, a feat comparable to the best classic syntheses of other natural products (89,174).

Butadiene and its derivatives form the basis for most of the synthetic rubbers. Thus, polymerization of 2,3-dimethylbutadiene with sodium gave a rubber which was important in Germany during World War I (18). During World War II, the Allies depended to a large extent on copolymers of butadiene with styrene ("GR-S") and acrylonitrile to replace the natural rubber cut off from the Far East.

In addition, a third diene polymer, that from 2-chlorobutadiene (neoprene), was discovered by W. H. Carothers and is used extensively where an oil resistant rubber is needed (18,48).

4. NONCONJUGATED DIENES

As mentioned earlier, divinyl compounds might be expected to produce highly branched, three-dimensional polymers. This occurs less readily with conjugated dienes, but will occur with other nonconjugated systems. Thus glycol dimethacrylate (I) will polymerize

$$CH_2{=}\overset{\overset{\displaystyle CH_3}{|}}{C}{-}\overset{\overset{\displaystyle O}{\|}}{C}{-}O{-}CH_2CH_2{-}O\overset{\overset{\displaystyle O}{\|}}{C}{-}\overset{\overset{\displaystyle CH_3}{|}}{C}{=}CH_2 \qquad CH_2{=}\overset{\overset{\displaystyle CH_3}{|}}{C}{-}\overset{\overset{\displaystyle O}{\|}}{C}{-}OCH_3$$

$$\text{(I)} \qquad\qquad\qquad\qquad \text{(II)}$$

under conditions similar to those which will polymerize methyl methacrylate (II). However, each group reacts independently, and the product from I has properties of a cross-linked polymer; that is, it is an infusible, insoluble solid. In contrast, poly(methyl methacrylate) is easily molded, and is soluble in many common organic solvents.

A specialized type of nonconjugated diene polymerization, cyclopolymerization, has recently been described by Butler (43), Marvel (118), and Jones (101). It is described in more detail in Chapter 6.

5. COPOLYMERS

Two or more vinyl monomers which polymerize with a given catalyst may be incorporated into the same polymer chain (1,16). In general, the product will have properties intermediate between the homopolymers.   There are four types of copolymers of monomers A and B:

(1)   *Random*
      —ABBAAABBBBBABAAB—
(2)   *Alternating*
      —ABABABABABABAB—
(3)   *Block*
      AAAAAABBBBBBBBBAAAAAA
(4)   *Graft*
      AAAAAAAAAAAAAAAAAAAA
         | | | |
        B   B   B   B
        B   B   B   B
        B   B   B   B
        B   B   B   B
        | | B   B
        | |
        | |

Preparation of each of these types requires specialized techniques.

A. Random Copolymers

The preparation of random copolymers is the most straightforward. Monomer A and monomer B are mixed, and the catalyst added. Normally, A and B will polymerize at different rates, so that the composition of a copolymer isolated before polymerization is complete will depend on the relative reactivity of A versus B*. This had led to the concept of reactivity ratios, in which a variety of monomers are compared to a standard monomer, usually styrene.   This concept has found wide application in the copolymer field (1,121).

The properties of polymers can be changed greatly by inclusion of minor amounts of a comonomer in this way.   Thus copolymerization of minor amounts of several vinyl monomers with acrylonitrile can give products with improved solubility characteristics, with built-in sites for chemically bonding or fixing dye molecules, etc., but with the desirable characteristics of pure polyacrylonitrile.   On the other hand, copolymerization of relatively large amounts of butadiene with acrylonitrile gives a polymer with the characteristics of an elastomer.

* If polymerization is allowed to go to completion, the copolymer will have a composition corresponding to the original ratio of A to B, since polymer formed toward the end will be richer in the slow component, the fast one having been consumed.   At any instant, the composition of polymer being formed is necessarily different from that being formed at any other instant.

B. Alternating Copolymers

Alternating copolymers represent a special case and require that each monomer be more reactive towards the other species than towards its own kind. Thus styrene radical has a great affinity for maleic

anhydride, but the maleic anhydride radical will not add to itself, hence a styrene molecule is added next to the growing chain.

This alternation continues until the chain is terminated (1,16,186).

Another particularly interesting and unusual case of alternation occurs during the copolymerization of terminal olefins with sulfur dioxide (71,77,95,158):

$$XCH_2-CH_2\cdot + SO_2 \longrightarrow XCH_2CH_2SO_2\cdot$$

$$\longrightarrow XCH_2CH_2SO_2CH_2CH_2\cdot \longrightarrow XCH_2CH_2SO_2CH_2CH_2SO_2\cdot, \text{ etc.}$$

An olefin —SO$_2$ complex has been suggested as an intermediate (26,57).

Another unusual "comonomer" which has been shown to alternate with styrene is oxygen (63,120,124).

$$\underset{\underset{\displaystyle XCH_2-CH\cdot}{|}}{C_6H_5} + O_2 \longrightarrow \underset{\underset{\displaystyle XCH_2CH-O-O-}{|}}{C_6H_5}$$

$$\longrightarrow X[-CH_2-\underset{\underset{\displaystyle CH-O-O]_n}{|}}{C_6H_5}$$

C. Block Copolymers

The third type of copolymer, the block, is rather difficult to attain unequivocally in a vinyl polymer. One of the best methods is Szwarc's (177,178) living polymer technique. Polymerization of a monomer is initiated by the anionic initiator X$^-$ and polymerization continues until all of the monomer is used up. The length of the chain at this point will depend on the ratio of monomer molecules to catalyst molecules:

$$X^{(-)} + nA \longrightarrow X(A)_n^{(-)}$$

The chains do not "die" when all of the monomer is exhausted, but remain alive. Addition of the monomer B then permits the chain to continue:

$$X(A)_n^{(-)} + mB \longrightarrow X(A)_n(B)_m^{(-)}$$

This alternation may, at least theoretically, be continued *ad infinitum*, provided subsequent monomers are polymerizable by the terminal anion.

Numerous other techniques for preparation of block polymers are reported in the literature. Each pair of monomers, however, requires development of specialized techniques so no generalization can be made.

D. Graft Copolymers

Preparation of graft polymers is basically simple and requires two steps:

First, monomer A is polymerized to a normal homopolymer:

$$A \longrightarrow AAAAAAAAAAAAAAAAAAA$$

Second, monomer B is polymerized in the presence of poly A in such a way that poly B is attached to poly A to give a backbone of A with branches of B:

This may be done in a variety of ways. High energy, ionizing irradiation of poly A can produce a few free radicals along the chain, which then initiate B. Reactive sites may be copolymerized with A. For example, if monomer A is copolymerized with acryloyl chloride, a condensation polymer (Cf. Chapter 3) can be grown from the vinyl backbone by low temperature techniques.

Characterization of graft polymers is difficult and time consuming and involves laborious fractionation experiments to prove that a true graft, and not a mixture of homopolymers, has been obtained.

II. Free Radical Polymerization of Vinyl Monomers—Experimental Methods

The number of examples which could be included in this section is quite large, since each of the many available monomers usually may be polymerized in a variety of ways, i.e., in bulk, suspension, emulsion, etc., and by a variety of catalysts which give free radicals. The monomers considered will be limited to those known to polymerize to high molecular weight readily, while satisfactory representative polymerization techniques will be described. No attempt will be made to consider exhaustively all methods for all monomers.

1. EQUIPMENT

In general, the free radical polymerization of a vinyl monomer may be carried out in rather simple systems. (Cf. Chapter 2). For monomers boiling above 40°C., a three-necked flask equipped with an efficient condenser, a nitrogen inlet, and a mechanical stirrer is all

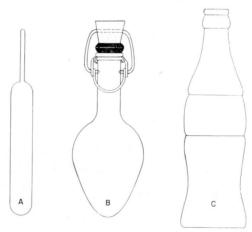

Fig. 4. 1. Pressure vessels for vinyl polymerization.

that is required.   Preferably, the flask should be immersed in a thermostatted bath which will usually be kept in the range of 40–50°C.
Polymerization is then carried out according to one of the techniques
described below, usually in a nitrogen atmosphere.

The polymerization of monomers boiling below about 40°C. may
be carried out by sealing the ingredients in a pressure vessel which
is then shaken or tumbled by a mechanical device in a constant temperature bath.   The vessel used may be a tube of the type used for
running pressure reactions (Fig. 4.1a).

Alternatively, the commercially available pressure bottles (Fig.
4.1b) or ordinary carbonated beverage bottles (Fig. 4.1c) with an
appropriate closure may be used where the pressures dealt with are
not excessive.   In any event, it should be recognized that any sealed
glass vessel of this type constitutes a potential bomb and must be
handled with extreme caution.   When glass pressure tubes are sealed
with an oxygen torch, care must be taken to build up a proper seal
which maintains the thickness of the wall of the tube.   All seals should,
of course, be annealed.   Furthermore, quantities of monomer larger
than those recommended in the experiments should not be used since
some of the polymerizations tend to be exothermic.   In the event of
an exothermic polymerization, quite excessive pressures may be built
up inside these tubes.   For this reason, all pressure tube reactions
should routinely be carried out behind adequate safety shielding, and
tubes should be opened cautiously behind a good barricade.

2. MONOMERS

The largest single factor in determining whether a polymerization
is successful or not is the purity of the monomer used.   It is absolutely
essential that the material be pure.

3. POLYMERIZATION SYSTEMS

Bulk polymerization is the simplest technique for converting monomer to polymer.   In this method catalyst is added to undiluted monomer and this mixture is carried through the polymerization cycle.   This
technique is useful because of its simplicity and because it makes
possible the direct preparation of castings, since the monomer-catalyst
mixture will polymerize to a solid shape controlled by the shape of the
polymerization vessel.   This method, however, suffers from certain

disadvantages.   For example, polymerizations which are exothermic are liable to form local hot spots within the polymerization with consequent charring of the product.   Other difficulties will be apparent during later discussion.

In order to obviate some of the difficulties encountered with bulk polymerization, solution polymerization has been used to some extent. In this technique the monomer is diluted by an inert liquid which makes control of the temperature of the reaction much simpler.   This technique, if the solvent is chosen properly, will give a solution of the polymer ready for casting or spinning.   However, many solvents have a deleterious effect on the molecular weights obtained, since they may act as chain transfer agents, thus lowering the molecular weight of the polymer.   Also, the last traces of solvents are sometimes quite difficult to remove.

Another technique which is used to compensate for the poor features of bulk polymerization is suspension polymerization.   In suspension polymerization, monomer is suspended rather than dissolved in an inert liquid, usually water.   Stabilizing agents such as starch may be used to keep the monomer in a state of suspension in the form of small droplets, each one of which constitutes a tiny individual bulk polymerization.   Mechanical agitation is required to maintain the liquid in suspension, and at the end of the polymerization the product is ordinarily obtained as a fine, granular product which is very easily filtered and handled.   It is necessary to wash and dry the polymer thoroughly to remove traces of the suspension stabilizer and the reaction medium, usually water.

The last technique to be considered is emulsion polymerization. In this system, again water is used as a carrier.   However, an emulsifying agent such as a synthetic detergent is added and the mixture of water, monomer, catalyst, and detergent is agitated quite vigorously. Under these conditions the monomer is dispersed in the aqueous phase in the form of very fine particles almost of a colloidal nature (5). One of the big advantages of emulsion polymerization is that it gives a fluid system in which temperature control can be achieved.   Rapid polymerization to very high molecular weights is easily achieved.

4. INITIATORS

There are a number of different techniques for initiating polymerization of vinyl monomers which depend upon the generation of free radicals. The simplest method is thermal polymerization in which free radicals are developed in the monomer simply by heating. About the only monomer with which this technique is satisfactory is styrene. In other cases it is necessary to add in small proportions an agent which will generate radicals *in situ*. The following compounds are popular and may be obtained commercially: benzoyl peroxide; acetyl peroxide; α,α'-azodiisobutyronitrile; *t*-butylhydroperoxide; cumene hydroperoxide; di-*t*-butyl peroxide; azodicyclohexylcarbonitrile; dimethyl-α,α-azodiisobutyrate; succinyl peroxide; dicumyl peroxide; and dichlorobenzoyl peroxide. All of these agents will produce free radicals. They differ in the end result in that different temperatures are required to bring about breakdown of the compound into radicals. It is claimed occasionally that a certain initiator has inherent advantages, for example, that it will give a less discolored product. However, this is something which is learned only by trial and error. These agents may be used in aqueous as well as inorganic media. In aqueous media, it is also possible to use certain inorganic oxidizing agents. Among those that are popular are hydrogen peroxide, sodium perborate, and various persulfates. The effectiveness of the radical catalyst can, in many cases, be enhanced greatly by the inclusion of a reducing agent, such as ferrous ion, and other modifiers. Thus the very important redox type of reduction-activated polymerization recipe contains a number of ingredients, each added for a specific purpose (18). For details on kinetics and mechanism of free radical catalyzed polymerizations, the reader should refer to a standard text on the subject.

It should be noted that the literature, in particular the patent literature, is replete with additional examples of compounds suitable for use as either sources of free radicals or as reducing agents for use in redox-type formulations. There is little point in attempting to list all of these. Only those which will actually be used in the preparation of polymer will be mentioned, and those in the appropriate place.

III. Free Radical Catalyzed Polymerization of Monosubstituted Ethylenes

The simplest olefin, ethylene, polymerizes to a high molecular weight, branched product with a melting point in the 110–135°C. range, depending on the amount of branching.

Low density polyethylene was first prepared in 1933 (2). It is ordinarily prepared in the laboratory on a small scale by free radical catalysts at high pressures and temperatures. For the laboratory preparation of high density polyethylene, a titanium-based catalyst at atmospheric pressure should be used. These experiments are described in a later section. It should be recognized that the polyethylene prepared with the titanium catalysts is of high density, with a low degree of branching. Polyethylene made at high pressure with free radicals will vary in properties from a nearly linear, high density product (109a) to highly branched, low density material (13,14), depending on polymerization variables.

Higher aliphatic 1-olefins such as propylene, 1-butene, etc., do not polymerize to high molecular weight with free radicals. Catalysts based on reduced transition-metal halides (e.g., $TiCl_3$), sometimes called coordination catalysts, or the various hydrogenation type catalysts, such as reduced chromium oxide, supported on alumina are required. The most common hydrocarbon type known to polymerize with free radicals (aside from ethylene) is styrene and ring-substituted derivatives, as well as other vinyl aromatics such as vinylnaphthalene, etc. Of these only polystyrene and polyvinyltoluene have achieved any technical importance.

Styrene homopolymerizes under a wide variety of conditions. A number of these will now be considered. It will be found that these techniques will be representative of those suitable for polymerization of most vinyls.

84. The Thermal Polymerization of Styrene in Bulk (62)

$$C_6H_5CH\!\!=\!\!CH_2 \longrightarrow [-\underset{\underset{C_6H_5}{|}}{C}H\!-\!CH_2\!-\!]_n$$

Pure styrene monomer polymerizes thermally without added initiator at a rate which increases rapidly with increasing temperature. Polymerization at room temperature may require months or years. However, at 150 °C. polymerization is over in a very short time. The temperature chosen for the thermal polymerization of the styrene should be somewhere in between these extremes since, although lower temperature requires much longer period of time, it also produces much higher molecular weight.

Preparation of polystyrene with a molecular weight of about 150,000 may be carried out at 125 °C. A polymer tube or pressure bottle is charged with approximately 50 g. of styrene monomer and is flushed and sealed under nitrogen. The container is immersed in a heating bath at approximately 125 °C.

and allowed to remain at this temperature for approximately 24 hr.   Under these conditions better than 90% of the monomer will be converted to polymer.   For complete conversion to polymer, it is necessary to allow the polymerization to run for 7 days or more and then finish the polymerization by heating at 150°C. for an additional 2 days.   This will reduce the content of volatile material to less than 1%.   However, for a volatile content of less than 10%, 24 hr. is all the time that is required at 125°C.

Heat transfer problems can be serious if the polymerization is scaled up. The polymerization may become violent, so a larger scale is not recommended.

If desired, the polymer may be purified by first grinding to a small particle size in, for example, a Wiley mill, then dissolving in benzene.   The benzene solution is poured into methyl alcohol agitated vigorously in a high speed mixer to precipitate the polymer in a finely divided condition.   The solid polymer is filtered and dried in a vacuum oven at 110°C.

85. Bulk Polymerization of Styrene with Peroxide Catalysis (62)

$$C_6H_5CH{=}CH_2 \longrightarrow [{-}\overset{\displaystyle C_6H_5}{\underset{\displaystyle |}{CH}}{-}CH_2{-}]_n$$

To 50 ml. of freshly distilled styrene contained in a suitable vessel such as a polymer tube, flask, or screw cap bottle is added 1.0 g. of benzoyl peroxide. This mixture is heated at 50°C. for approximately 3 days.   At the end of this period, a solid plug of polymer is obtained which should have a molecular weight of about 700,000.   The rate of polymerization can be increased markedly by carrying out the reaction at temperatures higher than 50°C.

Polymerization mixtures of this type are suitable for preparing castings or embedding small objects in a polystyrene matrix.   For example, polymerization of the mixture of styrene and benzoyl peroxide indicated above may be carried to the point where the polymerized mixture is so viscous it is difficult to pour.   It may be then transferred to a mold, such as a square box, and the object to be embedded is immersed in the very viscous mixture.   Polymerization is then continued at elevated temperatures until the polystyrene solidifies around the object to be imbedded.   It is possible to suspend the object in the viscous mixture, if it has a tendency to sink, by use of a very fine thread or wire which may be removed when the polystyrene reaches a gel-like state.   Alternatively, the casting may be built up in layers.   Half of the mold is cast and hardened.   The object to be embedded is laid down, the remainder of the viscous prepolymer added, and polymerization completed.   Any bubbles which occur in the final casting may be removed simply by drilling a hole with a fine drill and injecting more styrene-catalyst mixture into the bubble to fill it.   Polymerization is then continued to polymerize the styrene which has been added to the air pockets.

Polystyrene molds can be made very easily, again from the viscous polymerizing mixture such as described above.   It is poured into the object to be reproduced and polymerization continued until the polystyrene is solid.   The polymer mass will, of course, take on the outline of the surrounding vessel.

Polystyrene does not adhere to glass; a coating of methyl cellulose or a silicone spray may be applied to objects which stick to polystyrene to facilitate separation.

It is not essential to use benzoyl peroxide for the polymerization of styrene in bulk; other peroxide or azo-type catalysts can be used. Techniques would be essentially the same as those described for benzoyl peroxide with the added precaution that some of the azo compounds may be more active toward producing free radicals at low temperatures.

The **polymerization of styrene in a solvent** offers little advantage over the bulk polymerizations described previously, since many solvents tend to react with the growing polymer chain, limiting the molecular weight obtainable. Furthermore, rather dilute solutions must be prepared, otherwise the viscosity of the polymer solution becomes so great that manipulation becomes a problem. However, it is possible to polymerize styrene satisfactorily in a solvent.

86. Solution Polymerization of Styrene

$$C_6H_5CH{=}CH_2 \longrightarrow [-\underset{\underset{C_6H_5}{|}}{C}H{-}CH_2{-}]_n$$

For example, (94), 50 ml. of styrene is mixed with 500 ml. of toluene and 0.5 g. of α,α'-azodiisobutyronitrile is added to the mixture. The temperature is raised to 100°C. and the mixture is stirred gently while the polymerization mixture becomes more viscous. After 24 hr., polymer may be isolated by pouring the solution into a precipitant such as an equal volume of methyl alcohol in a high speed mixer. The precipitated polymer is isolated by filtration and dried in a vacuum oven. It may be molded into sheets or bars and has properties characteristic of polystyrene prepared by other methods. Thin sheets or films may be obtained by casting the original polymer solution on a glass plate.

87. Emulsion Polymerization of Styrene with Persulfate (16,105)

$$C_6H_5CH{=}CH_2 \longrightarrow [-\underset{\underset{C_6H_5}{|}}{C}H{-}CH_2{-}]_n$$

For the simple laboratory polymerization of styrene in an emulsion, the following experiment (16,105) is quite satisfactory. In a soda pop or beer bottle is placed 100 g. of water, 0.05 g. of potassium persulfate, 0.05 g. of sodium hydrogen phosphate, and 1.0 g. of sodium laurylsulfate. When this mixture has dissolved, 50 g. of styrene is added. Nitrogen is bubbled through the mixture to replace the air and disperse the styrene. The nitrogen tube is removed and the bottle is capped and sealed. The bottle is wrapped with some wire screen to prevent serious damage in the event the polymerization gets out of control and maintained with intermittent agitation at 70°C. for 2 hr. then at 95 °C. for 2 hr.   The polymer latex, so produced, is precipitated by adding alum solution and boiling of the resulting mixture.   Polystyrene is separated by filtration, washed, and handled in the usual way.

88. Emulsion Polymerization of Styrene with Peroxide

$$C_6H_5CH{=}CH_2 \longrightarrow [{-}\overset{\displaystyle C_6H_5}{\underset{|}{C}H}{-}CH_2{-}]_n$$

One hundred g. of styrene, 250 ml. of water, and 0.2 g. of 30% hydrogen peroxide is stirred vigorously with 1 g. of sodium oleate emulsifying agent under nitrogen in a round bottom flask.   (There are a large number of other emulsifying agents which would serve this purpose satisfactorily, for example, polyacrylic acid, ammonium oleate, or a variety of other soap-like substances.) This mixture forms a colloidal suspension and is polymerized for 12 hr. at 80 °C.   The resulting latex is broken up by the addition of concentrated hydrochloric acid, and the polystyrene is filtered, washed with water, and dried.

89. Suspension Polymerization of Styrene (88)

$$C_6H_5CH{=}CH_2 \longrightarrow [{-}\overset{\displaystyle C_6H_5}{\underset{|}{C}H}{-}CH_2{-}]_n$$

The following ingredients are added to a 2 l. round bottom flask equipped with a mechanical stirrer and a condenser, and maintained at a temperature of about 80 °C.: 500 ml. of water, 0.1 g. sodium laurylsulfate, 1.5 g. of sodium polyacrylate, 5 g. of sodium sulfate, 150 g. of styrene, 1.5 g. of stearic acid, and 1 g. of benzoyl peroxide.   This mixture is stirred vigorously and maintained at 80 °C. for 12–24 hr.   At the end of this time, the beads of polystyrene are filtered, washed with water, and dried in an oven.   A somewhat simpler recipe for the suspension polymerization of styrene is the following: A 2 l., three-necked flask, equipped with a condenser and a very efficient mechanical stirrer, is charged with 750 ml. of water and 300 ml. of styrene containing about 2 g. of benzoyl peroxide.   This mixture is agitated vigorously and heated on the steam bath.   Polymerization will proceed at this temperature and eventually the finely divided droplets which are suspended in the aqueous phase will solidify into round beads of polystyrene.   It is necessary that agitation be effective until the beads attain a solid consistency, otherwise the droplets will tend to fuse together.   For this reason, it is generally preferable to add, in addition to the basic constituents described above, a small amount of a suspending agent.   Gelatin or sodium polymethacrylate have been used quite extensively.

90. Preparation of Foamed Polystyrene (122,127,155)

An interesting product may be made by polymerizing styrene in a low boiling solvent under pressure.   For example, styrene is mixed with isobutylene and ethylene at low temperatures and sealed in a steel pressure vessel with some initiator, such as benzoyl peroxide.   The mixture is allowed to polymerize at elevated temperatures then cooled to $-30°$ or less. The vessel is opened and allowed to warm. The mixture will begin to swell, and may expand (with gentle warming) to thirty times the original volume by expansion of the entrapped gases. The foam so obtained is similar in all respects to the polystyrene foam used extensively in the preparation of Christmas ornaments and display materials.

Of the **vinyl halides,**

$$\underset{\underset{\text{H}}{\diagdown}}{\overset{\overset{\text{H}}{\diagup}}{}} \text{C}{=}\text{C} \underset{\underset{\text{H}}{\diagup}}{\overset{\overset{\text{X}}{\diagdown}}{}}$$

where $X = F$, Cl, Br, I

only vinyl fluoride and vinyl chloride have given useful high polymers. Poly(vinyl fluoride), a highly crystalline moldable polymer, melts about $100°$C. higher than polyethylene. It requires polymerization conditions similar to those used for polyethylene, namely a high temperature and pressure, hence it cannot be made satisfactorily without special equipment (51,52,53). **Vinyl fluoride** is not known to polymerize under any other conditions.

Vinyl chloride, on the other hand, has been known to polymerize to a useful plastic material since before World War I, and important commercial products began to appear around 1930. Although vinyl chloride is a gas, b.p. $-14°$C., it does not present undue problems due to excessive pressure in sealed vessels at temperatures of $40–50°$C. Most published preparations of poly(vinyl chloride) are scaled to multi-ton lots. The following is a description of the manipulation of a large scale polymerizer which was successfully operated during World War II in Germany (33,66).

91. Polymerization of Vinyl Chloride with Persulfate (33,34)

$$CH_2{=}CHCl \longrightarrow [-CH_2-CHCl]_n$$

To a well-jacketed, glass-lined autoclave (13.5 m.^{3} capacity) equipped with an agitator, 6000 l. of pure water, 1500 l. of a 10% emulsifier solution, and 100 l. of a 1% potassium persulfate solution is charged. The reaction vessel is sealed and evacuated, then 1800 l. of vinyl chloride is pumped in by means of a specially designed pump. Water is circulated in the jacket of the polymerizer and polymerization is allowed to proceed. Samples are withdrawn at regular intervals and the density of the polymer dispersion is measured. When the density reaches 1.024, an additional 380 l. of vinyl chloride is pumped in. Thereafter, check points are established at every 0.008 g. increase in the density of the polymerized mixture.

The polymerization reaction is exothermic and great quantities of heat have to be dissipated through the walls of the polymerizer to the cooling medium in the jacket. In order to obtain better heat transfer once the polymerization begins, refrigerated brine is circulated in the cooling jacket at about $-20°C$. Very accurate control of the temperature of the emulsion is necessary since the molecular weight is extremely sensitive to variation in temperature. High molecular weight material is obtained with internal temperatures of 48–50°C. The polymer latex is converted to dry polymer by spraying onto counter rotating heated rollers.

This preparation can be carried out on a 40 ml. scale in a sealed glass pressure tube by freezing the aqueous components in the tube cooled in dry ice, adding the vinyl chloride from a cylinder, sealing the tube and then warming it in a thermostat for about 24 hr. at 40°C. with agitation. The polymer is isolated by evaporation of the aqueous phase, or by precipitation by the addition of salt. In either event it is washed thoroughly with water to separate inorganic matter.

Many other free radical initiators may be used; for example, **hydrogen peroxide** gives a good poly(vinyl chloride) in an emulsion system.

92. Polymerization of Vinyl Chloride with Peroxide (33,66)

$$CH_2{=}CHCl \longrightarrow [-CH_2-CHCl]_n$$

This polymerization must be carried out in a pressure vessel, such as a glass-lined, stainless steel autoclave, which can be agitated or stirred at a constant temperature. The aqueous phase for this emulsion polymerization is prepared by mixing 1 l. of distilled water with about 50 g. of soap or detergent and about 5.5 g. of 30% hydrogen peroxide.

This solution is placed in the reaction vessel, and cooled in dry ice. About 500 g. of vinyl chloride is now condensed from a cylinder into the reaction vessel. The mixture is maintained at temperatures between 40 and 50°C. for approximately 20 hr. At the end of this period, polymerization should be complete. At this point, the vessel is cooled to room temperature, vented, and the polymer latex broken by the addition of salt. The polymer is filtered, washed with water, and dried. Alternatively, the emulsion is dried directly and the dried material is washed free of occluded salts. The dried polymer obtained in either manner is suitable for conversion to high quality moldings or film.

93. Polymerization of Vinyl Chloride in Bulk (97)

$$CH_2{=}CHCl \longrightarrow [-CH_2CHCl-]_n$$

A polymer tube of approximately 150–200 ml. capacity is flushed with nitrogen and cooled in a Dry Ice-acetone mixture. Approximately 50 g. of vinyl chloride is condensed into the nitrogen filled tube from a cylinder. To the tube is now added approximately 0.15 g. of benzoyl peroxide. The tube is flushed again with nitrogen and sealed. Note that considerable pressures will develop during the polymerization process, hence the tube itself and the seal must be adequate to protect the tube against explosion. The sealed tube is now transferred to a heating bath maintained at approximately 50°C., and polymerization is allowed to proceed for approximately 24 hours. The tube is cooled to room temperature, carefully broken and the polymer plug removed. It is a slightly discolored clear, glassy solid with a molecular weight in the range 50–75,000.

94. The Suspension Polymerization of Vinyl Chloride (147)

$$CH_2=CHCl \longrightarrow [-CH_2-CHCl]_n$$

The dispersing solution is prepared by mixing 1600 ml. of water, 30 g. of a dispersing agent (such as the sodium salt of a sulfonated paraffin oil), 4.3 g. of ammonium persulfate and 1.6 g. of sodium bisulfite. The pH of this solution is adjusted to 2.4, using dilute sulfuric acid. A glass pressure vessel is charged with 100 ml. of this solution and cooled to −15–20°C. To the cooled tube is added 50 g. of vinyl chloride. The free space is swept with nitrogen and the vessel is sealed. The contents of the vessel are allowed to warm to 40°C. and the vessel, which is under considerable pressure, is agitated at that temperature for a period of about 2 hr. At the end of this period, the tube is cooled again, opened and allowed to warm to room temperature. The polymer, which is obtained in the form of coarse particles, is filtered, washed, and dried. The yield is approximately 98%. This polymer can be molded into tough sheets in a press.

Vinyl chloride becomes easier to handle on a laboratory scale **in a solution** since much lower pressures are developed in the presence of a solvent. As an example, consider the polymerization of vinyl chloride in cyclohexane with an azo-catalyst (94).

95. Solution Polymerization of Vinyl Chloride (94)

$$CH_2=CHCl \longrightarrow [-CH_2-CHCl]_n$$

A glass pressure vessel with a volume of approximately 250 ml. is charged with 50 ml. of cyclohexane and 0.8 g. of α,α'-azodiisobutyronitrile. The tube is flushed with nitrogen and cooled to about −50°C. with dry ice. About 40 g. of vinyl chloride is condensed into the cooled tube and then the tube is again flushed with dry nitrogen and sealed. It is agitated at 40–50°C. for 24 hr. and cooled. The cold tube is then opened and excess vinyl chloride is allowed to escape. The polymer plus cyclohexane is placed in a dish and the cyclohexane is allowed to evaporate. The residual polymer is washed with alcohol and water. The yield is approximately 85%. The inherent viscosity of the product is about 1.0 in cyclohexane at 0.1% concentration.

The properties of unplasticized poly(vinyl chloride) do not allow it to be successfully melt spun since it tends to degrade at the temperatures needed for spinning. Furthermore, the solubility is not great enough to allow dry spinning. It is possible to modify the properties of poly(vinyl chloride) by copolymerization, or by chemical after-treatment. One technique which was used to give an acetone-soluble polymer which could be dry spun was **after-chlorination.** A fair amount of fiber of this type was prepared and used in Germany during World War II, but the product was not very strong and degraded easily (33,66).

96. Chlorination of Poly(vinyl chloride) (33,66)

$$[-CH_2CHCl]_n \xrightarrow{\text{Cl}_2} [-CHClCHClCH_2CHCl]_{n/2} \text{ (approximate composition)}$$

In a 2 l., three-necked flask equipped with a stirrer, gas inlet tube, and a reflux condenser connected to a gas scrubbing device, is placed 100 g. of poly-(vinyl chloride) in a finely divided state and 1000 g. of *sym*-tetrachloroethane. The mixture is stirred and the temperature raised to 60°C., at which temperature chlorine gas is admitted from a cylinder. Chlorination proceeds readily and the internal temperature of the reaction mixture rises from 60 to approximately 150°C. During the course of the addition of chlorine, samples of the reaction mixture are removed, added to methyl alcohol, and the precipitated polymer is filtered and tested for acetone solubility. When the chlorine content rises from the original value of approximately 57 to about 64%, the polymer becomes soluble in acetone. Chlorination is stopped at approximately this chlorine content and the product is obtained by precipitation of the tetrachloroethane solution with methanol at 0°C. with vigorous stirring. The polymer is filtered, washed with water, and dried at 50–60°C. in a vacuum for about 24 hr. The acetone-soluble, chlorinated poly(vinyl chloride) has been used for the production of fibers and filaments by conventional dry spinning techniques.

Dehalogenation of poly(vinyl chloride) is another chemical transformation which can be carried out satisfactorily. It may be done with either zinc (117) or lithium aluminum hydride (55). With zinc, the product loses about 85% of the chlorine and appears to be a polymer containing cyclopropane rings with isolated halogen. Statistical calculations (69) predict that about 14% of the halogen would be isolated by reaction of adjacent groups in the formation of this type of structure. Reduction of poly(vinyl chloride) with lithium aluminum

hydride (55) gives a product which appears to be essentially chlorine free, by a typical hydride hydrogenolysis of a halide (98,145).

97. Dehalogenation of Poly(vinyl chloride) (117)

$$[-CH_2CHCl-CHCH_2Cl]_n \longrightarrow [-CH_2-CH-CH-]_n$$
$$\underset{CH}{\diagdown\diagup}$$

A mixture of 150 ml. of peroxide-free dioxane and 0.5 g. of poly(vinyl chloride) is refluxed with 4 g. of zinc dust which was purified by treating first with dilute hydrochloric acid, then washing with water to remove excess acid, then drying by slurrying with acetone, and filtering under nitrogen. After about 150–160 hr. refluxing, the mixture is cooled and filtered from excess zinc. The polymer may be isolated by evaporation of the dioxane or by addition of water to the filtrate. The product is a rubbery mass which is soluble in carbon tetrachloride. Solutions do not give a test for unsaturation.

98. Reduction of Poly(vinyl chloride) with Lithium Aluminum Hydride (55)

$$[CH_2CHCl]_n \longrightarrow [-CH_2CH_2-]_n$$

Tetrahydrofuran is purified by distillation from potassium hydroxide followed by refluxing over lithium aluminum hydride for 5 hr. The solvent is then distilled directly into the reaction vessel. (Do not distill to dryness!) Reaction is carried out by dissolving 13.3 g. of poly(vinyl chloride) and 13.3 g. of lithium aluminum hydride in 1 l. of tetrahydrofuran. This mixture is refluxed under nitrogen for about 150 hr. Essentially all of the halogen is removed from the polymer under these conditions. The polymer is isolated by the addition of water (Caution!), filtered, washed with dilute hydrochloric acid, water, and dried. The degree of polymerization of the product is essentially the same as the degree of polymerization of the original poly(vinyl chloride). The product has properties similar to high pressure polyethylene.

Acrylonitrile, the next monosubstituted ethylene to be considered, polymerizes with the greatest of ease with a wide variety of catalysts, both free radical and anionic (Chapter 4, Section VII). Solution, suspension, and emulsion techniques have been successfully employed, but the polymerization is too exothermic to make bulk-polymerization satisfactory.

99. Polymerization of Acrylonitrile in a Slurry (169)

$$CH_2=CHCN \longrightarrow [CH_2-CHCN]_n$$

Commercial acrylonitrile contains an inhibitor (usually a hydroquinone derivative) which is best removed before polymerization. Immediately before use commercial acrylonitrile is passed through a column of silica gel about 24 in. long and 1 in. wide. It is maintained under a slight head of nitrogen and is collected at the bottom of the column and used immediately. If it is retained without the inhibitor, it may polymerize of its own volition.

A 500 ml. three-necked flask is equipped with a stirrer, condenser, and a nitrogen inlet and surrounded by a constant temperature bath maintained at about 40°C.   Three hundred ml. of water which has previously been deaerated by boiling for 10 min. and 22 g. of purified acrylonitrile are placed in the flask and stirred gently for 10 min. to allow the mixture to come to bath temperature.   The initiator is now added.   It is composed of 0.3 g. of potassium persulfate dissolved in 10 ml. of water, followed after 1 min. by 0.15 g. of sodium bisulfite, also in 10 ml. of water.   Almost immediately, the colorless, aqueous solution becomes somewhat opalescent and white polymer begins to precipitate. After 3 hr. the polymerization should be complete.   The solid product is filtered, washed with water, and dried in a vacuum oven at 60°C. overnight. The yield of polymer is 80–90%.   The inherent viscosity as measured in DMF will be about 2.0 (0.5%, 25°C.).

100. Emulsion Polymerization of Acrylonitrile (29)

$$CH_2{=}CHCN \longrightarrow [-CH_2-\overset{\displaystyle CN}{\underset{\displaystyle |}{CH}}-]_n$$

A 500 ml. three-necked, round bottom flask is fitted with a nitrogen inlet, a stirrer, and a reflux condenser.

The flask is thermostatted in a bath at about 35°C. and flushed for 15 min. with nitrogen.   Then 120 ml. of freshly boiled distilled water is added, stirring is started, and the nitrogen flow is reduced to a very slow rate over the surface. To this flask is now added, in order, 2 g. of sodium "Lorol" sulfate detergent, 80 g. of acrylonitrile freed of inhibitor by the method described in the previous experiment, 0.1 g. of potassium persulfate and 0.033 g. of sodium bisulfite. Evidence that the polymerization has started is the appearance of a milkiness, usually in about 5–20 min.   If the milkiness does not appear within about 1 hr., an additional amount of initiator and activator may be added.   Once begun, polymerization is usually complete in 2–3 hr.   However, a small additional yield may be obtained by allowing it to stand overnight.   A nearly quantitative yield of polymer is obtained as a stable dispersion.   The particles are nearly spherical with a diameter of approximately 0.1 μ.   The polymer is isolated by pouring the dispersion into approximately 500 ml. of water, then slowly adding salt with stirring to coagulate the suspension.   The product is collected by filtration.   It is washed with water and dried in air at room temperature.   The molecular weight of the polymer prepared in this manner is extremely high, the inherent viscosity usually being of the order of 10.5 as measured in DMF (0.5%, 30°C.).

Polyacrylonitrile homopolymer is very resistant toward most chemical reagents.   It is, however, degraded by alkali and by heat. A most interesting **transformation** occurs when an acrylonitrile fiber, such as Orlon*, is **heated** in a controlled fashion (182) at 200°C. and

---

* Trademark for du Pont's acrylic fiber.

over. The originally white, flammable yarn or fabric turns black, and becomes fireproof without losing its identity as a fiber. The density of the polymer increases from 1.17 to 1.60, while the tensile strength of the yarn decreases, perhaps as much as 50%, though it is still equivalent or superior to many commercial yarns. It has been suggested (182) that this product is produced by the following transformation:

This structure, however, has not been completely proved.

101. Thermal Condensation of Polyacrylonitrile (92a,182)

For this preparation, almost any type of a forced draft oven capable of operating at temperatures in the range of 250°C. or more can be used successfully. The condensation product may be prepared in the form of either fabric or yarn. However, it is more convenient to use a portion of fabric made, for example, from Orlon acrylic fiber. The fabric is placed in a forced draft oven and heated for a period of time suitable for converting the polyacrylonitrile to the black modification. The time varies; at 250–275°C. the time required is 4–6 hr. It should be noted that the conversion of polyacrylonitrile to the black modification is an extremely exothermic reaction, so that the material being treated should not be wadded together or compressed as this will tend to give a charred product from its own heat of reaction. It should be noted also that oxygen is necessary for the conversion. The optimum oxygen content fortunately is about 20%, so air is the most satisfactory medium in which to carry out this conversion. Black fabric produced as described has a remarkable resistance to fire. A sample of the fabric can be held directly in a flame. The only effect will be that the sample will glow around the edges. If left in the flame for any length of time, the fabric will lose its strength completely. However, under no conditions will it show signs of burning.

Another chemical reaction which may be carried out on **polyacrylonitrile** is the **reaction with hydroxylamine** (12). The resulting **polyamideoxime** is formed without cleavage of the backbone, hence has the same degree of polymerization as the parent polymer. The product is film- and fiber-forming.

102. Conversion of Polyacrylonitrile to Polyacrylamideoxime (40)

$$[-CH_2-CH-]_n + NH_2OH \longrightarrow [-CH_2-CH-]_n$$

$$CN \qquad\qquad\qquad\qquad C$$

$$NH_2 \quad NOH$$

A 1 l. three-necked flask containing 300 ml. of dimethylformamide and 50 g. of polyacrylonitrile is equipped with a mechanical stirrer and maintained at a temperature of 75 °C. by an external water bath.   Twenty g. of hydroxylamine hydrochloride and 15 g. of anhydrous pulverized sodium carbonate are added to the flask and the resulting mixture is stirred and heated for 3 hr.   At the end of this time, the polymer solution is filtered, precipitated into methanol, and the product washed with methanol and dried.   The nitrogen content will vary between 23 and 25%.   This is not too different from the nitrogen content of pure polyacrylonitrile, suggesting that some hydrolysis of amideoxime groups has occurred.   That some chemical reaction has taken place on the polymer is evidenced by the fact that although the polymer remains in solution during the reaction the precipitated and dried product no longer will dissolve in dimethyl formamide.   However, it will dissolve in dilute hydrochloric acid and dilute sodium hydroxide.   The dilute hydrochloric acid solution gives a deep red-to-violet color with ferric chloride, indicative of the formation of a ferric chelate of the amideoxime group.

Vinyl acetate may be polymerized by a variety of free radical catalysts.   Several typical recipes are given.

103. Solution Polymerization of Vinyl Acetate in Benzene

$$OCOCH_3$$

$$CH_2=CHOCOCH_3 \longrightarrow [-CH_2-CH-]_n$$

A 2 l. three-necked flask, equipped with a stirrer, condenser, nitrogen inlet, and a thermometer is charged with 200 ml. of vinyl acetate and 300 ml. of dry benzene.   The vinyl acetate is purified by distillation, then passed through a silica column just before use.   The mixture is heated to reflux under nitrogen and about 0.2 g. of α,α'-azodiisobutyronitrile is added.   Polymerization is allowed to proceed at reflux temperature for about 2 hr. and the mixture is treated with steam to remove unreacted monomer and solvents.   The polymer is broken up, filtered, then dried.   This polymer has an inherent viscosity in chloroform of greater than 1 (0.5% at 25 °C.).

104. Solution Polymerization of Vinyl Acetate in Isopropanol

$$OCOCH_3$$

$$CH_2=CHOCOCH_3 \longrightarrow [-CH_2-CH-]_n$$

A 2 l. flask maintained in a thermostatted bath at 50°C. is equipped with a stirrer, thermometer, nitrogen inlet, and reflux condenser. It is charged with 1000 g. of vinyl acetate, 100 g. of isopropyl alcohol, and 1.4 g. of α,α'-azobis-(α,α-dimethylvaleronitrile). This reaction requires about a 15 min. induction period, then proceeds spontaneously. The temperature of the reaction is not permitted to exceed 50°C. In about 2 hr. polymerization should be terminated by addition of a trace of dinitrobenzene inhibitor. The polymerization mixture is then treated with a jet of steam to remove unreacted monomer and solvent, and the polymer is ground up and dried at 150°C. The yield is approximately 30% and the inherent viscosity in chloroform should be about 1.0 (0.5%, 30°C.).

105. Emulsion Polymerization of Vinyl Acetate

$$CH_2{=}CHOCOCH_3 \longrightarrow [-CH_2-\overset{\displaystyle OCOCH_3}{\overset{|}{CH}}-]_n$$

The polymerization of vinyl acetate may be carried out satisfactorily in a typical redox system such as is described by Marvel and coworkers (114). In a 2 l., round bottomed flask, equipped with a reflux condenser, mechanical stirrer, nitrogen inlet, and thermometer, is placed 200 g. of vinyl acetate purified by distillation, 400 g. of water, 10 g. of emulsifying agent, 0.5 g. of benzoyl peroxide, 1.4 g. of ferrous ammonium sulfate hexahydrate, and 6.0 g. of sodium pyrophosphate decahydrate. The flask is thermostatted at approximately 40°C. and the reaction mixture is blanketed with nitrogen. After approximately 1 hr., the polymer is isolated as above, washed with water, and dried. The inherent viscosity, as determined in chloroform solution, should be greater than 1.0 (0.5%, 30°C.).

106. Suspension Polymerization of Vinyl Acetate (94)

$$CH_2{=}CHOCOCH_3 \longrightarrow [-CH_2-\overset{\displaystyle OCOCH_3}{\overset{|}{CH}}-]_n$$

In a 3 liter, three-necked flask equipped with a stirrer, an efficient condenser, and a nitrogen inlet is placed 300 g. of pure vinyl acetate, 800 ml. of water, 3 g. of commercial sodium dodecyl sulfate detergent, 3 g. of sodium dihydrogen phosphate monohydrate, and 1.5 g. of α,α'-azodiisobutyronitrile. The vessel is swept with nitrogen to remove the air and the mixture is maintained with stirring at a temperature of about 40°C. for 17 hr. The reaction mixture is then treated with steam to remove unpolymerized vinyl acetate, cooled, and the solid polymer is filtered from the aqueous phase, washed with water, and dried. The polyvinyl acetate is obtained in the form of tiny spheres or granules which are easily handled. The reaction time may be decreased by increasing the amount of catalyst.

High molecular weight poly(vinyl acetate) is a clear, glassy solid soluble in many organic solvents. It softens at a fairly low temperature and discolors above 200°C. It is amorphous.

Poly(vinyl acetate) is readily **hydrolyzed** in alcohol solution **to poly(vinyl alcohol)**, the polymer of the unknown vinyl alcohol, or acetaldehyde enol. This polymer is less readily soluble in organic media, but dissolves in water. The bulky acetoxy group has been replaced by the smaller —OH, so the polymer can now crystallize; fibers with high crystallinity and orientation can be obtained. Poly-(vinyl alcohol) of various degrees of hydrolysis and of several different molecular weight ranges are available commercially.

107. Hydrolysis of Poly(vinyl acetate) (83,84,85,126)

$$[CH_2-\underset{\underset{OCOCH_3}{|}}{CH}-]_n \longrightarrow [CH_2-\underset{\underset{OH}{|}}{CH}-]_n$$

Fifty g. of high molecular weight poly(vinyl acetate) is dissolved in about 500 ml. of boiling methanol in an appropriate sized flask equipped with a condenser and a mechanical stirrer. Five per cent sodium methoxide in methyl alcohol is added to the stirred refluxing polymer solution in 5–10 ml. portions at intervals of 5 min. Approximately 25–30 ml. of the solution is sufficient to catalyze the methanolysis. The reaction, once begun, proceeds rapidly with the precipitation of the polyvinyl alcohol which is insoluble in methanol. If the hydrolysis proceeds at too great a rate, the reaction may be moderated by the addition of 100–200 ml. of methanol and by external cooling. After the reaction has subsided, refluxing is continued for about 3 min. and the mixture is filtered. If the product is gel-like, it may be broken up by vigorous agitation in a Waring Blendor with cold methanol. The product is filtered and washed several times with alcohol and then dried.

Alternatively, the hydrolysis of poly(vinyl acetate) may be carried out in acidic media. For example, 30 g. of poly(vinyl acetate), 100 g. of water, and 1 g. of 95% sulfuric acid is heated and stirred for 6–8 hr. at 95°C., or until a clear solution is obtained. Steam is then passed through the solution to remove acetic acid and complete the hydrolysis. The poly(vinyl alcohol) is isolated by precipitation with concentrated salt solution or the aqueous acid solution may be used directly, for example in the preparation of poly(vinyl butyral) described below.

108. Films and Fibers of Poly(vinyl alcohol) (92,195)

The preparation of poly(vinyl alcohol) films may be carried out by dissolving polymer in solvent to a solid content of 15–20% and casting the solution on a glass plate or a polished metal surface with a doctor knife (See Chapter 2) of appropriate clearance. Poly(vinyl alcohol) is hygroscopic. Therefore, drying of the film cast from water is relatively difficult and slow. It is preferable to use a solvent such as alcohol-water (30–70) for this purpose. It is also preferable to carry out the drying of the film in a closed container in a slow stream of dry air.

It is interesting to note that poly(vinyl alcohol) film will react with iodine very much in the same manner as starch to form a sorption complex. If these films are stretched, the complex is oriented to a structure which is light polarizing. This is the basis of many of the polarizing filters now in use (109).

Fibers of poly(vinyl alcohol) can be prepared rather simply by extrusion of aqueous solutions into precipitating baths consisting of aqueous solutions of salts in a high concentration or into an organic nonsolvent. The fiber is then further processed by stretching in the usual manner. Such fibers are sensitive to cold water and usually will dissolve in hot water. It is interesting to note that these fibers are less soluble in water when under tension than when relaxed. The following represents a typical preparation of a poly(vinyl alcohol) fiber.

A 20% solution of high molecular weight poly(vinyl alcohol) in water is prepared at a temperature of about 75 °C. It is placed in a spinning apparatus such as the ones described in Chapter 2 maintained at this temperature, and extruded by a mechanical pump through a spinneret into a 40% aqueous solution of ammonium sulfate at about 50 °C. The rate of extrusion should be such that the filaments are completely coagulated and capable of supporting their own weight when removed at the other end of the bath. The fibers are wound up on a mechanical windup and the yarn is washed on the bobbin in 50% acetone–water mixture. Finally, the yarn is treated with 95% acetone–H_2O and the yarn is then allowed to dry overnight at room temperature. The yarn is then stretched to its maximum degree at 75–100 °C. and wound onto a cone.

The techniques of precipitation of poly(vinyl alcohol) solution in strong salt solutions may also be applied to the preparation of **poly-(vinyl alcohol) film.**

Thus, a 50% aqueous solution of poly(vinyl alcohol) at 75 °C. to which has been added approximately 0.01 of sodium dioctylsulfosuccinate is cast on a glass plate using a doctor knife of approximately 0.004 in. clearance. The plate and film are then immersed in a saturated aqueous solution of sodium sulfate or of ammonium sulfate, maintained at a temperature of 40–50 °C. The solution is allowed to coagulate for 5 min. or more, then the plate is removed and immersed in a 50% aqueous acetone solution. After 3 hr. the film is removed from the plate and washed with fresh portions of the aqueous acetone. It is finally washed with pure acetone. The product is a strong self-supporting film of poly(vinyl alcohol).

It is also possible to use organic media for the precipitation of poly(vinyl alcohol) solutions in fiber or film form. Thus, a solution of 14% by weight poly(vinyl alcohol) in water at 60 °C. is extruded into a precipitating bath consisting of 94% acetone and 6% water at about 30 °C. The polymer solution is precipitated in the form of a thread which is wound up at a rate sufficiently slow such that the thread, on issuing from the bath, is completely self-support-ing.   The yarn is then stretched approximately 5 times its former length in a mixture of 50% diethylene glycol monomethyl ether and 50% water at about 30°C.   The yarn so obtained should have tenacities of better than 2 g./denier.

Poly(vinyl alcohol) may be plasticized by a number of hydroxylic materials such as ethylene glycol or glycerol.   Two examples of **plasticized poly(vinyl alcohol)** given in the patent literature are as follows.

109. Preparation of Plasticized Poly(vinyl alcohol) (58)

A mixture of 100 g. of poly(vinyl alcohol), 35 g. of glycerol, 45 g. of water, and 12 g. of ammonium bromide is thoroughly mixed together, preferably by milling on a rubber mill.   The resulting highly plasticized material is obtained as a rather rubbery sheet which will remain flexible for long periods of time throughout a wide temperature range.

Similarly, a plasticized composition of poly(vinyl alcohol) may be made by blending 100 g. of poly(vinyl alcohol), 45 g. of water, 10 g. of formamide, 35 g. of ethylene glycol, and 12 g. of ammonium bromide.   This material again is tough and very flexible and retains its flexibility to quite low temperatures.

Poly(vinyl alcohol) with its free hydroxyl groups offers consider-able latitude for **chemical transformation.**   Thus acetylation converts it back to the parent poly(vinyl acetate) while, for example, butyric anhydride, will produce **poly(vinyl butyrate).**

110. Preparation of Poly(vinyl butyrate) by Esterification

$$\left[\begin{array}{c} -CH_2-CH- \\ | \\ OH \end{array}\right]_n \longrightarrow \left[\begin{array}{c} -CH_2-CH- \\ | \\ OCOCH_2CH_2CH_3 \end{array}\right]_n$$

Ten. g. of poly(vinyl alcohol) is refluxed with a mixture of 50 ml. of pyridine and 50 ml. of butyric anhydride until a clear, homogeneous solution results. The product is precipitated by pouring into water.   The solid polymer is filtered, washed thoroughly, and dried.   In order to obtain a pure product, it is preferable to dissolve the polymer in a solvent such as methanol and repre-cipitate by pouring into a Waring Blendor containing water agitated at a high rate of speed.   The slurry is filtered and the polymer dried.   It exhibits properties similar to those of poly(vinyl acetate), except that it is somewhat less brittle at lower temperatures.

Since poly(vinyl alcohol) is a 1,3 glycol, it forms **cyclic acetals** with aldehydes.   For example, water insoluble fibers may be prepared by extrusion of aqueous poly(vinyl alcohol) into aqueous formaldehyde. Acetalization occurs, together with an occasional cross-link, rendering the fiber insoluble.

111. Preparation of Water Insoluble Poly(vinyl alcohol) Fibers (106)

$$
\begin{bmatrix} -CH_2CH_2-CH_2-CH-CH_2-CH \\ \quad\quad\quad\ OH \quad\quad\ OH \quad\quad\ OH \end{bmatrix}_n \longrightarrow \begin{bmatrix} -CH_2-\triangle-CH_2-CH- \\ \quad\quad O\ \ O \quad\quad\quad O \\ \quad\quad\quad\quad\quad\quad -CH_2 \end{bmatrix}_n
$$

A 16% by weight solution of poly(vinyl alcohol) in water is prepared. The precipitating bath consists of 40% aqueous ammonium sulfate maintained at 50°C. to which has been added 10% formaldehyde (as 37% aqueous solution) and $1/4$ mole of sulfuric acid for every mole of ammonium sulfate. The aqueous solution of poly(vinyl alcohol) is extruded into this acidic salt solution of formaldehyde. The polymer sets up into strong fibers which should have tenacities of the order of 2–2.5 g. per denier after being removed from the spinning bath, stretched and dried.

It is obvious that other aldehydes could be substituted for the formaldehyde, giving a whole family of polymers, each with different characteristics with respect to melting point, stiffness, solubility, etc. Furthermore, acetalization may be carried out on the finished yarn, or film. For example, a film such as was made in an earlier preparation, soaked in an aqueous solution of benzaldehyde (10%) and phosphoric acid (1%) in hot ethanol will pick up a substantial weight of benzaldehyde in an acetal structure, during the course of several hours.

An important plastic which finds use in safety glass is **poly(vinyl butyral),** made from poly(vinyl alcohol) and butyraldehyde.

112. The Preparation of Poly(vinyl butyral) (173)

$$
\begin{bmatrix} --CH_2-CH-CH_2-CH-- \\ \quad\quad\quad OH \quad\quad\quad OH \end{bmatrix}_n \xrightarrow{C_3H_7CHO} \begin{bmatrix} -CH_2-\triangle- \\ \quad\quad O\ \ O \\ \quad\quad\ \vee \\ \quad\quad C_3H_7 \end{bmatrix}_n
$$

A solution of 100 g. of poly(vinyl alcohol), 80 ml. of methyl alcohol, and 0.3 of sulfuric acid in 820 ml. of water is prepared by mixing the ingredients with warming in a vessel equipped with a mechanical stirrer. To the agitated solution is added 80 g. of butyraldehyde. Three hundred g. of this solution is placed in a 2 l., three-necked flask equipped with mechanical stirrer and a condenser. Eighty g. of butyraldehyde is then added with vigorous stirring, followed by the remainder of the poly(vinyl alcohol) solution over a period of about 20 min. During this time the internal temperature should rise to about 70°C. At the conclusion of this period, 600 ml. of hot water at approximately 70°C. is added over a period of 15–20 min. The resulting mixture is agitated for an additional 10 min., then 3 g. of concentrated sulfuric acid, dissolved in 25 ml. of water, is added. The reaction mixture is allowed to stir for an additional 1 hr., then the resin is filtered and washed repeatedly with water. A product is obtained, if the agitation is satisfactory, of a particle size which is appropriate for easy handling and filtering.

The poly(vinyl butyral) prepared in this way must be washed thoroughly with dilute alkali to remove the last traces of acid which would catalyze decomposition.

The major use of poly(vinyl butyral) is in the preparation of safety glass in which a thin layer of plasticized polymer is sandwiched between two sheets of glass. The poly(vinyl butyral) has outstanding adherence to the glass. It is elastic and tough and serves admirably for this purpose.

In order to prepare a **plasticized poly(vinyl butyral),** 100 g. of polymer is mixed with a plasticizer such as Flexol* 3GH, which is triethylene glycol di-2-ethylbutyrate. The polymer and plasticizer are blended together, with enough ethanol to form a plastic mass. This material can be spread or rolled into a sheet and the solvent allowed to evaporate. The resulting product may be dusted with talc to decrease the tackiness of the material, if it is to be stored. In order to prepare a laminate with two pieces of glass, a sheet of the butyral is washed and placed between carefully cleaned pieces of glass. The seal is effected by heating in a Carver Press or similar source of heat and pressure at temperatures of 150–175°C. and moderate pressures. For the preparation of commercial glass laminates, it is necessary to finish the process by heating at higher temperatures and pressures. Specialized equipment, however, is necessary.

Other groups reactive toward secondary hydroxyls will also transform poly(vinyl alcohol). For example, **cyanoethylation** occurs readily, without chain cleavage.

* Trademark of Union Carbide Corporation.

113. Cyanoethylation of Poly(vinyl alcohol) (91)

$$\begin{bmatrix} CH_2\!-\!CH \\ | \\ OH \end{bmatrix}_n + CH_2\!\!=\!\!CH\!-\!CN \longrightarrow \begin{bmatrix} -CH\!-\!CH\!- \\ | \\ OCH_2CH_2CN \end{bmatrix}_n$$

A slurry of 45 g. of high viscosity poly(vinyl alcohol), 265 g. of acrylonitrile, and 5 g. of a 5% aqueous solution of sodium hydroxide is placed in a 500 ml., three-necked flask fitted with a mechanical stirrer and a reflux condenser. The mixture is heated externally to reflux. After about $1/2$ hr., the poly(vinyl alcohol) begins to go into solution and forms a gel. After another 15 min. at reflux, the external heat is discontinued and the reaction mixture is cooled and then neutralized with glacial acetic acid. The resulting viscous, light tan product, which consists of a solution of polymer in acrylonitrile, is poured into about 2 l. of diethyl ether and a taffy-like precipitate is obtained. This precipitate is dissolved in 300 ml. of acetone and again precipitated by pouring into diethyl ether. The product is then dried in a vacuum over phosphorus pentoxide. The yield is about 95 g.

Acrylic acid, its **salts, amides, esters,** and **acid chlorides** can be polymerized.

The preparation of a vinyl polymer of a high degree of reactivity is made possible by the availability of **acryloyl chloride** (116) which can be **polymerized to a polymeric acid chloride.** It has the expected high degree of sensitivity toward hydroxylic reagents and amines, and can be prepared only in anhydrous media and handled only in a dry box. Homopolymerization is not particularly easy. However, minor proportions of acryloyl chloride can be copolymerized (78) with other vinyl monomers. Cross-linking reactions such as treatment with a diamine can then be carried out to give insoluble, infusible products with improved tensile properties. These will be discussed in a later section.

114. Polymerization of Acryloyl Chloride (165a)

Three milliliters of freshly distilled acryloyl chloride is mixed in a polymer tube with 3 ml. pure dioxane and 50 mg. of α,α'-azodiisobutyronitrile. The tube is sealed under nitrogen and the mixture is warmed at 50°C. for 48 hours. Evaporation of the solvent gives an 84% yield of poly(acryloyl chloride) with a molecular weight of about 36,000.

Acrylamide will undergo vinyl polymerization via free radical catalysis, to give a polymer having pendant carboxamide groups. (Cf. Chapter 3, Preparation 29 for a Michael addition-type polymerization of acrylamide.) Water soluble polymers can be prepared in an aqueous system, as in the following example.

115. Solution Polymerization of Acrylamide (20a)

$$CH_2{=}CH{-}\overset{\displaystyle O}{\overset{\|}{C}}{-}NH_2 \longrightarrow \left[\begin{array}{c} -CH_2{-}CH{-} \\ | \\ C{=}O \\ | \\ NH_2 \end{array}\right]_n$$

Acrylamide is Toxic.   Use Care in Handling.

In a 1 l. three-necked flask equipped with stirrer, gas inlet, thermometer, and condenser are placed 51.8 g. acrylamide (Chapter 3, Preparation 29 for purification) and 414.7 g. distilled water. The acrylamide solution is stirred and heated to 68°C. under a rapid stream of carbon dioxide. Then 7.7 g. isopropyl alcohol and 0.096 g. potassium persulfate are added. The temperature of the reaction rises to 75–80°C., where it is maintained by a heating bath for 2 hr. The product is obtained in a clear, colorless solution having a very high viscosity. The polymer can be precipitated in methanol, washed well with methanol, and dried in a vacuum at 50°C. The inherent viscosity is about 1.0 (1 N solution of sodium nitrate, 0.5% polymer conc., 30°C.). The relationship of intrinsic viscosity to molecular weight is

$$[\eta] = 3.73 \times 10^4 \, M^{0.66}$$

where M is weight average molecular weight.

The polymerization of **acrylate esters** can be carried out readily. The acrylate esters form hard, glassy materials similar to the methacrylates, but inferior in properties. For this reason the methacrylate esters have achieved considerably greater popularity in clear, plastic materials. The polymerization of **methyl acrylate** is typical of the preparation of the acrylate esters. An extensive series of poly(acrylate esters) has been prepared and reported in the literature (119).

116. The Polymerization of Methyl Acrylate (119)

$$CH_2{=}CHCO_2CH_3 \longrightarrow \left[\begin{array}{c} -CH_2{-}CH{-} \\ | \\ CO_2CH_3 \end{array}\right]_n$$

A three-necked flask is fitted with a stirrer, a reflux condenser, and a thermometer. The flask is charged with 400 ml. of water, 2 g. of Triton*720, which is an alkyl arylether sulfonate, 2–4 g. of Tergitol** paste, which is sodium 2-methyl-7-ethylhendecyl-4-sulfate penetrant, and 0.01 g. of ammonium persulfate. The solution is stirred slowly and 200 g. of distilled methyl acrylate is added. Heat may be applied to the reaction vessel in order to induce poly-

* Trademark of the Rohm & Haas Co.
** Trademark of the Union Carbide Corp.

merization. If polymerization does not start within 10 min. after refluxing has occurred, additional ammonium persulfate may be added. If excessive quantities are required the monomer is not of sufficient purity. Once initiated the polymerization usually proceeds at a rate sufficient to cause refluxing without external heating for 15–30 min. After about 30 min., heat is applied, and the refluxing temperature is allowed to rise until it is about 95 °C., at which point the polymerization may be considered to be complete. The resulting polymer emulsion is steam distilled for 15–30 min. to remove excess monomer and is run slowly into twice its volume of hot 5% sodium chloride solution. The polymer is precipitated in the form of discrete particles which are filtered and washed with hot water until free of salt. It is then air dried. The yield is quite good in all cases.

Higher alkyl acrylates may be polymerized using the identical recipe described in the previous paragraph. The properties of a whole series of such esters will be found in Ref. 119.

A number of *N*-**vinyl lactams** have been prepared by the reaction of acetylene with the lactam. The most important of these is *N*-vinyl pyrrolidone (68,153,166,188).

This monomer polymerizes readily with most free radical catalysts, under a variety of conditions to give a water-soluble high polymer. This material has been used successfully as a blood plasma substitute.

117. Polymerization of *N*-Vinyl Pyrrolidone (68,153,166,188)

A mixture of 30 g. of distilled *N*-vinyl pyrrolidone and a solution of 40 g. of neutral potassium sulfite in 200 ml. of water is stirred vigorously in an atmosphere of nitrogen for 24 hr. at a temperature of 35–40 °C. At the end of 24 hr. the polymerization product, which is a viscous solution, is decanted into a dish and evaporated under a stream of dry air or nitrogen on a steam bath with stirring. The product, poly(vinyl pyrrolidone), is obtained in good yield in the form of a clear, horn-like solid mass mixed with potassium salts. It will dissolve in water to give a viscous solution. The polymer can be separated from the potassium salts by extraction into alcohol, or by dialysis of an aqueous solution in, for example, a cellophane bag, against running water.

118. Polymerization of Vinyl Pyrrolidone with Hydrogen Peroxide (68,153,166,188)

$$\text{CH}=\text{CH}_2 \longrightarrow (-\text{CH}-\text{CH}_2-)_n$$

A 1 l., three-necked flask equipped with a stirrer and a condenser is charged with 60 g. of vinyl pyrrolidone, 140 ml. of water, 2 ml. of 30% hydrogen peroxide, and 1 ml. of concentrated aqueous ammonia. This mixture is stirred gently and maintained at a temperature of 50°C. in an atmosphere of nitrogen for about 8 hr. The very viscous solution may be poured into a dish and evaporated. The clear, solid plastic remaining after complete drying of the product is ground to a fine white powder, which is hygroscopic and should, therefore, be kept under anhydrous conditions. It will redissolve readily in water to give viscous solutions.

Unsaturated ketones will polymerize readily with peroxide catalysts. Methyl vinyl ketone and methyl isopropenyl ketone give products which are structurally similar to poly(methyl acrylate) and poly(methyl methacrylate):

$$\left[-\text{CH}_2-\overset{\text{CH}_3}{\underset{\text{CO}_2\text{CH}_3}{\text{C}}}- \right]_n$$
Poly(methyl methacrylate)

$$\left[-\text{CH}_2-\overset{\text{CH}_3}{\underset{\text{COCH}_3}{\text{C}}}- \right]_n$$
Poly(methyl isopropenyl ketone)

$$\left[-\text{CH}_2-\underset{\text{CO}_2\text{CH}_3}{\text{CH}}- \right]_n$$
Poly(methyl acrylate)

$$\left[-\text{CH}_2-\underset{\text{COCH}_3}{\text{CH}}- \right]_n$$
Poly(methyl vinyl ketone)

They are, however, inferior in properties to the acrylates, so have not met with wide commercialization.

119. Polymerization of Methyl Vinyl Ketone (54)

$$\text{CH}_2=\text{CH}-\overset{}{\underset{\text{O}}{\text{C}}}-\text{CH}_3 \longrightarrow \left[-\text{CH}_2-\underset{\text{COCH}_3}{\text{CH}}- \right]_n$$

In a 1 l., three-necked flask or resin kettle, equipped with a condenser, nitrogen inlet and a mechanical stirrer is placed 100 g. of freshly distilled methyl vinyl ketone and 100 ml. of ethyl acetate. Five g. of benzoyl peroxide is then added and the mixture is stirred for 3 hr. at a temperature of 75°C. maintained by an external water bath. Approximately 95–100% of the monomer is converted to polymer. The solution in ethyl acetate may be precipitated into a nonsolvent for the polymer, such as cyclohexane, with stirring in a high speed mixer, or it may be poured out and the solvent allowed to evaporate. The product in the latter case will be a clear slab of hard colorless polymer.

1. Miscellaneous Monomers

Conceivably, any monosubstituted ethylene, R—CH=CH₂, could give high polymer, although the monomers just considered are the most common to free radical vinyl technology. Many other monomers have been prepared and polymerized, but the polymers have not been thoroughly characterized. Table 4.1 lists those which have been studied and appear to be of some interest, particularly as comonomers to change physical or chemical properties of a given homopolymer.

TABLE 4.1

Name	Structure	References
Vinyl isocyanate	$CH_2=CH-NCO$	49,50,96
Nitroethylene	$CH_2=CH-NO_2$	189,99
Vinyl azide	$CH_2=CH-N_3$	79,190
Vinylsulfonyl fluoride	$CH_2=CHSO_2F$	81
Vinylsulfonyl chloride	$CH_2=CHSO_2Cl$	100,171
Vinylsulfonic acid	$CH_2=CHSO_3H$	100,20,87
Butyl vinyl sulfone	$CH_2=CH-SO_2C_4H_9$	146
Vinyl triethoxy silane	$CH_2=CH-Si(OC_2H_5)_3$	128
Ethyl vinyl sulfoxide	$CH_2=CH-SO-C_2H_5$	164,181
Ethyl vinyl sulfone	$CH_2=CH-SO_2C_2H_5$	164,181
Acrolein	$CH_2=CH-CHO$	160,161

IV. Free Radical Polymerization of 1,1-Disubstituted Ethylenes

The number of 1,1-disubstituted ethylenes which have been successfully polymerized by free radicals is less than the number of monosubstituted ethylenes, but some very important homopolymers are found in this group. Techniques are essentially the same, and the following representative polymers will be considered: poly(methyl methacrylate) and related higher esters, poly(methyl-α-chloroacrylate), poly(α-methacrylonitrile), poly(α-chloroacrylonitrile), poly(vinylidene chloride).

Probably the most important monomer of this group is **methyl methacrylate,** the monomer on which Lucite* and Plexiglas** as

* Trademark for du Pont's acrylic resins.
** Trademark for Rohm & Haas' acrylic resins.

well as numerous acrylic paints and sprays are based. It will polymerize readily to a very clear, colorless polymer. Suspension and bulk methods give representative products. Emulsion techniques may also be used (56,176).

120. Suspension Polymerization of Methyl Methacrylate

$$CH_2{=}C\begin{smallmatrix}CH_3\\\\CO_2CH_3\end{smallmatrix} \longrightarrow \left[{-}CH_2{-}\underset{CO_2CH_3}{\overset{CH_3}{C}}{-}\right]_n$$

A mixture of 200 g. of monomeric methyl methacrylate (freshly distilled) with 2.5 g. of α,α'-azodiisobutyronitrile, 40 ml. of a 5% aqueous poly(methacrylic acid) solution, 20 g. of disodium hydrogen phosphate dodecahydrate, and 400 ml. of water is placed in a 1 l., three-necked flask, mounted on a steam bath, and equipped with a nitrogen inlet, an efficient stirrer, a thermometer, and a reflux condenser. The reaction mixture is stirred vigorously and heated to boiling in a steam bath, under an atmosphere of nitrogen. The initial reflux temperature will be about 82°C. As polymerization continues, the temperature will rise to 93°C. At this temperature, polymerization is essentially complete. The granular polymeric methyl methacrylate is filtered, washed in water, and dried. The total time required for the polymerization is approximately 20 min.

Alternatively, polymerization may be carried out without added initiator. This is not a true thermal polymerization, but is initiated by adventitious impurities. Highly purified monomer will not polymerize under these conditions. In a 1 l. three-necked flask equipped with condenser and stirrer is placed 100 g. of methyl methacrylate and 200 ml. of water containing about 4 g. of poly(vinyl alcohol) dispersing agent. This mixture is stirred vigorously and heated at about 80°C. for approximately 40 min. The internal temperature begins to rise at this point and will reach a maximum of 85°C. At this point, the mixture is cooled to 60°C. by the addition of cold water to the flask. The granules of polymer are separated, washed with water, and dried at 100°C. The poly(methyl methacrylate) may be converted to molded objects.

Methyl methacrylate may be safely **bulk polymerized** under mild conditions. In this way it is possible to prepare castings by *in situ* polymerization at 40°C.

121. Bulk Polymerization of Methyl Methacrylate(94)

$$CH_2{=}\underset{CO_2CH_3}{\overset{CH_3}{CH}} \longrightarrow \left[{-}CH_2{-}\underset{CO_2CH_3}{\overset{CH_3}{C}}{-}\right]_n$$

One hundred g. of freshly distilled monomeric methyl methacrylate is mixed with 3 g. of high molecular weight poly(methyl methacrylate) thickener, 0.007 g. of methacrylic acid, and 0.05 g. of α,α'-azodiisobutyronitrile. The viscous mixture is maintained in an oven at about 40°C., under which conditions it will polymerize in about 25–30 hr. to a clear, solid block in the shape of the polymerization vessel. For example, the viscous mixture may be poured between two glass plates which are separated by a compressible gasket. If this assembly is maintained in the oven at about 40°C., as previously described, for 25–30 hr., a clear sheet of poly(methyl methacrylate) is obtained. It may be separated from the glass regaining plates by raising the temperature to 95°C.

Poly(methyl methacrylate) has a Vicat softening temperature (see Chapter 2) of about 120°C.

Objects may be embedded in poly(methyl methacrylate) using the same techniques given for polystyrene (Preparation 85).

If methacrylic acid is esterified with other alcohols, polymers with different softening points will be obtained.

122. Polymerization of *n*-Butyl Methacrylate

$$\underset{\underset{CO_2C_4H_9}{|}}{\overset{\overset{CH_3}{|}}{CH_2{=}C}} \longrightarrow \left[\underset{\underset{CO_2C_4H_9}{|}}{\overset{\overset{CH_3}{|}}{-CH_2{-}C{-}}} \right]_n$$

This monomer may be polymerized exactly as methyl methacrylate. The polymer is a solid, but the softening point is now 30°C. (56,176).

123. Polymerization of *n*-Amyl Methacrylate

$$\underset{\underset{CO_2C_5H_{11}}{|}}{\overset{\overset{CH_3}{|}}{CH_2{=}C}} \longrightarrow \left[\underset{\underset{CO_2C_5H_{11}}{|}}{\overset{\overset{CH_3}{|}}{-CH_2{-}C{-}}} \right]_n$$

This monomer may be polymerized exactly as in the preceding examples. Poly(*n*-amyl methacrylate) is an elastomer, with a softening point below room temperature (56,176).

124. Polymerization of Glycol Dimethacrylate

$$\left[CH_2{=}C\overset{CH_3}{\underset{C}{\diagdown}}\overset{O}{\underset{OCH_2{-}}{\diagup}} \right]_2 \longrightarrow \text{3-Dimensional network polymer}$$

Glycol dimethacrylate is purified before use by distillation at 84°C./1 mm. It may be polymerized exactly as the above methacrylate esters. The product is, however, completely insoluble and infusible. This monomer is used in dental fillings, of the type which are polymerized *in situ*.

The **nitrile of α-methacrylic acid, methacrylonitrile,** may also be polymerized by free radicals. The product softens lower than polyacrylonitrile, hence can be molded, although it tends to discolor on molding.

125. Polymerization of Methacrylonitrile (170)

$$CH_2{=}C\begin{smallmatrix}CN\\\\CH_3\end{smallmatrix} \longrightarrow \left[-CH_2-C\begin{smallmatrix}CN\\\\CH_3\end{smallmatrix}-\right]_n$$

A mixture of 100 g. of freshly distilled methacrylonitrile, 300 ml. of water, 0.5 g. of "Duponol"* ME detergent, and 0.5 g. of potassium persulfate is placed in a sealed glass tube or in a stainless steel bomb. This mixture is maintained at 50 °C. for 24 hr.; it is either stirred or tumbled in order to agitate the contents of the reaction vessel. At the end of 24 hr., the temperature is raised to 85 °C. for an additional 4 hr. At the end of this period, a 90% yield of a stable, white polymer latex is obtained. The polymer may be taken out of solution by the usual techniques. It may be frozen or it may be precipitated by the addition of an organic solvent or an electrolyte. The dried polymer is colorless when prepared in the described manner and can be injection molded or formed into film at temperatures of 135–155 °C. and pressures of 1500–4000 p.s.i.

Methyl α-chloroacrylate and **α-chloroacrylonitrile** both polymerize readily. The products are higher melting, but are less stable thermally, than are the methyl analogs.

126. Preparation of Methyl α-Chloroacrylate (149)

$$ClCH_2CHCl{-}CO_2CH_3 \longrightarrow CH_2{=}CClCO_2CH_3$$

Caution. Methyl α-chloroacrylate is a potent lachrymator.

Methyl α,β-dichloropropionate is prepared by the addition of chlorine to methyl acrylate. One hundred g. of methyl α,β-dichloropropionate is mixed with 35 g. of concentrated sulfuric acid to give a clear solution. This solution is heated cautiously in a distillation set-up without fractionation at a temperature ranging from 80 to 150 °C. During the course of this heating, hydrogen chloride is evolved and methyl α-chloroacrylate distills. The product is washed with dilute alkali, then with water, and dried. It is fractionated through an efficient column, b.p. 57–59 °C./55 mm.

This monomer polymerizes with greater ease than methyl methacrylate (113,115).

* Trademark for du Pont's surface active agent.

127. Polymerization of Methyl α-Chloroacrylate

$$CH_2=\overset{\overset{\displaystyle Cl}{|}}{\underset{\underset{\displaystyle CO_2CH_3}{|}}{C}} \longrightarrow \left[-CH_2-\overset{\overset{\displaystyle Cl}{|}}{\underset{\underset{\displaystyle CO_2CH_3}{|}}{C}}- \right]_n$$

This monomer may be polymerized exactly as methyl methacrylate (see Preparation 121 and 122). The polymer tends to form discolored castings, but is more resistant to scratching and has a softening temperature about 40°C. higher than the corresponding methacrylate polymer.

128. Preparation of Trichloropropionitrile (110)

$$CH_2=CH-CN + Cl_2 \longrightarrow ClCH_2-CCl_2CN$$

A one l., three-necked flask equipped with a stirrer, a condenser, and a gas inlet tube and cooled externally by an ice-water bath is charged with 265 g. of acrylonitrile containing a small amount of polymerization inhibitor such as hydroquinone. Chlorine gas is bubbled slowly into the acrylonitrile with external cooling until a total of 419 g. of chlorine is absorbed. This chlorinated product is distilled at 30 mm. to give 560 g. of a product boiling at 70–75°C. This material may be purified further by redistillation; b.p. 80–81°C./63 mm. However, the once distilled material is satisfactory for the next experiment.

129. Preparation of α-Chloroacrylonitrile (38)

$$ClCH_2CCl_2CN \overset{Mg}{\longrightarrow} CH_2=CClCN$$

A dehalogenating agent is prepared as follows in a three-necked flask equipped with a stirrer and a condenser. In the flask is placed 29 g. of metallic magnesium together with 51 g. of iodine dissolved in 350 ml. of butyl ether containing 0.5–1 g. of hydroquinone. After the iodine color disappears, the flask containing the agent is heated in an oil bath at 150°C. while 99 g. of α,α,β-trichloropropionitrile is added dropwise over 30–45 min. During the entire operation the mixture is stirred vigorously. An exothermic reaction takes place with the removal by distillation of the lower boiling products together with the butyl ether. Stirring and heating is continued after the addition of the trichloropropionitrile is complete, until approximately 250 ml. of distillate has been obtained. This distillate is shaken with mercury to remove free iodine and is then fractionated. Approximately 20 g. of α-chloroacrylonitrile with a boiling point of 85–88°C. is obtained. Prior to polymerization the α-chloroacrylonitrile should be freshly redistilled. The refractive index is reported to be 1.4205 at 32°C.

130. Polymerization of α-Chloroacrylonitrile (36)

$$CH_2=\overset{\overset{\displaystyle Cl}{|}}{\underset{\underset{\displaystyle CN}{|}}{C}} \longrightarrow \left[-CH_2-\overset{\overset{\displaystyle Cl}{|}}{\underset{\underset{\displaystyle CN}{|}}{C}}- \right]_n$$

A mixture of 109 g. of freshly distilled chloroacrylonitrile, 300 g. of deaerated distilled water, 1 g. of ammonium persulfate, 2.0 g. of sodium metabisulfite, 0.6 g. of edible-grade gelatin, and 0.72 g. of sodium phosphate is placed in a three-necked flask equipped with stirrer and condenser. The mixture is stirred at 55 °C. for about 24 hr.

The suspension is cooled to room temperature and the polymer, which is present as a fine, white powder, is filtered to give about 100 g. of poly-α-chloro-acrylonitrile.

Copolymers of α-chloroacrylonitrile with diethylmaleate, vinyl chloride, ethyl acrylate, methyl methacrylate, styrene, etc., may be prepared. The homopolymer may be made into a viscous solution (37) suitable for spinning or casting by dissolving in a solvent comprised of 40 parts of nitromethane, 1.2 parts of water, and 12 parts of phenol.

Vinylidene chloride is a low boiling (32 °C.) liquid which polymerizes readily. Bulk polymerization may be carried out at 40–50 °C. in sealed tubes, but should not be done on a large scale, since the polymerization may get out of control if efficient dissipation of heat is not possible. It is best polymerized in an emulsion. The polymer may be molded, but the molding temperature (Ca. 200 °C.) is rather high and some decomposition occurs. Vinylidene chloride is found most frequently in copolymers. Some are described in a later section.

Caution! Vinylidene chloride monomer tends to form peroxides and phosgene in contact with air, giving a mixture which may explode on heating (151). Anyone planning to work with this monomer should acquaint himself fully with the hazards (61).

131. Polymerization of Vinylidene Chloride (35)

$$CH_2{=}CCl_2 \longrightarrow [-CH_2{-}CCl_2{-}]_n$$

In a 1 l., three-necked flask equipped with a nitrogen inlet, a condenser, and a stirrer is placed 100 g. of pure vinylidene chloride, 300 ml. of an aqueous solution containing 3 g. of ammonium persulfate, 1 g. of sodium hydroxide, 1.5 g. of sodium thiosulfate, and 3 g. of a detergent, such as sodium "Lorol" sulfate. The air in the reaction vessel is displaced by nitrogen and the temperature is maintained at 30 °C. with stirring. After about 6 hr., polymerization is essentially complete and a polymer emulsion is obtained. This is removed from the reaction vessel and the polymer is precipitated by the addition of 100–150 ml. of saturated salt solution with stirring. The easily filterable, finely divided white powder is removed, washed with water, and dried. The yield is approximately 85 g.

In view of the low boiling point of vinylidene chloride (32 °C.) a nitrogen sweep should not be used. Instead, the reaction vessel should be kept under a slight positive pressure of nitrogen. If desired, pressure bottles can be used for the polymerization.

V. The Free Radical Polymerization of Other Di-, Tri- and Tetrasubstituted Olefins

In sharp contrast to the number of mono- and 1,1-disubstituted olefins known to homopolymerize by a free radical mechanism, there are only very few **1,2-disubstituted olefins** which give high polymer. It is interesting to note that most of the 1,2-disubstituted olefins which polymerize well (including those which polymerize by other mechanisms, cf. acenaphthylene) are unsaturated 5-membered cyclic compounds.

The most interesting 1,2-olefin is **vinylene carbonate,** first reported in the literature by Newman and Addor (142,143). It is prepared by chlorination of ethylene carbonate, followed by dehydrohalogenation. Polymerization is carried out with benzoyl peroxide (67,142,143) or an azo catalyst (67,179).

It is essential that the monomer be very pure if high molecular weight polymer is to be obtained. A thermal treatment has been claimed (179), but treatment with sodium borohydride is preferred (67).

132. Preparation of Vinylene Carbonate (67)

Vinylene carbonate is prepared essentially in the manner described by Newman and Addor (142,143). It is preferable, however, to dilute the ethylene carbonate with carbon tetrachloride and chlorinate for 5–10 hr. in the illumination of a photo-flood lamp. The monomer is dehydrohalogenated with triethylamine as described in the reference and the crude product is distilled through an efficient fractionating column. It boils at 162°C. at atmospheric pressure.

For purification of vinylene carbonate, it is treated with approximately 1% by weight of sodium borohydride and refluxed for 1 hr. at a pressure of 35 mm., at which pressure the b.p. is about 75°C. The monomer is distilled without further fractionation and treated a second time if desired with an additional portion of sodium borohydride in a similar manner. The purified monomer may be stored at room temperature for several days without protection. Monomer which has not been purified as described will darken on exposure to light and will not consistently give high polymer.

133. Polymerization of Vinylene Carbonate (67)

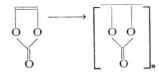

Twenty-five ml. of monomer is placed in a polymer tube together with 50–75 mg. of α,α'-azodiisobutyronitrile. The polymer tube is alternately evacuated and flushed with nitrogen three times and then sealed under vacuum. It is maintained at 60°C. for approximately 18 hr., then opened and the polymer plug removed and ground up with alcohol to separate unreacted monomer. The yield of polymer under these conditions is 67–69%; the inherent viscosity should be greater than 3.0 as measured in a 0.5% dimethylformamide solution. This solution should be prepared at room temperature since some decomposition may occur in hot solvent.

This polymer has good color and the high molecular weight is evident from the high viscosity of solutions. Solutions of the polymer in dimethylformamide may be cast into strong, clear, water-white films. These films have a pronounced metallic rattle when shaken in the hand. The polymer begins to discolor badly at about 250°C. It is soluble in dimethylformamide, dimethylsulfoxide, ethylene carbonate, and acetone containing a small amount of dimethylformamide.

Other 1,2-disubstituted monomers of a similar structure will, in some cases, polymerize or at least copolymerize. These include N-substituted maleimides (25,34,79), and maleic anhydride (183). In addition, the noncyclic maleonitrile will form copolymers (136).

Tetrasubstituted monomers known to polymerize satisfactorily include **chlorotrifluoroethylene** (I), (72,99,165) and **tetrafluoroethylene** (II) (102,148,157).

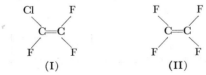

(I)   (II)

These compounds polymerize only under pressure and are very dangerous to handle; therefore, the polymerizations should not be attempted except by those experienced in the handling of these materials. Both polymers are available commercially. "Teflon" is du Pont's trademark for its fluorocarbon resins, including tetrafluoroethylene polymers, and "Kel-F" is the trademark of Minnesota Mining and Manufacturing Co.'s poly(chlorotrifluoroethylene) resin.

VI. Cationic Polymerization of Vinyl Compounds

Cationic polymerization of vinyl compounds is not nearly so universally applicable as is free radical polymerization. The growing chain has a terminal carbonium ion together with its counter ion and polymerization is ordinarily much more rapid and vigorous. Cationic polymerizations are ordinarily initiated at low temperatures in order to suppress undesirable chain-terminating side reactions. The choice of solvent, catalyst concentration, co-catalyst, etc., is extremely important. It is, of course, essential that the solvent, if used, should be completely unreactive towards strong Lewis acids. The theoretical implications of general cationic catalysis are discussed at length in the literature (12).

The following experimental examples illustrate some of the different types of techniques used in the polymerization of several vinyl compounds. It will be noted that the procedures are quite different from those used in the polymerization of vinyl monomers by typical free radical recipes.

One of the few monomers which responds satisfactorily to cationic as well as to free radical catalysis is **styrene,** although it is admittedly difficult to get a product of as high molecular weight with cationic catalysis as is possible with free radical.

Substitution of styrene with an α-methyl group gives a monomer which will polymerize readily with typical cationic catalysts. Again, it is necessary to operate at very low temperatures in order to obtain high molecular weight. For example, Hershberger, Reid and Heiligmann polymerized α-**methyl styrene** in ethyl chloride at $-130\,°C$. according to the following procedure.

134. Cationic Polymerization of α-Methyl Styrene (86)

$$C_6H_5 \cdot CCH_3{=}CH_2 \longrightarrow \left[-CH_2-\underset{\underset{CH_3}{|}}{\overset{\overset{C_6H_5}{|}}{C}}- \right]_n$$

The monomer must be carefully purified of possible oxidation products, such as formaldehyde and acetophenone, so it is distilled immediately before use. There may also be some residual cumene with the α-methyl styrene used, which might act as a chain transfer agent. The solvent employed is ethyl chloride purified by passing over silica gel. The reaction vessel, used by the original workers, was of copper and consisted of a simple container protected from air and moisture and which could be maintained in liquid nitrogen for

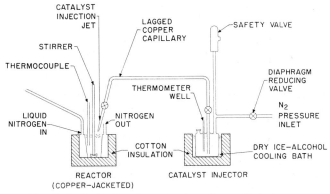

Fig. 4. 2. Cationic polymerization of α-methyl styrene.

external cooling (Fig. 4.2).   More conventional modifications may be used if desired.   The reactor is charged with a mixture of α-methyl styrene diluted with ethyl chloride in a ratio of approximately 14 parts of solvent to 1 part of monomer.   The mixture is cooled until the internal temperature is about −130°C., when a catalyst solution is sprayed in.   The catalyst is prepared by making up a 1% solution of anhydrous aluminum chloride in ethyl chloride. The amount of catalyst used should be approximately 1 g./200 g. of polymer desired.   The yield of polymer will be between 80 and 90%.   The tube used for injection of the catalyst into the monomer-solvent mixture should not extend below the surface of the liquid, otherwise it will become plugged with polymer.   When polymerization appears to be complete, the catalyst is inactivated by the addition of ethyl alcohol and the solvent is allowed to evaporate.   The polymer is broken up, treated with steam to remove the remaining unreacted monomer and solvent and dried.   It is a clear, relatively hard solid with a polymer-melt temperature of slightly over 200°C.

α-Methyl styrene may be copolymerized with isobutylene to give rubbery products.   However, they have little advantage over corresponding styrene derivatives.

Probably the most important monomer which is polymerized commercially by a cationic catalyst is **isobutylene.**   It polymerizes very easily at low temperatures to high molecular weight polymers which are relatively soft and rubbery.   Isobutylene is not affected by free radical type catalysts.   However, the cationic polymerization of carefully purified monomer may occur with almost explosive violence, hence it is ordinarily necessary to moderate this reaction by using very low boiling diluents such as ethyl chloride or ethylene.   The following represents a typical technique for polymerizing isobutylene with a cationic catalyst.

135. Polymerization of Isobutylene with Cationic Catalyst

$$CH_2=C \begin{array}{c} CH_3 \\ \\ CH_3 \end{array} \longrightarrow \left[-CH_2-\underset{CH_3}{\overset{CH_3}{C}}- \right]_n$$

A mixture of 100 g. of isobutylene with approximately 50 g. of anhydrous dry ice is stirred at −80°C. and approximately 0.5 parts of boron fluoride gas is introduced. Polymerization is initiated almost at once and polymer is produced, the heat of reaction being dissipated by the dry ice present in the reaction vessel. The product is a high molecular weight, clear, nontacky, elastomeric material. It is obvious that employment of this technique requires dry ice from which all traces of moisture are absent, since moisture will inhibit the activity of the catalyst (135).

A better method (137) of dissipating heat and moderating violence of the polymerization is to use a low-boiling diluent. For example, a mixture of 20 parts of pure isobutylene and 80 parts of ethane (b.p. −88°C.) or ethylene (b.p. −104°C.) is cooled in a liquid nitrogen bath (−196°C.) and treated with 0.2 parts of boron fluoride gas. Polymerization occurs rapidly and the product is of high molecular weight. The mixture of polymer and solvents is allowed to warm to room temperature and is dried in a vacuum oven at 50°C. The product is a chunk of clear, rubber-like plastic.

Two other monomers which polymerize with Lewis acids are *N*-vinyl carbazole and acenaphthylene. The following techniques illustrate preparation of polymers from these monomers.

136. The Polymerization of *N*-Vinyl Carbazole (152,159)

Fifty g. of freshly distilled *N*-vinyl carbazole and 150 ml. of methylene chloride in a 1 l., three-necked flask equipped with a stirrer, an inlet tube, and an outlet tube is cooled in a dry ice bath to −60°C. with exclusion of atmospheric moisture by means of suitably placed drying tubes. The solution is stirred rapidly and 0.1 ml. of boron fluoride etherate solution is added by means of a hypodermic syringe through the inlet tube which may be capped by a piece of thin rubber sheeting, or a serum type stopper (Chapter 2). Polymerization is initiated almost immediately and the temperature of the reaction mixture rises. After approximately 5 min., the gel-like reaction mixture is treated with 1 ml. of concentrated aqueous ammonia to neutralize the catalyst present and the polymeric solution is coagulated by stirring with methyl alcohol in a high speed mixer. The polymer is filtered and is obtained as a white mass in a yield of about 80–85%.

It is possible to carry out this experiment at room temperature or even at higher temperatures, but lower molecular weight polymer is always obtained. Other solvents may be used such as toluene, carbon tetrachloride, etc., but they are all inferior to methylene chloride in that lower molecular weight products are invariably obtained.

The polymerization of N-vinyl carbazole will take place under a wide variety of conditions. For example, highly purified monomer may be heated in the absence of catalyst at temperatures of 85–120°C. to give a nearly colorless clear product similar in appearance to polystyrene. Again it must be emphasized that it is essential for the monomer to be very pure, otherwise high molecular weight material will not be obtained. The monomer should be distilled, or recrystallized from a suitable solvent such as methyl alcohol or cyclohexane. Poly(vinyl carbazole) can be molded at temperatures of 210–270°C. to sheets which are clear and stiff. The polymer is soluble in chloroform, trichloroethylene, aromatic hydrocarbons, etc. The polymer has excellent electrical properties, but has not found widespread use in this field mainly because of the high cost of the monomer.

137. Polymerization of Acenaphthylene (125)

A solution of about 9 g. of the hydrocarbon dissolved in ether at −50°C. is treated briefly with a slow stream of boron trifluoride gas. The solution is then allowed to warm to 25°C. After 4 hr., the precipitated polymer is removed by filtration, dissolved in benzene, and reprecipitated with methyl alcohol. The polymer has a molecular weight in the range of 183,000–341,000.

Alternatively, polymerization may be carried out by treating a solution of 50 g. of acenaphthylene in 140 ml. of chlorobenzene maintained at −50° to −20°C. with a very slow stream of boron trifluoride gas for about 30 min. The polymer is obtained from the chlorobenzene by precipitation with alcohol. It is dissolved in benzene and reprecipitated with methanol. The yield is approximately 37 g. of very high molecular weight material.

Another class of vinyl compounds which is generally susceptible to cationic polymerization is the **vinyl ethers.** One of the more important of these monomers is **vinyl isobutyl ether.** This material may be polymerized under two conditions—either at very low temperatures or at relatively high temperatures. The polymers obtained under these two types of conditions differ in that the one prepared at very low temperature has a **stereoregular** structure (140,162), very similar to that observed in the isotactic polyhydrocarbons to be described later. The stereoregular polymer is crystalline, orientable, and gives a typical fiber diagram, whereas the nonstereoregular polymer is noncrystalline and elastomeric.

138. Cationic Polymerization of Vinyl Isobutylether at Low Temperatures (162)

Vinyl isobutyl ether monomer should be washed at least 5 times with successive portions of distilled water, dried, then distilled through a fractionating column. The pure product boils at 80°C. The polymerization may become quite vigorous, hence should not be carried out on a particularly large scale. If the equipment is available, a three-necked elongated flask (Fig. 4.3) is

Fig. 4. 3. Elongated flask for exothermic polymerizations.

recommended rather than a typical round bottom flask, since the increased surface area makes cooling of the contents of the flask more efficient. The reaction vessel is equipped with a stirrer. It is cooled in a mixture of acetone and dry ice under a blanket of oxygen-free nitrogen and approximately 40 ml. of propane is condensed into the flask, followed by 10 ml. of vinyl isobutylether. The mixture is stirred at −70°C. and 3 drops of redistilled boron trifluoride etherate is added. The polymerization takes place in a heterogeneous manner around the insoluble droplets of catalyst. After about $1/2$ hr., 3 more drops of catalyst are added and polymerization is continued for another 90 min. The reaction mixture is allowed to warm to room temperature with evaporation of propane and excess monomer. A 57–60% yield of white solid is obtained with an inherent viscosity of about 1.5 in toluene (0.1% concentration). The polymer is crystalline by x-ray and has a crystalline melting point of 90°C. It may be pressed to rubbery, tough film.

The crystallinity of the poly(vinyl isobutylether) can be increased by carrying out polymerization at lower temperatures, or reduced to zero by carrying out the polymerization at higher temperatures or by using flash polymerization techniques such as were employed in Germany to prepare this polymer. The technique for flash polymerization of vinyl isobutylether is as follows:

Liquid propane (30 ml.) is condensed in a suitable vessel with a dry ice condenser attached and allowed to reflux. Boron fluoride is dispersed in the liquid propane at a concentration of at least 0.01%. This catalyst dispersion is mixed rapidly with vinyl isobutylether (10 ml.), purified as described above, in 20 ml. of propane. Prior to mixing each of the two solutions should be cooled to $-69°C$. to $-70°C$. Reaction occurs almost instantaneously, and gaseous propane evolves rapidly from the heat of reaction. The white solid polymer is isolated by allowing the propane to evaporate. It is rather tacky and rubber-like and cannot be converted to satisfactory films. An x-ray diagram shows the material to be noncrystalline.

The polymerization of vinyl isobutylether at relatively low temperatures to produce isotactic polyether is interesting since it is a cationic polymerization which proceeds at a relatively slow rate compared to the usual cationic vinyl polymerization. Examination of the polymerization at low temperature indicates that the polymer appears to grow on the surface of the frozen boron fluoride-etherate catalyst particles. Considerable emphasis has been placed on this mode of growth during discussions of the mechanism of this polymerization (140,162).

VII. Anionic Polymerization of Vinyl Compounds

The least well developed type of vinyl catalysis examined is that of anionic initiation, assuming that coordination catalysis (see following) is not anionic in nature. However, several rather interesting examples are known. **Polymerizations by free alkali metals** are included in this category, since a free radical propagation is apparently not involved, as witness the ready polymerization of α-**methyl styrene** by metallic potassium. The initiator is probably

$$
\begin{array}{ccc}
& CH_3 & CH_3 \\
& | & | \\
C_6H_5\!-\!\!C\!-\!CH_2CH_2\!-\!C\!-\!C_6H_5 \\
& | & | \\
& K & K
\end{array}
$$

139. Polymerization of α-Methyl Styrene by Metallic Potassium (187)

$$C_6H_5-\overset{\overset{\displaystyle CH_3}{|}}{C}=CH_2 \longrightarrow \left[-CH_2-\overset{\overset{\displaystyle C_6H_5}{|}}{\underset{\underset{\displaystyle CH_3}{|}}{C}}-\right]_n$$

In a glass wall polymer tube of at least 150 ml. content are placed 72.5 g. of freshly distilled α-methyl styrene together with about 2 g. of metallic potassium (**Danger**!) in the form of wire or pellets. The mixture is sealed under vacuum and agitated at 15°C. for about 12 hr. An induction period of about 7 hr. is noted followed by a polymerization period of about 5 hr. The reaction mixture is removed from the tube and the viscous liquid is separated from metallic potassium by filtration. Unpolymerized α-methyl styrene is removed from the mixture by heating at 190°C./1 mm., or by blowing with steam, after removal of the potassium. The product remaining in the flask consists of about 35–40 g. of polymeric α-methyl styrene, with an inherent viscosity of about 0.7–0.8 as measured in toluene (0.5%, 25°C.).

α-Methyl styrene may be polymerized using similar conditions with metallic sodium, metallic lithium or alloys of the alkali metals. The reaction with metallic sodium is considerably slower than with potassium, while lithium is intermediate.

Catalysts for the anionic polymerization of vinyls are ordinarily salts of very weak bases. The classic example is the **polymerization of methacrylonitrile by Grignard reagents, or triphenylmethyl sodium,** as described by Beaman (30).

140. Polymerization of Methacrylonitrile with Triphenylmethyl Sodium (30)

$$CH_2=\overset{\overset{\displaystyle CN}{\diagup}}{\underset{\underset{\displaystyle CH_3}{\diagdown}}{C}} \longrightarrow \left[-CH_2-\overset{\overset{\displaystyle CN}{\diagup}}{\underset{\underset{\displaystyle CH_3}{\diagdown}}{C}}-\right]_n$$

Triphenylmethyl sodium is prepared by the method described in *Organic Syntheses* (151A) from 4.5 g. of triphenylmethyl chloride and 0.82 g. of sodium amalgamated with 82 g. of mercury. This solution of triphenylmethyl sodium in ether at −75°C. is mixed with 15 g. of freshly distilled methacrylonitrile diluted with about 50 ml. of anhydrous ether and precooled before adding to the sodium derivative. A dark green precipitate is formed at −75°C. very rapidly. The mixture is allowed to warm to room temperature and any excess sodium alkyl is decomposed by the addition of water or alcohol. The solid is collected by filtration, washed with water, and dried. The product is obtained in a yield of approximately 12 g. with a relatively low inherent viscosity.

141. Polymerization of Methacrylonitrile with Sodium in Liquid Ammonia (30)

$$CH_2=\underset{CH_3}{\overset{CN}{C}} \longrightarrow \left[-CH_2-\underset{CH_3}{\overset{CN}{\underset{|}{C}}}- \right]_n$$

A 500 ml. round bottom, three-necked flask, equipped with a dry ice condenser, a stirrer, and a gas inlet is cooled in a dry ice bath, and about 100 ml. of anhydrous liquid ammonia is condensed into the flask. Approximately 0.4 g. of metallic sodium is now introduced into the liquid ammonia and allowed to dissolve to give the intense blue solution characteristic of sodium dissolved in liquid ammonia. To this solution, maintained at $-75°C.$, is added 15 g. of freshly distilled α-methacrylonitrile. The blue color is discharged almost instantaneously. After approximately 15 min., 2 g. of solid ammonium chloride is added to decompose any organometallic compounds present and the ammonia is allowed to evaporate. The residual solid polymer is washed with water to remove inorganic salts, filtered, and dried. The yield of polymer is quantitative, the inherent viscosity in the neighborhood of 0.8 as measured in dimethylformamide solution (0.5%, $25°C.$).

Another effective type of catalyst for anionic polymerization is **sodium naphthalene,** or **sodium benzophenone,**

$$Na^+ \,_{(-)} \qquad \text{and} \qquad \underset{C_6H_5}{\overset{C_6H_5}{\diagdown}}C-O^{(-)}$$

which are ion-radicals, but appear to initiate anionic polymerization (41,177,178,184) as follows:

$$\underset{C_6H_5}{\overset{C_6H_5}{\diagdown}}\cdot C-\bar{O} + CH_2=\underset{Y}{\overset{X}{C}} \longrightarrow \phi_2CO + \cdot CH_2-\underset{Y}{\overset{X}{C}} \;(-)$$

The radicals dimerize and the chain grows anionically in both directions, until terminated. Catalysts of this type will polymerize **styrene** and **acrylonitrile** to high molecular weight products, provided adequate precautions are taken to maintain purity of reagents.

142. Preparation of Lithium and Sodium Naphthalene Catalysts (167,168)

$$\text{(naphthalene)} + Li \longrightarrow \text{(naphthalene)}^{(-)} Li^+$$

Lithium naphthalene catalyst is prepared in the following manner. A three-necked reaction flask of suitable size is equipped with a gas inlet, a stirrer, a stopper and a means for allowing the inert gas to exit, which is protected by a drying tube. The flask is flamed out under nitrogen, or better, argon, and 50 ml. of tetrahydrofuran, purified by distillation from lithium aluminum hydride, is added followed by 15 g. of resublimed naphthalene. To this solution at room temperature is added 1.5 g. of metallic lithium in small pieces, or as a lithium dispersion. The reaction begins almost at once as evidenced by the appearance of the dark greenish black color of lithium naphthalene. The reaction proceeds so rapidly that it is exothermic and becomes warm to the touch, and if lithium dispersion is used external cooling may be necessary. After 2 hr. of stirring, the reaction is considered to be complete. A 3 ml. aliquot may be withdrawn at this point and quenched in methanol. The titer is then determined with standard hydrochloric acid. The solution should ordinarily contain approximately 1.6 milliequivalents of base/ml. when prepared in the above manner.

Sodium naphthalene is prepared in an identical manner to the lithium naphthalene described in the preceding paragraph. Again the solution is standardized by titration of a quenched sample with dilute hydrochloric acid.

143. Anionic Polymerization of Styrene (41,177,178,184)

$$C_6H_5CH{=}CH_2 \longrightarrow (-\overset{\displaystyle C_6H_5}{\underset{\displaystyle |}{C}H}-CH_2)_m(CH_2-\overset{\displaystyle C_6H_5}{\underset{\displaystyle |}{C}H}-)_n$$

In order to successfully polymerize styrene to high molecular weight polymer with an anionic initiator, it is necessary that all liquid reagents be distilled and maintained under nitrogen until required. The nitrogen used in flushing the equipment under which the reagents are to be stored should be previously purified by passing through silica gel. All solid reagents used should be dried in desiccators for at least one week. All glass equipment should be flamed out under dry nitrogen after assembly and immediately prior to use. All reaction vessels should be maintained under a positive nitrogen pressure.

A 100 ml., three-necked flask fitted with a stirrer, a nitrogen inlet, and a side arm for the introduction of reagents is assembled. To the flask is added 10 ml. of styrene, 50 ml. of glycol dimethyl ether purified by stirring with sodium dispersion for several hours, followed by distillation at atmospheric pressure under nitrogen. This solution is cooled to −70°C. by an external dry ice bath and 50 mg. of sodium naphthalene catalyst is added. The polymerization proceeds very rapidly and the solution assumes a bright red color, due to the styrene anion. This color persists for long periods of time, presumably indefinitely if reactive agents are excluded. The polymerization is quenched by the addition of some alcohol which causes immediate disappearance of the color. The mixture is allowed to warm to room temperature and the polymer is filtered, mixed with alcohol, and dried. The yield is quantitative; the inherent viscosity will run between 1.0 and 1.5 in toluene at 0.5% concentration.

An interesting example of anionic polymerization is afforded by the so-called "**living polymers**" (177). As previously suggested, an initiator such as sodium naphthalene will produce an ion-radical from a vinyl monomer, which dimerizes, then grows in both directions:

$$\cdot CH_2\overset{\displaystyle X}{\underset{\displaystyle Y}{C}}\ (-) \longrightarrow (-)\ \overset{\displaystyle X}{\underset{\displaystyle Y}{C}}-CH_2-CH_2\overset{\displaystyle X}{\underset{\displaystyle Y}{C}}\ (-)$$

The resulting polymer will grow until the monomer is exhausted, the average chain length depending on the ratio of initiator to monomer. The chain ends remain active and further polymerization can occur on addition of more monomer, which may be different from that first used. This affords a simple way to prepare block copolymers. Alternatively, a reagent capable of reacting with organometallic compounds is added. For example, carbon dioxide will give a macrodicarboxylic acid.

144. Preparation of a Polystyrene with Carboxyl Ends (41,103,177,178, 184)

$$C_6H_5CH{=}CH_2 \longrightarrow HO_2C(-\overset{\displaystyle C_6H_5}{\overset{|}{C}}H-CH_2)_m(CH_2-\overset{\displaystyle C_6H_5}{\overset{|}{C}}H-)_nCO_2H$$

Polymerization is carried out in a three-necked reaction vessel, preferably a creased flask of the type originated by Morton and coworkers (132). This flask is equipped with a nitrogen flush, a stirrer, stopper, and a means for the nitrogen to escape. The flask is flamed under nitrogen prior to addition of the reagents. To the flask is now added 250 ml. of purified tetrahydrofuran. In order to make certain that the tetrahydrofuran is completely free of impurity, a few drops of the lithium naphthalene catalyst is added until the greenish black color of the organometallic reagent persists. At this point, a quantity of solution containing 21.9 milliequivalents of catalyst is added. The flask is then immersed in a dry ice bath and cooled until a temperature of about $-77°C$. is reached. At this point, 150 milliequivalents (13.6 g.) of styrene is added via a hypodermic syringe inserted through a serum type rubber stopper (Chapter 2) in one of the necks of the flask. The green-black color of the lithium naphthalene catalyst is completely changed to the dark red color of the dianion of styrene. The relatively nonviscous solution is allowed to come to room temperature when 35 g. of dry, solid carbon dioxide is quickly added. The dark red solution immediately becomes colorless and considerably more viscous. After the solid carbon dioxide has all evaporated, dilute hydrochloric acid is added to liberate the macrodicarboxylic acid. The mixture is precipitated with methanol and the solid filtered and washed repeatedly with water and alcohol until free of salts and mineral acid. The solid is dried overnight in an 80°C. oven.   The yield is approximately 90%.   On the basis of the suggested ratio of ingredients, the degree of polymerization should be approximately 30.   Experimentally, the value will not differ from this calculated figure appreciably.   If a higher or lower degree of polymerization is desired, this may be obtained by varying the ratio of lithium naphthalene to monomeric styrene in the initial charge.

Again it should be stressed that in experiments of this type it is essential to maintain all glass equipment and all reagents absolutely free of impurities which might tend to either inactivate the catalyst or act as chain terminators. When due precaution is taken, no problems are encountered in preparing living polystyrene molecules which can be terminated with carboxyl groups in the manner indicated above.   It is possible to vary the molecular weight of the material obtained over a fairly wide range.   The difunctionality of the resulting product is almost theoretical.

Acrylonitrile may be polymerized in essentially the same manner as described above for styrene with sodium naphthalene or sodium benzophenone.   With acrylonitrile, it is convenient to use dimethylformamide as a reaction medium, in which case the polymer obtained remains in solution and may be used directly for further applications.   A variation on this anionic polymerization technique uses a salt of a somewhat stronger (but still very weak) acid, namely, **sodium cyanide.** This salt in dimethylformamide at very low temperatures acts as a very efficient anionic chain initiator for the polymerization of acrylonitrile.

145. Anionic Polymerization of Acrylonitrile (64)

$$CH_2{=}CHCN \longrightarrow [-CH_2-\overset{\displaystyle CN}{\underset{\displaystyle |}{CH}}-]_n$$

A 250 ml., three-necked, round bottom flask is fitted with a stirrer, an inlet tube for the introduction of nitrogen, and an outlet tube.   As in the previous experiments, the nitrogen must be dried by passing it through silica gel and the equipment should be flamed out under nitrogen immediately prior to use.   In the flask is placed 60 ml. of freshly distilled dimethylformamide and 10 ml. of acrylonitrile recently distilled under nitrogen.   The flask with its contents is immersed in a cooling bath consisting of dry ice and alcohol, and the temperature is lowered to about −50°C.   The initiator, 2 ml. of a saturated solution of anhydrous sodium cyanide in dry dimethylformamide, is rapidly introduced by means of a hypodermic syringe inserted in a serum type rubber stopper. Sodium cyanide can be dried by storing in a vacuum desiccator over silica gel for several days prior to use.   A saturated solution of this salt in dimethylformamide contains somewhat less than 1 g. of cyanide in 100 g. of dimethylformamide.

Within a few seconds of adding the initiator, the temperature of the reaction mixture will rise rapidly and the solution may become so viscous it may climb up the stirrer shaft. The contents of the flask is allowed to stir for about 30 min. in the cooling bath. At the end of this reaction time, 5 ml. of 3% sulfuric acid in dimethylformamide is added to destroy unreacted initiator and to adjust the acidity of the mixture to a value of pH of 7 or less. The polymer may be isolated by precipitation in water, or the solution may be used directly for other purposes. The yield is quantitative; the inherent viscosity measured in dimethylformamide is 2–3 (0.5%, 30°C.).

Vinylidene cyanide, $CH_2 = C(CN)_2$, has been studied extensively (e.g., 23,24,75). It polymerizes readily by an anionic mechanism, but the polymer is easily depolymerized. It is more useful in copolymers, and will be considered there (Preparations 165–168).

VIII. Stereospecific Polymerization of Olefins

It was stated earlier that among the olefins, only ethylene and styrene can be readily polymerized by radicals, the former most commonly at high pressure and temperature. It has been found that catalysts obtained by the reduction of transition metal halides with organometallic reducing agents will polymerize ethylene and substituted α-olefins to high molecular weight, crystalline orientable polymers.

These catalysts (21,22,39,197,198), now known popularly as coordination catalysts, polymerize olefins at room temperature and atmospheric pressure, hence are admirably suited to small scale operations in laboratory glassware. The polymers are generally very high in molecular weight, sometimes too high for suitable fabrication. In this case it may be possible to thermally crack the polymer to an equally crystalline, but lower molecular weight material.

With higher olefins, such as propylene, these catalysts usually give high melting products which have a stereoregular structure (138, 139,141). In normal polymerization of a substituted olefin, a new asymmetric center is produced as each monomer unit is added, but there is no control of the configuration of each succeeding center.

$$\text{\textasciitilde\textasciitilde CH}_2\text{—CH· + CH}_2\text{=CH} \longrightarrow \text{—CH}_2\text{—CH—CH}_2\text{—CH\textasciitilde\textasciitilde}$$

The result is a completely random configuration of the chain.

These configurations may be visualized by imagining the carbon-carbon polymer chain laid out on a plane in the extended zigzag con-

formation.   If the substituents from the monosubstituted vinyl monomer are arranged at random above and below the plane of the carbon
chain, the polymer lacks stereochemical regularity and is called *atactic:*

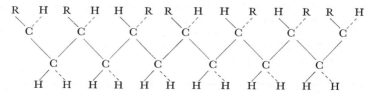

The titanium-based catalysts give, by a mechanism which is still unclear, a stereoregular chain in which each succeeding asymmetric carbon has the same configuration as the preceding one:
    If the substituents all fall on one side of the plane, the polymer is said
to be *isotactic:*

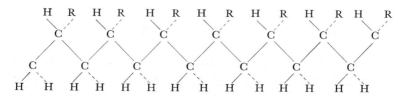

Finally, if the substituents fall alternately above and below the plane of
the chain, the polymer is designated *syndiotactic:*

The stereoregularity permits the chains to crystallize, hence the properties of the polymers differ markedly from the random counterpart.
Thus, free radical polystyrene is clear, noncrystalline, and low melting,
while stereoregular polystyrene is hazy like nylon, crystalline, orientable,
and high melting. The nature of R also affects the melting point markedly; the bulkier it is the higher melting the polymer (47,150). The
preparation of some selected polymers follows.
    The stereoregular polymers have been described by Natta (138,139,
141), who has also described other types of stereoregularity.

146. Preparation of Lithium Aluminum Tetradecyl (21,22,39)

$$\text{LiAlH}_4 + \text{C}_8\text{H}_{17}\text{CH}{=}\text{CH}_2 \longrightarrow \text{LiAl}(\text{C}_{10}\text{H}_{21})_4$$

A mixture of tetrahydronaphthalene (700 ml.), 1-decene (150 ml.) and lithium aluminum hydride (7.6 g.) is heated with stirring to 135°C. A mildly exothermic reaction occurs and the temperature is allowed to rise to about 180°C. It is maintained at this temperature for about 2 hr., then cooled. The originally clear liquid containing lumps of white hydride has become a solution in which is suspended a gray-black flocculent solid. The flask is transferred to a nitrogen-filled dry box and filtered while still warm through a Celite pad. The filtered solution is stored and the pyrophoric residue on the funnel destroyed at once with isopropanol. For standardization, a 5.0 ml. aliquot of the solution is removed, dissolved in some alcohol, then 200 ml. of water is added. The resulting mixture is titrated potentiometrically to pH 7 with standard acid. Under these conditions, only the lithium is titrated, and normality = molarity. This preparation should have concentrations of around 0.2 M. It is necessary to prevent contact of oxygen and moisture with the lithium aluminum tetradecyl solution. Otherwise, no problems should be encountered during storage.

147. Preparation of Titanium Tetrachloride Solution

A commercial product is distilled at 136.5°C. after removal of an appreciable forecut. A stock solution is made up in cyclohexane in 500 ml. batches as needed. A convenient concentration which should be sought for is about 0.5 M. The exact concentration is determined gravimetrically.

148. Preparation of Catalyst and Polymerization: General Procedure (21,22,39,47)

In general, measured amounts of the catalyst components (titanium tetrachloride and lithium aluminum tetradecyl) are mixed in some inert solvent, usually cyclohexane. Stirring is rapid during mixing and during polymerization. The major cause of trouble in polymerizations is oxygen which is excluded during all phases of the polymerization and catalyst preparation. Also, water and other electron-rich substances must be excluded, since they also inactivate the catalyst.

In the actual experiments listed, the volumes and concentrations used are taken directly from the literature (47). It is obvious that other concentrations could be used, the volumes of the component solutions being adjusted accordingly.

If aluminum triisobutyl is on hand, it may be advantageous to use this material. However, it should be recognized that it is a very dangerous reagent. A catalyst is then prepared as follows.

A 1 1., three-necked flask equipped with stirrer, a nitrogen inlet, a thermometer, a dropping funnel, and a condenser is flushed with nitrogen and maintained with an atmosphere of nitrogen throughout the entire preparation. One hundred ml. of decahydronaphthalene is introduced into the reaction flask and heat is applied through a heating mantle. To the decahydronaphthalene is added in succession 6 ml. of 1 M titanium tetrachloride, and 2 ml. of 1 M triisobutylaluminum, both solutions having previously been made up in decahydronaphthalene. Addition of the aluminum alkyl causes precipitation of a brownish black product. The temperature of the flask is then increased as rapidly as possible to 180–185°C. and maintained at this temperature for 40 min. The color of the suspended complex changes to a deep violet which is quite intense. The solution is now cooled and 400 ml. of cyclohexane is added followed by 12 ml. of 1 M aluminum triisobutyl solution. The violet color becomes at once a deep purplish-black.

All of the polymers described below are prepared in essentially the same manner. A three-necked flask or a resin kettle is equipped with a stirrer, a nitrogen inlet, and a simple outlet. A catalyst suspension is prepared in the flask by mixing appropriate amounts of the catalyst components under nitrogen with or without additional solvent. Monomer is then added and the polymerization is allowed to proceed. The polymer is isolated by addition of alcohol followed by filtration. It is purified by washing in a high speed home mixer with additional quantities of alcohol, then freed of organic solvents in an appropriate manner, usually either with steam or with dry nitrogen at 100–120°C.

149. Preparation of Crystalline Polystyrene (47,141)

$$\underset{\overset{|}{\text{CH}_2=\text{CH}}}{\text{C}_6\text{H}_5} \longrightarrow \underset{\overset{|}{[-\text{CH}_2-\text{CH}-]_n}}{\text{C}_6\text{H}_5}$$

The polymerization of styrene over a titanium-containing organometallic catalyst proceeds relatively slowly. However, the product obtained has properties which makes it different from all other kinds of polystyrenes previously described.

The catalyst is prepared by mixing 50 ml. of 0.44 M titanium tetrachloride and 175 ml. of lithium aluminum tetradecyl (0.14 M) without additional solvent. The concentration of the reactant may be different than specified, but the total quantity should be equivalent. Styrene (40 g.) is added all at once and the resulting mixture is stirred for 20 hr. The polymer solution is then treated with 200 ml. of isopropanol and stirred under a stream of air to discharge most of the color due to the lower valent titanium. The polymer is isolated by filtration and the solid washed repeatedly with alcohol. The product is a white, rather rubbery solid, obtained in a yield of 9–11 g. This polymer is fractionated as follows. First, it is extracted with 200 ml. of anhydrous ether. The insoluble fraction (6–7 g.) is collected and dried. The filtrate on evaporation gives 3–4 g. of a tacky, low molecular weight, noncrystalline polystyrene. The ether-insoluble fraction may be purified further by extraction with boiling toluene. The toluene-soluble fraction, which amounts to only about 0.5–1.0 g., is partially crystalline material which is probably a block polymer containing crystalline and noncrystalline segments. The toluene-insoluble portion can be pressed into film at temperatures of the order of 150°C. The product has a crystalline melting point of the order of 240–

250°C.   It is moderately soluble in tetrachloroethane and has an inherent viscosity of about 6 (0.5% concentration) in this solvent at room temperature.

It is interesting to contrast polystyrene made in this manner with polystyrene made by a conventional free-radical type catalyst with respect to solubility in a series of common solvents such as benzene, chloroform, acetone, tetrahydrofuran, etc. and with respect to clarity when in film form, with respect to behavior on a hot surface at 200°C., and with respect to its ability to stretch and orient over a hot surface.

150. Preparation of Linear Polyethylene (21,22,39,109a)

$$CH_2{=}CH_2 \longrightarrow [-CH_2{-}CH_2]_n$$

A three-necked, 4 l. resin kettle is equipped with a stirrer, a gas inlet tube, and an outlet consisting of a simple glass tube 24 in. long, protected with a drying tube.   The kettle is flushed with nitrogen and a catalyst suspension is prepared in the following manner.   Two l. of cyclohexane is added to the kettle followed by 200 ml. of a 0.2 molar solution of lithium aluminum tetradecyl as previously made.   The mixture is cooled externally in a water-ice bath and 0.029 moles of titanium tetrachloride is added as a cyclohexane solution.   The mixture immediately becomes brownish black and is now an active catalyst for the polymerization of ethylene.   A cylinder of ethylene is attached to the gas inlet tube through a safety trap.   Ethylene is bubbled through the vigorously stirred catalyst suspension, and polyethylene begins to separate with the evolution of some heat.   The polymerization may be continued as long as desired until the solution becomes unstirrable.   The slurry of polymer and solvent containing catalyst is poured into a large excess of isopropyl alcohol with vigorous stirring and the finely divided, precipitated polymer is isolated by filtration.   The product is usually obtained as a white powder which can be molded to clear, tough films or extruded to tough fibers.   The product has a crystalline m.p. in the range of 130°.

151. Preparation of Isotactic Polypropylene

$$CH_2{=}CHCH_3 \longrightarrow [-CH_2{-}\overset{\overset{\textstyle CH_3}{|}}{CH}-]_n$$

Polypropylene may be polymerized over either the catalyst prepared in the previous experiment or over a catalyst prepared as follows.   In a 4 l., three-necked resin kettle equipped with a stirrer, gas inlet, and an outlet consisting of a simple glass tube 24 in. long protected with a drying tube, is placed 500 ml. of decahydronaphthalene.   The flask is swept with nitrogen and heated moderately with a heating mantle.   To the decahydronaphthalene is added, in succession, 30 ml. of 1.0 molar titanium tetrachloride and 10 ml. of 1.0 molar triisobutyl aluminum, both the latter solutions in decahydronaphthalene. Addition of the aluminum alkyl causes precipitation of a brownish black product.   The temperature of the flask is then increased as rapidly as possible to about 185°C. and maintained at this temperature for 40 min.   The color of the suspended complex changes to a deep violet.   This suspension is now cooled and 2000 ml. of cyclohexane is added, followed by 60 ml. of 1.0 molar aluminum triisobutyl solution. The purplish black suspension is now an effective catalyst for the polymerization of gaseous propylene. The propylene is bubbled through the catalyst suspension as in the previous experiment and the slurry of polypropylene is precipitated into isopropyl alcohol, filtered, washed, and dried. Isotactic polypropylene can be pressed to clear, tough films and molded to other objects. The crystalline m.p. is about 165°. The yield is determined by the length of time the propylene is bubbled into the catalyst.

152. Preparation of Poly(4-methyl-1-pentene) (47)

$$CH_2{=}CH{-}CH_2\underset{\underset{\textstyle CH_3}{\diagdown}}{\overset{\overset{\textstyle CH_3}{\diagup}}{CH}} \longrightarrow [-CH_2-\underset{\underset{\textstyle CH_2-CH(CH_3)_2}{|}}{CH}-]_n$$

A three-necked, 4 l. resin kettle is equipped with a stirrer, nitrogen inlet, and an outlet consisting of a simple glass tube 24 in. long. The kettle is flushed with nitrogen and a catalyst suspension is prepared in the following manner. Two l. of cyclohexane is added to the kettle followed by 200 ml. of a 0.20 M solution of lithium aluminum tetradecyl as previously made. The mixture is cooled in a water bath and 33 ml. of a 0.87 molar titanium tetrachloride solution in cyclohexane is added. The mixture immediately becomes brownish black and is now an active catalyst for the polymerization of an α-olefin. To the catalyst suspension is now added 450 g. of distilled, dry 4-methyl-1-pentene, which may be obtained commercially. The mixture warms up moderately and rapidly becomes viscous. Polymerization may be allowed to proceed for 12 hr. It is essentially complete in a much shorter time and the reaction may be worked up after 2 hr. if it is desired, although the yield may be diminished by a few per cent. Since the polymerization is mildly exothermic, a certain amount of monomer may be lost by distillation and entrainment from the reaction vessel. This may be trapped in a condenser system if desired.

After a 12 hr. period the polymerization is essentially complete and the reaction mixture has the appearance of a solid, blackish brown lump of rubber. This mass of polymer which is swollen by the cyclohexane present, is cut up into convenient sized lumps with scissors or a knife and then cut up very finely in a high-speed cutter, such as a household blender, with isopropyl alcohol. The color of the original polymer is discharged immediately on contact with the alcohol and the resulting product is isolated by filtration as a pure, white, rather granular product. The polymer may be washed repeatedly with alcohol and then dried either in a vacuum oven at pressures less than 1 mm. and temperatures of 100°C. for 8 hr. or by treatment with a rapid stream of live steam or nitrogen at 100°C. with vigorous agitation. The yield of dry polymer is about 250 g. and the inherent viscosity will be 4–6, measured at 130°C. on a 0.1% solution in decahydronaphthalene. The extremely high molecular weight product may be fabricated directly to a clear tough film by pressing at temperatures in excess of 250°C. It also may be extruded from a spinning cell in the form of a continuous filament which may be after-drawn on a hot pin at

100–150°C. The polymer shows a crystalline melting point of about 240°C. as measured on a polarizing microscope.

4-Methyl-1-pentene may also be polymerized over a catalyst prepared as above from aluminum triisobutyl. To this catalyst solution is added 100 ml. of 4-methyl-1-pentene. The mixture is stirred for a period of 90–100 min., at which time the mixture is so thick that it wraps around the stirrer blade and breaks away from the walls of the vessel. The polymer is isolated then dried in a vacuum oven at 50°C. by methods previously described. Polymer prepared in this manner is essentially the same as prepared in the previous experiments. Yields will be of the order of 65–80%. The inherent viscosity is 2–4 (0.1% in decahydronaphthalene at 130°C.).

If the polymer obtained is too high in molecular weight for the desired use, the molecular weight may be conveniently lowered by a cracking process.

154. Thermal Cracking of Poly(4-methyl-1-pentene) (45)

One hundred g. of finely divided poly(4-methyl-1-pentene)prepared as in the previous experiment is freed of low molecular weight atactic polymer by extraction at room temperature with 500 ml. of petroleum ether followed by 500 ml. of cyclohexane. The extracted polymer is dried, then preferably molded into a solid object such as a circular plug, and placed in a glass tube. It is heated at approximately 280°C. in a high vacuum for 8 hr. Polymer with an inherent viscosity of 4–6 should be reduced to polymer with a viscosity between 1.2 and 1.9. The viscosity of the polymer may be checked at the end of this heating period and if it is desired to lower it further, an additional heating period may be carried out.

155. Polymerization of 3-Methyl-1-butene (47)

$$CH_2{=}CH{-}CH \overset{CH_3}{\underset{CH_3}{\diagdown}} \longrightarrow [{-}CH_2{-}\overset{\overset{\displaystyle CH_3 \quad CH_3}{\diagdown\diagup}}{\underset{\displaystyle CH}{CH}}{-}]_n$$

A catalyst suspension is prepared as in the preceding experiment by mixing in a 4 l. resin kettle under nitrogen 250 ml. of 0.19 molar lithium aluminum tetradecyl and 40 ml. of 1.08 molar titanium tetrachloride in 1 l. of cyclohexane. One hundred ml. of 3-methyl-1-butene, b.p. 20°C., is collected in an ice bath and added to the mixture. After 20 hr. the polymer is isolated by filtration and washed with alcohol. Only 13.8 g., approximately 22%, is isolated in this manner. The inherent viscosity cannot be determined since the product is incompletely soluble in decahydronaphthalene. The crystalline melting point (310°C.) is much higher than that of poly(4-methyl-1-pentene) and it is necessary to go to temperatures above 310°C. in order to fabricate the polymer into a clear, transparent film. Strips of this film can be oriented by stretching at temperatures of the order of 250–300°C. or fibers may be drawn from the melt at 310°C. Oriented film strips or fibers show extremely high crystallinity and very high orientation. The crystalline melting point is of the order of 310°C.

156. Poly(4-methyl-1-hexene) (47)

$$CH_2\!\!=\!\!CH\!-\!CH_2\!-\!\underset{\underset{CH_2CH_3}{\diagdown}}{\overset{\overset{CH_3}{\diagup}}{CH}} \longrightarrow [-CH_2-\underset{\underset{CH_2}{|}}{CH}-]_n$$

with the side chain: CH_3CH_2 CH_3 → CH → CH_2

In order to illustrate further the effect of structure of the olefin on the properties of the resulting polymer, 4-methyl-1-hexene, b.p. 86.5 °C., is made from *sec*-butyl magnesium chloride and allyl chloride (47) and is polymerized in a manner similar to that described in the previous experiments. The polymer is a hard solid quite similar in appearance to poly(4-methyl-1-pentene). It may be pressed to film or extruded to fiber. It may be stretched over a hot pin to get a highly oriented crystalline sample. However, the crystalline melting point is only 160 °C. This illustrates the effect of breaking up the symmetry of the branch on the side chain.

157. Preparation of 4-Phenyl-1-butene (76,156)

$$C_6H_5CH_2MgCl + BrCH_2CH\!\!=\!\!CH_2 \longrightarrow C_6H_5CH_2CH_2CH\!\!=\!\!CH_2$$

A Grignard reagent is prepared from 172 g. of benzyl chloride and 33 g. of magnesium metal turnings in the usual way. To this solution is added over a period of 2 hr. a solution of 170 g. of allyl bromide dilute with 600 ml. of ether. The mixture is allowed to stir overnight, then it is cautiously hydrolyzed with water and the ether layer is separated and distilled. 4-Phenyl-1-butene is obtained in a yield of approximately 130 g. (72%) with a boiling point of 86–87 °C./35 mm. The product is distilled through a precision fractionating column prior to use.

158. Polymerization of 4-Phenylbutene-1 (28,47)

$$C_6H_5CH_2CH_2CH\!\!=\!\!CH_2 \longrightarrow [-CH_2-\underset{\underset{CH_2CH_2C_6H_5}{|}}{CH}-]_n$$

A catalyst suspension is prepared by mixing 100 ml. of 0.18 molar lithium aluminum tetradecyl, 15 ml. of 1.08 molar titanium tetrachloride, and 180 ml. of dry cyclohexane. To this suspension is added 50 ml. of 4-phenyl-1-butene. Polymerization is quite rapid and after 1 hr. the mixture is very viscous. The polymer may be isolated at this point or polymerization may be allowed to proceed for several hours, in which case the yield will be slightly increased. The polymer is isolated by pouring the very viscous solution into isopropyl alcohol which is being agitated rapidly in a high speed mixer. The polymer is isolated and dried by heating in a stream of steam for 1 hr. The yield is approximately 24 g.; the inherent viscosity is in the range of 3–4 (0.1%, in decahydronaphthalene at 130 °C.). The polymer can be pressed to clear, very tough film at 200°C. Strips of film may be drawn at 125°C. over a hot surface. The oriented crystalline polymer shows a crystalline melting point of 160°C.

IX. Copolymers

As described earlier in this chapter, there are several types of copolymers, namely random, alternating, block, and graft. It is obvious that an almost infinite number of copolymers could be described. However, the discussion will be limited to a few illustrative examples of each type.

The **random copolymer** is the simplest to prepare. In its simplest manifestation, two monomers are mixed and polymerization is initiated as described in earlier examples of homopolymerizations. If the rate of polymerization of the individual monomers are too greatly different, it may be necessary to add the faster monomer slowly to the polymerization zone containing the slower monomer.

The usual reason for preparing a random copolymer is to tailor a product with desirable features lacking in the homopolymers. For example, polyacrylonitrile homopolymer is soluble with some reluctance and in fiber form dyes very poorly. Copolymerization of minor amounts of, for example, vinyl pyridine, acrylamide, or vinyl acetate will improve markedly the solubility and dyeing characteristics of this polymer. Indeed, it is not uncommon to use several different comonomers in minor proportions, each to impart some desirable property not inherent in the homopolymer. The following examples have been chosen from the vast literature on copolymers.

159. Preparation of a Copolymer of Acryloyl Chloride and Methyl Methacrylate (78)

$$CH_2=CH-\overset{\displaystyle O}{\underset{\displaystyle Cl}{C}} \quad + \quad CH_2=CH-\overset{\displaystyle O}{\underset{\displaystyle CO_2CH_?}{C}} \quad \longrightarrow \quad Copolymer$$

A mixture of 50 g. of freshly distilled methyl methacrylate and 50 g. of acryloyl chloride is placed in a thoroughly dried polymer tube under an atmosphere of dry nitrogen. To this mixture is added 0.2 g. of α,α'-azobis-(α,γ-dimethylvaleronitrile). The tube containing this mixture is fitted with an ordinary capillary inlet reaching beneath the surface of the monomer and is further protected with a drying tube on the outlet. The mixture is heated in a water bath at approximately 50°C. while a slow stream of nitrogen is passed through the capillary. The material becomes quite viscous after 1 hr.

and the capillary is raised to just above the surface of the polymerizing mass. Heating is continued for a total of 3–4 hr., at the end of which time the contents of the polymer tube has set to a hard, clear, colorless solid. The copolymer is isolated in nearly quantitative yield by breaking the glass tube in a nitrogen filled dry box in order to prevent hydrolysis of the acid chloride. The inherent viscosity of polymers made in this manner will lie in the range of 1–2.4 (0.5%; methylene chloride).

160. Preparation of Cross-linked Products from Acryloyl Chloride Copolymers (78)

A solution of the acryloyl chloride copolymer prepared above is made at approximately 10% concentration in anhydrous methylene chloride or a closely related unreactive solvent. A film is dry cast (Chapter 2) on a glass plate under an atmosphere of nitrogen in a dry box. It is advisable to use a casting knife of approximately 30 mils clearance since the solution is relatively dilute. The film is removed from the glass plate and a portion of it is soaked in a 15–20% aqueous solution of ethylene diamine for approximately 10 min. The film is then washed carefully with water and dried. The effect wrought by the cross-linking with diamine is quite marked. The uncross-linked film is not form stable and is likely to be tacky and difficult to handle. The cross-linked material shows a considerable increase in form stability as well as improved tensile properties.

Similar experiments may be carried out on fibers by wet spinning solutions of acryloyl chloride copolymers into a precipitating bath containing a cross-linking agent such as ethylene diamine.

161. Preparation of a Copolymer of Acrylonitrile and Isopropenyl Toluene (107)

$$CH_2\!=\!CHCN + CH_2\!=\!\overset{\overset{\displaystyle CH_3}{|}}{C}\!-\!\langle\!\!\!\bigcirc\!\!\!\rangle\!CH_3 \longrightarrow \text{Copolymer}$$

In a 3 l., three-necked flash equipped with a condenser, stirrer, and a gas inlet is placed 450 g. of acrylonitrile and 150 g. of isopropenyl toluene. To this mixture of acrylonitrile and isopropenyl toluene is added 1200 ml. of water and 1.2 g. of benzoyl peroxide followed by 400 ml. of an emulsifier solution. The latter may be made by dissolving 25 g. of the sodium salt of the di-octyl ester of sulfosuccinic acid and 10 g. of sulfonated castor oil in 100 parts of water.

The polymerization mixture is agitated vigorously and heated on the steam bath for about 14 hr., internal temperature being maintained at about 70–72°C. The mixture is then steam distilled to eliminate any unreacted monomeric materials and in this manner 225–250 g. of polymer is obtained. This polymer is washed with water and soaked in hot ethyl alcohol for several hours to remove additional traces of monomeric materials. After drying, the polymer, which weighs about 200 g., is obtained as a tough, white, board-like material. This polymer can be molded at temperatures of about 120–150°C. to give clear films or other molded objects.

162. Copolymerization of Vinylidene Chloride and Acrylonitrile (80)

$$CH_2\!\!=\!\!CHCN + CH_2\!\!=\!\!CCl_2 \longrightarrow \text{Copolymer}$$

Seventy-five g. of vinylidene chloride and 25 g. of acrylonitrile are mixed with 0.5 g. of benzoyl peroxide and sealed in a pressure vessel maintained at about 45°C. for 10 days.   Gradually the mixture becomes viscous and finally a light yellow nearly transparent glassy mass is obtained.   This material may be molded at 170°C. into films or other objects.

It is possible to prepare copolymers of vinylidene chloride and acrylonitrile of any desired composition by simply varying the ratio of monomers.   These polymerizations are best carried out in a sealed, heavy-wall glass tube behind barricades.

163. Preparation of a Vinyl Chloride–Vinyl Acetate Copolymer

$$CH_2\!\!=\!\!CHCl + CH_2\!\!=\!\!CHOCOCH_3 \longrightarrow \text{Copolymer}$$

Copolymerization of vinyl acetate with vinyl chloride gives a polymer which is tougher than vinyl chloride homopolymer.   Such a copolymer is prepared in the following manner.

In a glass polymer tube is placed 100 ml. of water, about 5 g. of a dispersing agent, such as the sodium salt of sulfonated paraffin oil, 0.25 g. of ammonium persulfate, and 0.1 g. of sodium bisulfite.   This mixture is cooled below the b.p. of vinyl chloride (-14°C.) with a dry ice acetone bath.   Five g. of vinyl acetate and 45 g. of vinyl chloride, measured by first condensing into a graduated vessel, are introduced into the pressure tube which is flushed with nitrogen and sealed.   The pressure tube is allowed to warm to 40°C., where it is agitated for a period of 2 hr.   The vessel is now cooled in ordinary ice water and opened.   The contents is transferred to a conveniently sized beaker, and an equal volume of water is added.   The mixture is heated to approximately 85°C. and the polymer is precipitated by the addition of 10% aluminum sulfate solution with vigorous stirring.   The mixture is heated and stirred for a short time.   Then the polymer is filtered, washed thoroughly with water, and dried. The yield is approximately 45%.   It is a snow-white product which can be formed in a hot press into very tough, light-colored sheets.

164. Copolymer of Vinyl Chloride and Vinylidene Chloride (191,192)

$$CH_2\!\!=\!\!CHCl + CH_2\!\!=\!\!CCl_2 \longrightarrow \text{Copolymer}$$

A buffered hydrogen peroxide catalyst is prepared by mixing 500 ml. of water, 4 g. of soap or other dispersing agent, 3 g. of 30% hydrogen peroxide, and 0.5 g. of acid ammonium phosphate.   This buffer is mixed in a 1 l. stainless steel, stirred autoclave with 42 g. vinylidene chloride and 126 g. of vinyl chloride measured from a pressure cylinder.   The sealed vessel containing the vinyl chloride–vinylidene chloride mixture is heated and agitated at 48°C. for about 20 hr.   Polymerization is complete at the end of this period and the resulting emulsion of copolymer is coagulated by the addition of salt.   The precipitated polymer is filtered, washed with dilute alkali, and then with copious quantities of water.   The copolymer so obtained contains about 25% by weight of vinylidene chloride and 75% of vinyl chloride.   It is satisfactory for molding. It is also soluble in most organic solvents, for example, butyl acetate, benzene, and acetone.   Solutions of the polymer may be used for casting film.

Vinylidene cyanide gives a homopolymer with almost any catalyst. However, the product depolymerizes readily.   With other vinyl

$$\left[-CH_2-C \begin{matrix} CN \\ \\ CN \end{matrix} \right]_n$$

monomers, it is possible to obtain copolymers which appear to be **alternating.   Copolymers of vinylidene cyanide** have found some success in a yarn produced by B. F. Goodrich under the trade name of Darvan.

165. Preparation of Di(acetyl cyanide) (75)

$$2KCN + 2(CH_3CO)_2O \longrightarrow CH_3COO-\underset{\underset{CN}{|}}{\overset{\overset{CN}{|}}{C}}-CH_3 + 2CH_3CO_2Na$$

In a 2 l., three-necked flask equipped with a stirrer, condenser, and dropping funnel and cooled with a water bath is placed 500 ml. of benzene and 100 g. of potassium cyanide.   (**Poison!**) To this stirred mixture is added 150 g. of acetic anhydride over a period of approximately $1/2$ hr.   Any excessive increase in temperature is moderated with the water bath.   The mixture is stirred for approximately 5 hr. at the reflux temperature after addition of acetic anhydride is completed.   The cooled reaction mixture is filtered and distilled.   The product obtained at 100–110°C. at 10 mm. should have a melting point of approximately 69°C.   If it is lower than this, the product should be recrystallized from carbon tetrachloride.   The over-all yield of di(acetyl cyanide) is about 60%.

166. Preparation of Vinylidene Cyanide (24)

$$CH_3COO-\underset{\underset{CN}{|}}{\overset{\overset{CN}{|}}{C}}-CH_3 \xrightarrow{\Delta} CH_2{=}C(CN)_2$$

An apparatus for pyrolyzing di(acetyl cyanide) is made as follows.   A tube of $85/15$ brass, 3 ft. long, $5/8$ in. inside diameter is wrapped with resistance wire and jacketed with asbestos.   It is equipped with a side thermocouple well and is packed with a tight roll of brass window screen.   Both ends of the tube are wound with four turns of small copper tubing through which water is circulated to prevent rubber-stopper connections from softening.   The tube may be used either vertically or at a slight incline from the horizontal.   The tube is maintained at a temperature of 600–650°C.   A 125 ml. distilling flask is connected to the inlet (top) of the tube and the outlet (bottom) is connected to a 250 ml. suction flask connected in turn to a vacuum source.   Eighty g. of diacetylcyanide is placed in the distilling flask and 2 g. of phosphorus pentoxide is placed in the suction flask.   The system is evacuated to 10 mm.   The receiving flask is cooled with a dry ice–acetone bath and the distilling flask is heated at 100°C.   The diacetyl cyanide distills smoothly through the pyrolysis tube in approximately 1 hr.   The pyrolysis product is allowed to warm to room temperature out of contact with moisture.   Seventy-two g. of light-yellow liquid is obtained which is approximately 40% vinylidene cyanide.

The pyrolysis product is purified by distilling through a 6 in. Vigreux column at 15 mm. pressure.   The fraction boiling at 54–57°C. is about 70% pure vinylidene cyanide.   This fraction diluted with $1/2$ its weight of dry chloroform is cooled slowly to -30°C. with stirring.   The filtrate is removed by suction with a filter stick and the crystals remaining are washed with cold (-30°C.) dry toluene in a quantity equal to the weight of chloroform used originally.   The washed, recrystallized vinylidene cyanide is distilled rapidly to yield 18 g. of pure monomer melting at 9°C.

167. Preparation of Alternating Copolymer from Vinylidene Cyanide and Vinyl Benzoate (75)

$$CH_2{=}C(CN)_2 + CH_2{=}\overset{\displaystyle OCO\phi}{\overset{|}{CH}} \longrightarrow \text{Copolymer}$$

A mixture of 174 ml. of benzene, 20 g. of pure vinylidene cyanide, and 38 g. of pure vinyl benzoate is treated with 0.06 g. of o,o'-dichlorobenzoylperoxide in a sealed tube.   The mixture is maintained for 17 hr. at about 43°C.   At the end of this time the copolymer is removed by filtration.

The composition of the polymer so obtained is virtually independent of the ratio of vinylidene cyanide to vinyl benzoate in the original charge.   Analysis of polymer made over a wide range of composition shows that the product is always essentially a 1:1 alternating copolymer.   The copolymer is soluble in dimethylformamide and solutions of polymer in this solvent can be spun to fibers which have shown excellent properties (75).

168. Preparation of Vinylidene Cyanide-Isobutylene Alternating Copolymer (23)

$$CH_2{=}C(CN)_2 + CH_2{=}\overset{\displaystyle CH_3}{\underset{\displaystyle CH_3}{C}} \longrightarrow \text{Copolymer}$$

One hundred and fifty ml. of dry benzene is placed in a polymer tube and 20 g. of vinylidene cyanide and 44 g. of isobutylene are added with cooling. Then, 0.06 g. of catalyst (0.06 g. o,o'-dichlorobenzoyl peroxide) is added and the polymerization vessel is sealed under nitrogen. The mixture is maintained for approximately 20 hr. at about 45°C. when polymerization is complete. The copolymer is separated from the solvent by filtration. The resulting copolymer is a 50/50 alternating copolymer which is again soluble in dimethylformamide. Fibers of excellent properties can be obtained from the dimethylformamide solution by conventional techniques (23).

Another interesting example of an **alternating copolymer in which one of the monomers is inorganic,** is the propylene–sulfur dioxide copolymer, obtained as follows.

169. Alternating Copolymer of Propylene and Sulfur Dioxide (71,77,95, 158)

$$CH_2{=}\overset{\overset{\displaystyle CH_3}{|}}{CH} + SO_2 \longrightarrow [{-}CH{-}\overset{\overset{\displaystyle CH_3}{|}}{CH}{-}SO_2{-}]_n$$

This experiment requires the use of high pressure equipment. To a 1 l. rocker bomb is added 0.5 g. of α,α'-azobis(α,γ-dimethylvaleronitrile). The bomb is pressure tested with nitrogen at 400 p.s.i. to detect leaks and then evacuated to less than 1 mm. for 3–4 hr. The bomb is chilled in a dry ice–acetone mixture and 42 g. of propylene and 240 g. of sulfur dioxide (99% purity) are distilled in. The bomb is sealed. Polymerization is allowed to proceed at 40–45°C. for 8 hr. The product, which is obtained in a yield of approximately 110 g., is removed from the bomb and washed twice with alcohol in a high speed mixer. The dry polymer is ground in a Wiley Mill, or similar device, to pass through a 20 mesh screen and rewashed with alcohol. It is dried at 80°C. overnight. The yield is 96 g. of a hard white product which has an inherent viscosity of 3.3 as measured in concentrated sulfuric acid at room temperature. The product has a PMT of 300°C. At this temperature, it decomposes into monomer.

Isotactic co-(polyhydrocarbons) can be made, as in the following example.

170. Random Copolymer of 4-Methyl-1-pentene and 1-Hexene (46)

$$CH_3CH_2CH_2CH_3CH{=}CH_2 + \quad \overset{\overset{\displaystyle CH_3}{\diagdown}}{\underset{\underset{\displaystyle CH_3}{\diagup}}{CH}}CH_2CH{=}CH_2 \longrightarrow Copolymer$$

In order to illustrate the effects of copolymerization on the properties of poly-α-olefins, the following experiments can be performed. A mixture of 40 ml. of 4-methyl-1-pentene and 10 ml. of 1-hexene is polymerized for 3 hr. as in Section VIII. The polymer is isolated by precipitation in alcohol followed by filtration. The inherent viscosity is approximately 2.5–3.5 as measured in cyclohexane (0.5%) at room temperature. This polymer may be pressed to clear film at about 120°C. It may be drawn and oriented at 125°C. These strips show a crystalline melting point of approximately 195°C. The interesting thing about this copolymer is that it is readily soluble in cyclohexane to give a very viscous but true solution in contrast to poly(4-methyl-1-pentene), which forms with cyclohexane a swollen, gel-like mass. The added 1-hexene has changed the solubility characteristics quite markedly.

X. Diene Polymers and Copolymers

The preparation of diene polymers and copolymers is an important technology which has occupied the attention of many scientists since before World War I. These polymers are, in general, elastomers and have gone far toward supplementing and, perhaps, ultimately supplanting natural rubber.

The volume of published work in this field is very large and has been well summarized in many excellent books (5,10,15,18) and papers. Briefly, dienes will polymerize by a variety of techniques and with a variety of catalysts. With butadiene, the resulting polymerization may give the following structural units:

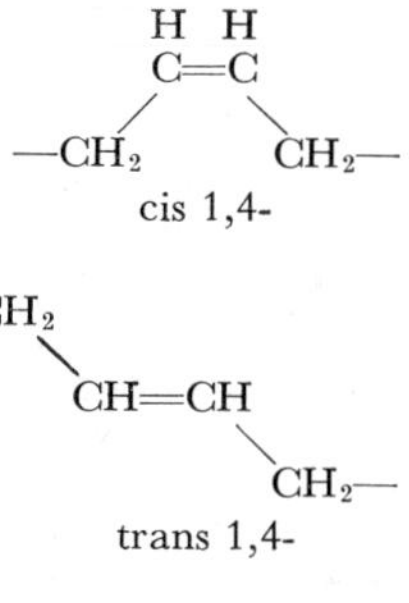

$$
\begin{array}{c}
\text{H \quad H} \\
\text{C}{=}\text{C} \\
\diagup \qquad \diagdown \\
-\text{CH}_2 \qquad \text{CH}_2- \\
\text{cis 1,4-}
\end{array}
$$

$$
\begin{array}{c}
-\text{CH}_2 \\
\diagdown \\
\text{CH}{=}\text{CH} \\
\diagdown \\
\text{CH}_2- \\
\text{trans 1,4-}
\end{array}
$$

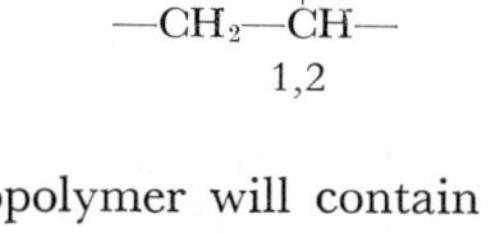

$$
\begin{array}{c}
\text{CH}{=}\text{CH}_2 \\
| \\
-\text{CH}_2{-}\text{CH}- \\
\text{1,2}
\end{array}
$$

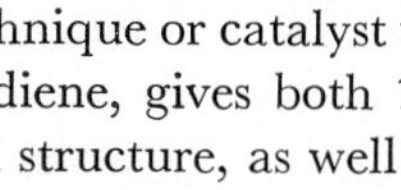

Ordinarily, the homopolymer will contain varying amounts of these structural units making it actually a copolymer. The proportion of units will vary with the technique or catalyst used.

Isoprene, 2-methylbutadiene, gives both 1,2- and 3,4-polymers because of its unsymmetrical structure, as well as cis- and trans-1,4. On the other hand, chloroprene, which is basically similar, appears to give only trans-1,4 polymerization.

$$\underset{\displaystyle CH_2=\overset{\displaystyle Cl}{\overset{|}{C}}-CH=CH_2}{} \longrightarrow \ [-CH_2-\overset{\displaystyle Cl}{\overset{|}{C}}=\underset{\displaystyle H}{\overset{|}{C}}-CH_2-]_n$$

2,3-Dichlorobutadiene polymerizes similarly. Interestingly, the product from this monomer is a hard plastic, and not an elastomer. The following experiments are illustrative of the preparation of diene polymers and copolymers.

Butadiene may be homopolymerized conveniently in a variety of ways. One of the more interesting techniques is that using the "**Alfin**" **catalyst,** discovered by Morton and co-workers (130,131,134). This is an organometallic system composed of a mixture of a metal alkyl, an alkali halide, and an alkali metal alkoxide. The rate of polymerization and the molecular weight of the product are very sensitive to changes in the alkyl group of the organometallic and the alkoxide.*

171. Preparation of "Alfin" Catalysts

$$2Na + C_5H_{11}Cl \longrightarrow C_5H_{11}Na + NaCl$$

$$NaCl + C_5H_{11}Na + 0.25(CH_3)_2CHOH \longrightarrow$$

$$0.75\ C_5H_{11}Na + 0.25(CH_3)_2CHONa + NaCl \xrightarrow{\ CH_2=CHCH_3\ }$$

$$0.75\ CH_2=CH-CH_2Na + 0.25(CH_3)_2CHOH + NaC$$

In order to prepare this catalyst successfully, it is necessary to use high speed stirring apparatus essentially as described by Professor Morton (132,133).

Amylsodium. In a 1 l., four necked flask attached to a high speed stirrer capable of at least 10,000 r.p.m., are placed 500 ml. of dry decane and 23.5 g. of metallic sodium. This mixture is heated to 105 °C. and stirred vigorously for 2 mins. The flask is cooled with stirring, then the sodium sand is allowed to settle. This mixture is now cooled to −20°C., and 62.5 g. of freshly distilled amyl chloride is added from a dropping funnel. After the addition of approximately 10–15 ml. of amyl chloride, the reaction mixture is stirred vigorously until a dark purple color develops indicating initiation of reaction. The remaining amyl chloride is now added over a period of 1 hr., maintaining the temperature at −20°C. The mixture is now allowed to warm to room temperature and stirred for an additional 30 min.

Amylsodium–Sodium Isopropoxide Catalyst. To 1 mole of amylsodium prepared as in the preceding paragraph is added 12.5 g. of isopropanol at room temperature with stirring.

---

* Freshly purified styrene may be polymerized by the "Alfin" catalyst essentially as is butadiene. The product obtained is of high molecular weight and has been reported to contain a crystalline fraction (193).

Allylsodium–Sodium Isopropoxide Catalyst. The combination of amyl-sodium–sodium isopropoxide prepared in the preceding paragraph is cooled to $-20\,°C$. and stirred vigorously. Propylene gas is bubbled in at $-20\,°C$. until the amylsodium is completely converted to allylsodium. The propylene is then bubbled through the suspension for an additional 3 hr. to insure completion of the reaction. The dark bluish purple suspension may be stored under nitrogen for future use.

172. Polymerization of Butadiene by an "Alfin" Catalyst

$$CH_2{=}CH{-}CH{=}CH_2 \longrightarrow (C_4H_6)_n$$

A flask equipped with high speed stirring, such as was used in the preparation of the organometallic catalyst, is charged with 250 ml. of anhydrous pentane, and 20 ml. of the catalyst suspension is added by means of a hypodermic syringe or other anaerobic method of transfer. The catalyst suspension is stirred rapidly, and 30 ml. of high purity butadiene in 30 ml. of cold pentane is added rapidly to the well-stirred mixture. Polymerization is allowed to proceed for approximately 2 hr. when dilute hydrochloric is added to quench the reaction and phenyl β-naphthylamine (approximately 4% by weight of the polymer expected) is added. The polymer is now isolated by evaporation of the pentane and the residue is placed in a vacuum oven at $40\,°C$. The resulting polybutadiene should be obtained in a yield of about 60% with an inherent viscosity of about 9 as measured in pentane (0.1, $25\,°C$.).

Ordinarily, polymers prepared with the "Alfin" catalyst are only partially soluble in pentane. The solubility may be, however, as high as 98% with the combination of alcohol and olefin used above in the preparation of the catalyst. The highest viscosity polymer is obtained when the catalyst is prepared as described in the preceding paragraph from isopropanol and propylene. The viscosity decreases with the use of higher olefins and higher alcohols. For example, using 2-heptanol and 2-pentene in place of isopropanol and propylene ordinarily gives a polymer with viscosities below 3, at a much slower rate than the preceding example. As is the case with all organometallic catalyzed polymerizations, both catalyst and monomer must be handled under anhydrous conditions.

Polymerization is usually very rapid, and it is allowed to go for 2 hr. only to insure completion and to allow for possible subnormal activity of the catalyst. The great speed of the polymerization can be demonstrated quite effectively. A few milliliters of active catalyst suspension is mixed in a cork-stoppered pop-bottle with 30 ml. of butadiene and 150 ml. of pentane. The contents will come swelling out of the bottle after 2–3 min. in spectacular fashion.

Butadiene also can be **polymerized in a typical emulsion system,** such as described earlier for vinyl monomers, or in a GR-S type system as in Preparation 171. It can be polymerized with **metallic sodium,** the following procedure being typical (112).

173. The Sodium Catalyzed Polymerization of Butadiene (112)

$$CH_2{=}CH{-}CH{=}CH_2 \longrightarrow (C_4H_6)_n$$

The reaction vessel used in this polymerization is a simple 4 oz. screw cap bottle which has been provided with a heavy rubber disk covered with a heavy tin foil disk underneath the screw cap. The bottle is flushed with gaseous butadiene and a volume of sodium dispersion in xylene or toluene containing about 0.15 g. of sodium is added to the bottle. Ten ml. of dry toluene is now added, followed by 60–70 g. of butadiene which has been condensed in an ice-salt bath. The mixture is allowed to boil gently for a short time in order to completely expel the air from the reaction vessel, then the cap plus the rubber gasket and heavy tin foil disk is placed on top of the bottle and the vessel is sealed. The bottle is maintained in a thermostatted bath and tumbled by a mechanical device at a temperature of approximately 50°C. As polymerization proceeds the contents of the bottle becomes viscous and eventually becomes solid. After 24 hr. the polymer can be isolated as follows.

Benzene containing 10% alcohol and a trace of phenyl-β-naphthylamine antioxidant is added to the cooled bottle. The mixture is removed and added to a large excess of benzene to give a homogeneous dispersion. Polymer is precipitated with methanol as a rubbery mass and pressed free of liquid, then mixed with about 2% of its weight of antioxidant. Drying is accomplished by placing in a circulating air oven at 70–80°C. for 6–8 hr.

Butadiene also will polymerize readily with organotitanium catalysts and with lithium and lithium alkyls, as is described subsequently for isoprene.

Polybutadienes prepared by the "Alfin," emulsion, sodium, and stereospecific techniques differ in average isomer content. The percentages also vary within a given type, depending on temperature of polymerization and the other factors. For example, emulsion polybutadiene runs about 80% total cis and trans 1,4 addition; "Alfin" polymer is about 70%, sodium polymer only 25–30% (59, 23), and lithium or organotitanium polybutadiene approaches 100% 1,4-cis.

Copolymers of butadiene have shown more usefulness in technical applications. Thus important copolymers with styrene, acrylonitrile, and isobutylene have been developed.

Copolymers of styrene with butadiene were the basis of the synthetic rubbers made in large amounts during World War II. They were prepared using the so-called "Mutual," or "**GR-S**" recipe, which was chosen for its simplicity and reproducibility.

174. Preparation of GR-S Rubber (5)

$$CH_2{=}CH{-}CH{=}CH_2 + \phi CH{=}CH_2 \longrightarrow Copolymer$$

Table 4.2 gives a recipe for "Mutual" or "GR-S" rubber in its simplest form.

TABLE 4.2

Constituent	Quantity, parts
Butadiene	75
Styrene	25
Commercial dodecyl mercaptan	0.5
Potassium persulfate	0.3
Soap flakes	5
Water (freshly boiled)	180

The mixture given in Table 4.2 is polymerized at 50°C. The conversion is approximately 6% per hour, and the polymerization is ordinarily short-stopped after about 75% conversion, that is, after about 12 hr. of polymerization.

Polymerization may be carried out in 4 oz. screw cap bottles mechanically tumbled end-over-end in a constant temperature bath. Bottles larger than 4 oz. should not be used since the reaction is exothermic and might get out of control if the heat cannot be dissipated rapidly. It should be borne in mind that all traces of air must be kept out of the system. That is, the water used should be boiled to deaerate it, while the reaction vessel should be flushed by allowing a small amount of the butadiene to boil out before capping.

After approximately 12 hr., the polymerization is short-stopped by adding 0.1% hydroquinone and the polymer latex so obtained is poured into a beaker of suitable size, and steam is passed through it to remove unreacted butadiene and styrene. To this stripped latex is now added an antioxidant such as phenyl-β-naphthylamine and the latex is coagulated. This may be done by first adding sodium chloride solution which causes partial coagulation ("creaming") of the mixture. Coagulation is then completed by the addition of dilute sulfuric acid which converts the dispersing salts to the free acids. The product is obtained in the form of crumbs, which are filtered, washed well with water, and dried.

Copolymers of butadiene and acrylonitrile achieved considerable importance in Germany as the oil resistant Buna-N, and later in the United States under a variety of names. The following procedure is typical.

175. Preparation of Nitrile Rubber (18)

$$CH_2{=}CHCN + CH_2{=}CH{-}CH{=}CH_2 \longrightarrow Copolymer$$

A recipe very similar to the GR-S recipe for styrene butadiene is quite satisfactory for the preparation of a nitrile rubber. The following ingredients (Table 4.3) are handled essentially in the manner described in Preparation 175.

TABLE 4.3

Constituent	Quality, parts
Butadiene	75
Acrylonitrile	25
Soap flakes	4.5
Stearic acid	0.6
tert-dodecyl mercaptan	0.5
Potassium chloride	0.3
Sodium pyrophosphate	0.1
Ferric sulfate (anhydrous basis)	0.02
Hydrogen peroxide (20% solution) (anhydrous basis)	0.35
Water (freshly distilled)	180

The mixture given in Table 4.3 may be polymerized in vessels such as described in the previous preparations. The solutions are made up in the following manner. The soap and stearic acid are dissolved in about 50 parts of water at 50°C. The sodium pyrophosphate, potassium chloride, and ferric sulfate are dissolved in about 5 parts of water. The excess water is first placed in the reactor followed by the soap solution, the ferric pyrophosphate solution, the acrylonitrile, the mercaptan, the butadiene, and finally, the hydrogen peroxide. The reactor is sealed and maintained with mild agitation at a temperature of 30°C. About 90% conversion is obtained in 24 hr. As in the previous preparations, the latex is discharged, steamed to boil off excess monomer, and stabilized by adding 2 parts of phenyl-β-naphthylamine antioxidant. The latex is coagulated by the addition of 0.5 parts of sodium alkyl benzene sulfonate, followed by 40 parts of saturated sodium chloride solution. The mixture is then acidified with dilute sulfuric acid to precipitate the polymer. It is washed repeatedly with water and dried at 60°C. It may be pressed into sheets by passing through a rubber mill.

The relative proportion of acrylonitrile is important in determining the properties of the resulting nitrile rubber. At 5% or below, the polymer will swell badly in the presence of oil. At 15% acrylonitrile, the resistance to oil is fair, at 25% it is fairly good, while at 35–40% the resistance to oil is very high. If the per cent of acrylonitrile is increased to 50–60%, the nature of the polymer will change. It is no longer the rubber-like material; it becomes a leathery plastic which has very high resistance to aromatics. As the percentage of acrylonitrile is increased beyond the 60% range, the properties approach those of pure polyacrylonitrile

Like butadiene, **isoprene** may be polymerized by a variety of techniques. High molecular weight polyisoprene has been obtained in a typical emulsion polymerization at 50°C., with metallic sodium, and with the organometallic catalysts described for polymerization of butadiene. Since natural rubber is a polyisoprene, it is not surprising that chemists have directed their attention to the synthesis of polyisoprene of the same chemical configuration as the natural product. The two principle types of naturally occurring polyisoprene are Hevea, which is about 97.8% cis-1,4 and 2.2% of 3,4-polyisoprene, and Balata, which is about 98.7% trans-1,4 and about 1.3% 3,4-polyisoprene. The synthetic polyisoprenes made in an emulsion system have approximately 12–14% of 1,2 product, while those made with sodium have between 50 and 55% 1,2 addition, the remainder being mainly trans-1,4 addition product, with some cis. It has been found that polymerization of isoprene with organotitanium compounds, with lithium alkyls, or with lithium aluminum alkyls produces a polyisoprene which is essentially identical to the cis-1,4-polyisoprene of Hevea rubber. Furthermore, although metallic sodium in a finely divided condition gives a product containing very large percentages of 1,2 addition, it has been found that finely divided lithium metal will give essentially the same results as the organometallic derivatives. The following preparations are typical of the polymerization of isoprene with this type of catalyst. In all these polymerizations it must be recognized that success depends on a number of factors, the most important of which is purity of the monomer and absence of contaminants such as moisture or air in the system.

176. Preparation of the Catalysts

The organotitanium type catalyst is prepared as described in the previous section on coordination catalysis (Section VIII). The butyl lithium may be purchased as a commercial product dissolved in pentane, or synthesized. Finely divided metallic lithium may also be obtained commercially (Chemical Appendix) and is much more satisfactory than any product which may be made in the laboratory with ordinary equipment.

177. Polymerization of Isoprene with n-Butyl Lithium (73,74)

$$CH_2{=}CH{-}\underset{\displaystyle |}{\overset{\displaystyle CH_3}{C}}{=}CH_2 \longrightarrow (C_5H_8)_n$$

The butyl lithium solution is standardized by hydrolysis and titration of lithium hydroxide with standard acid. The concentration is adjusted with n-pentane to 1.0 molar. The polymerization is carried out very simply by adding 84 ml. of pure isoprene, 180 ml. of petroleum ether, or n-pentane, and 3.0 ml. of the butyl lithium solution to a round bottomed flask which should be dried thoroughly and flushed with an inert gas, preferably helium or argon. All transfers should be made under absolutely anaerobic and anhydrous conditions.

The flask is stoppered and placed in a water bath at 30°C. Polymerization time is approximately 18 hr. At the end of this period, the flask is removed from the water bath and the contents poured into methyl alcohol which contains about 3% based on weight of polymer of an antioxidant such as phenyl-β-naphthylamine. The polymer is coagulated, filtered, washed thoroughly with methyl alcohol, and dried in a vacuum at 50°C. Polymer made in this way is approximately 77.4% cis-1,4, 13.0% trans-1,4, and about 9.5% 3,4.

178. Polymerization of Isoprene over Finely Divided Lithium (175

$$CH_2{=}CH{-}\overset{\overset{\displaystyle CH_3}{|}}{C}{=}CH_2 \longrightarrow (C_5H_8)_n$$

Polymerization of isoprene over finely divided lithium is most conveniently carried out in the laboratory according to the following technique. To purify isoprene, it is refluxed over metallic sodium for 4 hr., then distilled, passed through a silica column, and used immediately. It is kept out of contact with air or moisture. The silica column should be freed of air before use by passing a stream of oxygen-free helium through the column. Absolutely dry glass bottles sealed with aluminum-lined crown caps are charged with 100 ml. of isoprene. To the isoprene contained in the crown-capped bottles is added 0.1 g. of lithium as a 35% dispersion in vaseline or petroleum oil. The cap is placed on the bottle loosely and the bottle and contents are brought to a vigorous boil. Approximately 10% of the total isoprene is allowed to boil out in order to completely free the reaction vessel of traces of oxygen and moisture. The bottle is now rapidly sealed and placed in a constant temperature bath at 30–40°C. It is allowed to remain at this temperature either agitated or unagitated until the content have been converted to a solid chunk of polymer. This may require 30 min. to 3 days, depending on the purity of the ingredients. The unagitated polymerization is somewhat slower. However, it is also safer, since polymerization is exothermic and may become dangerous if not properly controlled.

When polymerization is deemed to be complete, the cooled bottle is broken and the solid chunk of polymer is removed and soaked in isopropanol containing a trace of acetic acid to remove the catalyst and a small amount of a suitable antioxidant such as phenyl-β-naphthylamine. Infrared examination of the polymer should indicate that it is of the order of 98% cis-1,4 structure, the remainder being 3,4. The product may be milled and compounded exactly as is natural rubber.

179. Polymerization of Isoprene over a Titanium-Based Catalyst (19,38a,90)

$$CH_2{=}CH{-}\overset{\overset{\displaystyle CH_3}{|}}{C}{=}CH_2 \longrightarrow (C_5H_8)_n$$

Petroleum ether is purified by treating with concentrated sulfuric acid until no further discoloration is observed. It is then washed with water, dried by passing through an alumina column, and distilled from metallic sodium.   The isoprene is distilled, then refluxed immediately prior to use with sodium, and passed through a silica column as described in the previous preparation.   The catalyst is prepared by mixing equimolar quantities of triisobutyl aluminum (Chemical Appendix) and titanium tetrachloride.   In view of the hazardous nature of triisobutylaluminum, all possible care must be taken in handling this material and the experimenter should be completely familiar with all the safety hazards inherent in triisobutylaluminum.   If desired, lithium aluminum tetra-alkyls may be used advantageously in place of the triisobutyl aluminum (38a). It is convenient to prepare a 1 molar solution of this compound in anhydrous, olefin-free heptane to be used as needed.   All monomers, solvents, and catalyst components are kept absolutely free of moisture and air and are stored in an inert atmosphere.   The bottles are conveniently capped with a self-sealing stopper of the type used on serum bottles (see Chapter 2).   A measured amount may be removed by use of a hypodermic syringe.

A mixture of 75 ml. of petroleum ether and 25 ml. of isoprene is placed in a beverage bottle and heated to vigorous boiling in a hot water bath.   A quantity of petroleum ether is distilled from the bottle sufficiently to insure the absence of all moisture and air from the polymerization vessel.   Two ml. of the 1 molar triisobutyl aluminum is now added under inert atmosphere, and the bottles are stoppered with a serum-type rubber stopper through which can be inserted a hypodermic syringe.   Bottles containing the monomer plus alkyl aluminum are cooled to the desired polymerization temperature and an equivalent amount of titanium tetrachloride is added from a hypodermic syringe.   The titanium tetrachloride may be added either as undiluted catalyst or as a pre-mixed 1 molar solution in heptane.   Polymerization is quite rapid and the mixture of catalyst and monomer rapidly becomes sufficiently viscous to disperse the catalyst particles making stirring unnecessary.   However, stirring or shaking during the first part of the polymerization cycle is recommended.

Polymerization is allowed to proceed for approximately 24 hr. when the polymer is isolated and soaked in alcohol for 24 hr. to destroy the catalyst components.   It is then mixed with an antioxidant, milled, or otherwise treated as in previous experiments.

In order to obtain polymer with a low gel content in high yield with a high inherent viscosity, it is necessary to have the molar ratio of trialkyl aluminum to titanium tetrachloride at about 1:1.   It may be desirable to have a very slight excess of alkyl aluminum since this appears to minimize the production of gel.

The temperature at which the polymerization is run is also important in determining the molecular weight of the resulting polymer and, to a lesser extent, the micro-structure of the polymer.   Temperatures between 5 and 25°C. appear to be most suitable for this purpose.   Above about 25°C. the molecular weights obtained are too low to be useful.   Polymer prepared at 25°C. is approximately 96% cis-1,4 and 4% 3,4 polyisoprene.   No trans-1,4 structure is observed if the polymer is made according to the instructions previously given.

180. Copolymerization of Styrene and Isoprene in the Presence of Lithium or Butyllithium (104)

$$CH_2{=}CH{-}\underset{\underset{CH_3}{|}}{C}{=}CH_2 + C_6H_5CH{=}CH_2 \longrightarrow \text{Copolymer}$$

Lithium metal as a dispersion in mineral oil and butyl lithium as a solution in normal pentane are suitable for use as catalysts (Chemical Appendix). However, they should be standardized by decomposing an aliquot with alcohol or water and titrating the liberated alkali.

Polymerizations are carried out in 4 oz. bottles equipped with self-sealing rubber stoppers. The bottle is approximately half filled with a 60/40 weight mixture of styrene/isoprene (both monomers carefully purified prior to use). Polymerization is initiated by introduction of either 100 mg. of lithium dispersion or approximately 1–10 millimoles/m. of monomer of butyl lithium. The bottles are sealed and magnetically stirred in a bath at 25°C. Polymerization is allowed to proceed for several hours and the polymer is isolated by precipitation with methyl alcohol. The copolymer prepared in the absence of any diluent will contain approximately 15% styrene and 85% isoprene unit. It can be pressed to tough, clear, rubbery film.

All the uses for polyisobutylene itself are somewhat limited by the fact that it is, even at high molecular weight, a relatively soft, plastic material. It was found by workers at Standard Oil (New Jersey) that **copolymerization of** a small amount of **a diene with isobutylene** gives a product which can be crosslinked (vulcanized) to a very useful product known as **butyl rubber** and used extensively in tires and inner tubes.

181. Preparation of an Isobutylene-Isoprene Copolymer by Cationic Catalysis (44,180)

$$CH_2{=}CH{-}\underset{\underset{CH_3}{|}}{C}{=}CH_2 + CH_2{=}\underset{\underset{CH_3}{\diagdown}}{\overset{\overset{CH_3}{\diagup}}{C}} \longrightarrow \text{Copolymer}$$

Pure isobutylene (100 ml.) and 1.5 ml. of pure isoprene are placed in a 1 l., three-necked flask equipped with a mechanical stirrer, a gas inlet tube, and a dry ice condenser. Approximately 300 ml. of methyl chloride is now added from a cylinder and the mixture is cooled to about −100°C. by means of a sludge of alcohol in liquid nitrogen. The solution of isobutylene and isoprene is stirred gently and successive 1 ml. portions of a solution of 0.2 g. of anhydrous aluminum chloride in 40 ml. of methyl chloride are added. As each portion is poured into the solution, an insoluble mass of copolymer is produced which floats in the cold solution. Catalyst may be added until conversion of the isobutylene-isoprene to copolymer is about 50%. Higher conversions give improper monomer balance to the copolymer because of the different reactivity of the monomers. The polymerization mixture is quenched by the addition of a small amount of isopropyl alcohol previously cooled to $-100°C.$ and the mixture is then allowed to warm to room temperature. The lumps of rubbery copolymer are removed, washed with alcohol, dried in a vacuum oven, and converted to sheet products by conventional techniques.

Chloroprene ($CH_2 = \overset{\overset{\displaystyle Cl}{\displaystyle |}}{C} - CH = CH_2$) is a monomer which duplicates in many ways the over-all geometry of isoprene; however, the polymer differs in many respects. This monomer is the basis for the neoprenes which have been successfully commercialized by the du Pont Co. in a variety of forms.

Chloroprene is synthesized by addition of hydrogen chloride to monovinyl acetylene. The vinyl acetylene is prepared by dimerization of acetylene, **an operation which is not recommended for anyone not familiar with the hazards of acetylene chemistry,** or by the dehydrohalogenation of 1,4-dichloro-2-butene (82). Chloroprene itself is relatively stable, and may be obtained commercially as a 50% solution in toluene. When pure, it will polymerize spontaneously in about 10 days to a high molecular weight, clear, tough product, the so-called "μ" polymer described by Carothers and co-workers (48). Polychloroprene shows a typical crystalline x-ray fiber diagram when stretched, and is essentially 100% trans-1,4 polymer.

182. Preparation of Chloroprene

$$CH_2 = CH - C \equiv CH + HCl \longrightarrow CH_2 = CH - CCl = CH_2$$

Vinylacetylene may be prepared in a number of ways. The most satisfactory method commercially is the oxidation of acetylene by cuprous salt (144). In the laboratory it may be prepared by the method of Willstatter and Wirth (194), or better from 1,4-dichlorobutene (82). It is a dangerous substance, and should be handled with care.

For the conversion of vinylacetylene to chloroprene, approximately 50 g. is distilled under nitrogen and maintained in an ice-salt bath. In a pressure bottle is placed 175 g. of concentrated hydrochloric acid, 25 g. cuprous chloride, and 10 g. of ammonium chloride. This bottle is cooled to below $0°C.$ and the cold vinyl acetylene is added. The pressure bottle is sealed and the bottle and contents placed in a water bath maintained at about $30°C.$ where it is shaken for several hours. The contents of the bottle are then placed in a separatory funnel and the lower aqueous phase is drawn off. The upper organic phase is washed with water and dried with calcium chloride and a small amount of an antioxidant such as pyrogallol or hydroquinone is added. It is now distilled in a vacuum through an efficient column with a low temperature head, cooled by circulating ice-salt water. The b.p. at 100 mm. pressure is 6.4 °C. This diene is a very reactive material and should be converted to polymer according to the following techniques immediately upon distillation. **Never try to polymerize chloroprene with an organotitanium catalyst, a violent explosion may result.**

183. Polymerization of Chloroprene (48)

$$CH_2{=}CH{-}\overset{\displaystyle Cl}{\underset{\displaystyle |}{C}}{=}CH_2 \longrightarrow [{-}CH_2{-}CH{=}\overset{\displaystyle Cl}{\underset{\displaystyle |}{C}}{-}CH_2{-}]_n$$

Chloroprene will polymerize under a variety of conditions to high molecular weight materials. Several different types of polymer have been described by Carothers in his original paper. The high molecular weight material which is known as the "μ" polymer is obtained in the following manner. About 40 ml. of chloroprene is placed in a 50 ml. bottle, closed with a cork stopper or a screw cap and allowed to stand at room temperature in the absence of direct light. Spontaneous polymerization begins almost at once and after 24 hr. the viscosity of the sample has increased considerably. After 4 days a stiff, colorless jelly plasticized by much unchanged chloroprene will be observed. After 10 days, polymerization has caused the jelly to contract somewhat in volume and to become tough and dense. The product is a colorless, or slightly yellow, transparent elastic material resembling a vulcanized soft rubber.

184. Polymerization of Chloroprene in an Emulsion (185)

$$CH_2{=}CH{-}\overset{\displaystyle Cl}{\underset{\displaystyle |}{C}}{=}CH_2 \longrightarrow [{-}CH_2{-}CH{=}\overset{\displaystyle Cl}{\underset{\displaystyle |}{C}}{-}CH_2{-}]_n$$

Emulsion polymerization of chloroprene may be carried out satisfactorily according to the following procedure. One hundred g. of freshly distilled chloroprene is emulsified in 150 ml. of water containing 4 g. of wood resin, 0.6 g. of sulfur, 0.8 g. of sodium hydroxide, 0.5 g. of potassium persulfate and 0.7 g. of the sodium salts of naphthalene sulfonic acid–formaldehyde condensation product, or other emulsifier. The progress of the polymerization is followed by means of specific gravity changes (27). The density of the emulsion increases with time and polymerization may be considered complete when the specific gravity is between 1.068 and 1.070. The polymer now may be precipitated by acidification with 2 ml. of dilute acetic acid or the emulsion may be allowed to age in the presence of tetraethylthiuram disulfide. During this ageing period, the polymer properties will improve to a more desirable level as a result of the action of the disulfide on sulfur linkages in the polymer (129), yielding a more soluble, plastic product. The coagulated polymer prepared by either method is filtered, washed thoroughly with water, and air dried at 120 °C. The polymer is then compounded for the specific purpose for which it is desired.

Finally, an interesting diene polymer which is a hard, tough, material and not an elastomer, is prepared by persulfate initiated polymerization of **2,3-dichlorobutadiene.** This polymer may be made by the methods described by Kuhn who has defined specialized conditions claimed to be necessary to produce a polymer which can be molded and shaped.

185. Preparation of 1,2,3,4-Tetrachlorobutane (93)

$$CH_2{=}CH{-}CH{=}CH_2 + 2Cl_2 \longrightarrow CH_2ClCHClCHClCH_2Cl$$

In a 2 l., three-necked flask equipped with a stirrer, a gas inlet tube, and a condenser is placed 600 ml. of chloroform. Butadiene (54 g.) and chlorine (140 g.) are passed into the chloroform from cylinders over a period of 45 min. The reaction vessel is maintained at a low temperature by means of an ice-salt bath. When all of the chlorine and butadiene is introduced, the resulting solution is fractionally distilled at atmospheric pressure. The fraction coming over between 209 and 220°C. is taken as 1,2,3,4-tetrachlorobutane of sufficient purity for the next stage.

186. Preparation of 2,3-Dichlorobutadiene-1,3 (93)

$$ClCH_2CHClCHClCH_2Cl \xrightarrow{\text{KOH}} {=}CClCCl{=}CH_2$$

Ninety-four g. of tetrachlorobutane prepared as above is dissolved in 32 g. of methanol. This mixture is introduced with agitation into 219 g. of 27% potassium hydroxide in methanol. This addition is carried out with the temperature being maintained at 10–15°C. throughout. Approximately 1 hr. should be required. The temperature is now allowed to rise to 25°C. and stirring is continued for an additional 2 hr. The reaction mass is then filtered and the filtrate is poured into 4 l. of distilled water. A lemon-colored oil separates which is removed and dried over calcium chloride, best in the presence of an inhibitor such as hydroquinone. When dried, the product is distilled at a pressure of approximately 80 mm., the product boiling in the range of 45–50°C. The monomer polymerizes very readily and should not be stored for any length of time. It should be used directly in one of the following recipes, after an additional distillation.

187. Polymerization of 2,3-Dichlorobutadiene (93)

$$CH_2{=}CClCCl{=}CH_2 \longrightarrow [{-}CH_2CCl{=}CCl{-}CH_2{-}]_n$$

A mixture of 330 ml. of freshly boiled distilled water, 100 g. of dichlorobutadiene, 1 g. of alkyl sodium sulfonate detergent, 0.02 g. of potassium persulfate, and 0.02 g. of thiophenol is sealed in a bottle under anaerobic conditions and agitated at 30–40°C. for 24–48 hr. The resulting polymer latex is coagulated by the addition of methyl alcohol and the precipitate is filtered, washed with water, and dried. This polymer should have an inherent viscosity of approximately 1.0 measured on a 0.5% solution in o-dichlorobenzene at 110°C.

The polymer can be extruded at temperatures of the order of 200–250°C. into filaments or may be pressed to clear, tough film. Both film and fibers can be stretched and oriented; the resulting products have a high crystallinity.

188. Thermal Polymerization of Dichlorobutadiene (93)

$$CH_2=CClCCl=CH_2 \longrightarrow [-CH_2-CCl=CCl-CH_2-]_n$$

A mixture of 120 g. of dichlorobutadiene and 0.2 g. of thiophenol is placed in a bottle which is then flushed with nitrogen and sealed. The mixture is agitated at 25°C. for 3 days. The resin is removed from the bottle and found to have an inherent viscosity of about 0.5 (0.5% in o-dichlorobenzene at 110°C.). This material is suitable for extrusion to fiber and molding to film and bars.

Although the double bond in the polymer chain of polydichlorobutadiene is relatively inert, it can cause difficulty in molding or spinning by crosslinking. **After-chlorination** of the double bond in the polymer is claimed to minimize this difficulty, at the same time increasing the solubility of the polymer.

189. Polymerization of Dichlorobutadiene Followed by Chlorination of Product (93)

$$[-CH_2CCl=CCl-CH_2-]_n \xrightarrow{Cl_2} [-CH_2-CCl_2-CCl_2-CH_2-]_n$$

Twenty-five g. of 2,3-dichlorobutadiene and 55 g. of methyl alcohol are mixed and the solution is refluxed for 3 hr. The precipitated polymer is recovered by filtration from the cooled solution and then dissolved in chloroform. Chlorine is passed from a cylinder through the chloroform solution for about 5 min. at 20°C. After this period, air is promptly blown through the solution to sweep out the unreacted chlorine. The chloroform in which the polymer is dissolved is then distilled, leaving a clear resin which melts at approximately 140°C.

This material is suitable for conversion to clear, tough films and fibers. For example, a portion of polymer weighing 2 g. is fused in a press at 150°C. between sheets of aluminum foil. The film prepared in this manner, which is approximately 0.01 in. in thickness, is removed from the press and quenched rapidly in cold water. The polymer sheet or film so produced is simultaneously pulled from all four sides to extend the area approximately 500%. The foil so produced, which is highly crystalline, is very flexible and transparent. It should have a tensile strength of between 10–15,000 p.s.i.

REFERENCES

The following references are books which treat the polymerization of vinyl compounds in a broader sense than in this chapter:

1. Alfrey, T., Jr., J. J. Bohrer, and H. Mark, *Copolymerization*, Interscience Publishers, New York, 1952.

2. Bamford, C. H., W. G. Barb, A. D. Jenkins, and P. F. Onyon, *The Kinetics of Vinyl Polymerization by Radical Mechanisms*, Academic Press, New York, 1958.
3. Billmeyer, F. W., *Textbook of Polymer Chemistry*, Interscience Publishers New York, 1957.
4. Boundy, R. H., and R. F. Boyer, editors, *Styrene, Its Polymers, Copolymers and Derivatives*, Reinhold, New York, 1952.
5. Bovey, F. A., I. M. Kolthoff, A. I. Medalia, and E. J. Meehan, *Emulsion Polymerization*, Interscience Publishers, New York, 1955.
6. Flory, P. J., *Principles of Polymer Chemistry*, Cornell University Press, Ithaca, N.Y., 1953.
7. Gaylord, N. G., and H. Mark, *Linear and Stereospecific Addition Polymers*, Interscience, New York, 1959.
8. Kainer, F., *Polyvinylchloride und Vinylchloride Mischpolymerisate*, Springer-Verlag, Berlin, 1951.
9. Krczil, F., *Kurzes Handbuch der Polymerisations-Technik*, Leipzig, Akademische verlagsgesellschaft, Becker and Erler, 1940–41.
10. Marchionna, F., *Butalastic Polymers*, Reinhold, New York, 1946.
11. Mark, H., ed., *Collected Papers of Wallace H. Carothers on High Polymeric Substances*, Interscience Publishers, New York, 1940.
12. Plesch, P. A., *Cationic Polymerization and Related Complexes*, Academic Press, New York, 1954.
13. Raff, R. A. V., and J. B. Alison, *Polyethylene*, Interscience Publishers, New York, 1956.
14. Renfrew, A., *Polyethylene: The Technology and Uses of Ethylene Polymers*, Interscience, New York, 1957.
15. Schildknecht, C. E., *Polymer Processes*, Interscience, New York, 1956.
16. Schildknecht, C. E., *Vinyl and Related Polymers*, Wiley, New York, 1952.
17. Staudinger, H., *Die Hochmolekularen Organischenverbindvngen*, Springer-Verlag, Berlin, 1932.
18. Whitby, G. S., ed., *Synthetic Rubber*, Wiley, New York, 1954.

The remaining references are of a more specific nature.
19. Adams, H. E., R. S. Stearns, W. A. Smith, and J. L. Binder, *Ind. Eng. Chem.*, **50,** 1507 (1958).
20. Alderman, V. U., and W. E. Hanford, U.S. Pat. 2,348,705 (May 16, 1944).
20a. American Cyanamide Co., New Products Bulletin, Coll. Vol. III.
21. Anderson, A., et al., U.S. Pat. 2,721,189 (Oct. 18, 1955).
22. Anderson, A. W., N. G. Merckling, and P. H. Settlage, U.S. Pat. 2,799,668 (July 16, 1957).
23. Ardis, A. E., U.S. Pat. 2,615,865 (Oct. 28, 1952).
24. Ardis, A. E., S. T. Averill, H. Gilbert, F. F. Miller, R. F. Schmidt, F. D. Stewart, and H. L. Trumball, *J. Am. Chem. Soc.*, **72,** 1305 (1950).
25. Arnold, H. W., M. M. Brubaker, and G. L. Dorough, U.S. Pat. 2,301,356 (Nov. 10, 1942).
26. Barb, W. G., *J. Am. Chem. Soc.*, **75,** 224 (1953).

27. Barrows, R. S., and Scott, G. W., *Ind. Eng. Chem.*, **40,** 2193 (1948).
28. Baxter, W. N., U.S. Pat. 2,842,531 (July 8, 1959).
29. Beaman, R. G., private communication.
30. Beaman, R. G., *J. Am. Chem. Soc.*, **70,** 3115 (1948).
31. Beasley, J. K., *J. Am. Chem. Soc.*, **75,** 6123 (1953).
32. Billmeyer, F. W., Jr., *J. Am. Chem. Soc.*, **75,** 6118 (1953).
33. BIOS Report, PB 19269.
34. British Pat. 505,120 (May 5, 1939).
35. British Pat. 570,711 (July 19, 1945).
36. British Pat. 741,236 (Nov. 30, 1955).
37. British Pat. 741,238 (Nov. 30, 1955).
38. British Pat. 741,239 (Nov. 30, 1955).
38a. British Pat. 776,326 (June 5, 1957).
39. British Pat. 777,538 (June 26, 1957).
40. British Pat. 786,960 (Nov. 27, 1957).
41. Brody, H., M. Ladacki, R. Milkovitch, and M. Szwarc, *J. Polymer Sci.*, **25,** 221 (1957).
42. Bryant, W. M. D., and R. C. Voter, *J. Am. Chem. Soc.*, **75,** 6113 (1953).
43. Butler, G. B., and R. J. Angelo, *J. Am. Chem. Soc.*, **79,** 3128 (1957).
44. Calfie, J. D., et al., U.S. Pat. 2,431,461 (Nov. 25, 1947).
45. Campbell, T. W., U.S. Pat. 2,842,532 (July 8, 1958).
46. Campbell, T. W., Italian Pat. 579,572 (July 16, 1958).
47. Campbell, T. W., and A. C. Haven, Jr., *J. Applied Poly. Sci.*, **1,** 79 (1959).
48. Carothers, W. H., I. Williams, A. M. Collins, and J. E. Kirby, *J. Am. Chem. Soc.*, **53,** 4203 (1931).
49. Coffman, D. D., U.S. Pat. 2,326,287 (Aug. 10, 1943).
50. Coffman, D. D., U.S. Pat. 2,334,476 (Nov. 16, 1943).
51. Coffman, D. D., and T. A. Ford, U.S. Pat. 2,419,008 (April 15, 1947).
52. Coffman, D. D., and T. A. Ford, U.S. Pat. 2,419,009 (April 15, 1947).
53. Coffman, D. D., and T. A. Ford, U.S. Pat. 2,419,010 (April 15, 1947).
54. Conaway, R. F., U.S. Pat. 2,008,577 (Aug. 3, 1937).
55. Cotman, J. D., Jr., *J. Am. Chem. Soc.*, **77,** 2791 (1955).
56. Crawford, J. W. C., *J. Soc. Chem. Ind.* (Trans.), **68,** 201 (1949).
57. Dainton, F. S., and K. J., Ivin, *Proc. Roy. Soc.* (*London*) A212, **66,** (1952).
58. Dangelmajer, C., U.S. Pat. 2,246,915 (June 24, 1941).
59. D'Ianni, J. D., *Ind. Eng. Chem.*, **40,** 253 (1948).
60. Dorough, G. L., U.S. Pat. 2,384,239 (Sept. 4, 1945).
61. Dow Chemical Company, Product Bulletin, *Handling Precautions for Vinylidene Chloride Monomer.*
62. Dow Chemical Company, Product Bulletin, *The Polymerization of Styrene.*
63. Elotson, R. M., and G. D. Jones, *J. Am. Chem. Soc.*, **76,** 210 (1950).
64. Evans, E. F., A. Goodman, and L. D. Grandine, private communication.
65. Fawcett, E. W., R. O. Gibson, and M. W. Perrin, U.S. Pat. 2,153,553 (April 11, 1939).
66. FIAT Report, PB 44674.
67. Field, N. D., private communication.
68. Fikentscher, H., and K. Herrle, *Modern Plastics*, **23,** 157 (1945).

69. Flory, P. J., *J. Am. Chem. Soc.*, **61,** 1518 (1939).
70. Forster, M. O., and S. H. Newman, *J. Chem. Soc.*, **97,** 2570 (1910).
71. Frazer, A. H., private communication.
72. French Pat. 922,429 (July 9, 1947).
73. German Pat. 1,040,795 (Oct. 9, 1958).
74. German Pat. 1,040,796 (Oct. 9, 1958).
75. Gilbert, H., and F. F. Miller, U.S. Pat. 2,615,867 (Oct. 28, 1952).
76. Gilman, H. and B. McGlumphey, *Bull. Soc. chim. Belg.*, **43,** 1326 (1928).
77. Glavis, F. J., L. L. Ryden, and C. S. Marvel, *J. Am. Chem. Soc.*, **59,** 707 (1937).
78. Hall, L. A. R., W. J. Belanger, W. Kirk, Jr., and Y. Sundstrom, *J. Applied Poly. Sci.*, **2,** 246 (1959).
79. Hanford, W. L., U.S. Pat. 2,396,785 (March 19, 1946).
80. Hanson, A. W., and W. C. Goggins, U.S. Pat. 2,238,020 (April 15, 1941).
81. Hedrick, R. M., U.S. Pat. 2,653,973 (Sept. 29, 1953).
82. Hennion, G. F., C. C. Price, and T. F. McKeon, Jr., *Org. Syn.*, **1958,** 70.
83. Herrmann, W. O., and W. Haehnel, *Ber.*, **60,** 1658 (1927).
84. Herrmann, W. O., and W. Haehnel, U.S. Pat. 1,672,156 (June 5, 1928).
85. Herrmann, W. O., and W. Haehnel, U.S. Pat. 2,109,883 (May 1, 1938).
86. Hersberger, A. B., J. C. Reid, and R. G. Heiligmann, *Ind. Eng. Chem.*, **37,** 1075 (1945).
87. Heuer, W., German Pat. 724,889 (Sept. 9, 1942).
88. Hiltner, J. R., and W. F. Bartoe, U.S. Pat. 2,264,376 (Dec. 2, 1941).
89. Horne, S. E., J. P. Kiehl, J. J. Shipman, V. L. Folt, E. A. Wilson, and M. A. Reinhart, 68th Meeting of the Division of Rubber Chemistry of the American Chemical Society, Philadelphia, Nov. 3, 1955.
90. Horne, S. E., J. P. Kiehl, J. J. Shipman, V. L. Folt, C. F. Gibbs, E. A. Wilson, E. B. Newton, and M. A. Reinhart, *Ind. Eng. Chem.*, **48,** 784 (1956).
91. Houtz, R. C., U.S. Pat. 2,341,553, (Feb. 15, 1944).
92. Houtz, R. C., U.S. Pat. 2,388,325 (Nov. 6, 1945).
92a. Houtz, R. C., Textile Research J., **20,** 796 (1950).
93. Hunt, L. B., Canadian Pat. 525,592 (May 29, 1956).
94. Hunt, M., U.S. Pat. 2,471,959 (May 31, 1949).
95. Hunt, M., and C. S. Marvel, *J. Am. Chem. Soc.*, **57,** 1691 (1935).
96. Iwakura, Y., et al., *Chem. of High Polymers* (Japan), **13,** 390 (1956).
97. Jenckel, E., H. Eckmanns-Mettegang, and B. Rumbach, *Makromol. Chem.*, **4,** 15 (1949).
98. Johnson, J. E., R. H. Blizzard, and H. W. Carhart, *J. Am. Chem. Soc.*, **70,** 3664 (1948).
99. Jones, G. D., *J. Org. Chem.*, **9,** 500 (1944).
100. Jones, G. D., and C. E. Barnes, U.S. Pat. 2,515,714 (July 18, 1950).
101. Jones, J. F., *J. Poly. Sci.*, **33,** 7, 15, 513 (1958).
102. Joyce, R. M., U.S. Pat. 2,394,243 (Feb. 5, 1946).
103. Jung, S. L., private communication.
104. Kelly, D. J., and A. V. Tobolsky, *J. Am. Chem. Soc.*, **81,** 1587 (1959).

105. Kolthoff, I. M., and W. J. Dale, *J. Am. Chem. Soc.*, **69,** 442 (1947).
106. Kranzlein, G., and H. Reis, Ger. Pat. 765,265 (Jan. 1, 1954).
107. Kropa, E. L., U.S. Pat. 2,446,049 (July 27, 1948).
108. Kung, F. E., U.S. Pat. 2,377,085 (May 29, 1945).
109. Land, E. A., and C. D. West, *Colloid Chemistry*, vol. 6, Reinhold, New York, 1946, p. 160.
109a. Larchar, A. W., and D. C. Pease, U.S. Pat. 2,816,883 (Dec. 17, 1957).
110. Lichty, J. G., U.S. Pat. 2,231,838 (Feb. 11, 1941).
111. Marks, B. M., U.S. 2,383,069 (Aug. 21, 1945).
112. Marvel, C. S., W. J. Bailey, and G. E. Inskeep, *J. Polymer Sci.*, **1,** 275 (1946).
113. Marvel, C. S., and J. C. Cowan, *J. Am. Chem. Soc.*, **61,** 3156 (1939).
114. Marvel, C. S., R. Deanin, C. G. Overberger, and B. M. Kuhn, *J. Poly. Sci.*, **3,** 128 (1948).
115. Marvel, C. S., J. Dec, H. G. Cooke, Jr., and J. C. Cowan, *J. Am. Chem. Soc.*, **62,** 3495 (1940).
116. Marvel, C. S., and C. L. Levesque, *J. Am. Chem. Soc.*, **61,** 3244 (1939).
117. Marvel, C. S., J. H. Sample, and Max F. Roy, *J. Am. Chem. Soc.*, **61,** 3241 (1939).
118. Marvel, C. S., and R. D. Vest, *J. Am. Chem. Soc.*, **79,** 5771 (1957).
119. Mast, W. C., and C. H. Fisher, *Ind. Eng. Chem.*, **41,** 790 (1949).
120. Mayo, F. R., and A. A. Miller, *J. Am. Chem. Soc.*, **78,** 1023 (1956).
121. Mayo, F. R., C. Walling, *Chem. Rev.*, **46,** 191 (1950).
122. McIntire, O. R., U.S. Pat. 2,515,250 (July 18, 1950).
123. Meyer, A. W., R. R. Hampton, J. A. Davison, *J. Am. Chem. Soc.*, **74,** 2295 (1952).
124. Miller, A. A., and F. R. Mayo, *J. Am. Chem. Soc.*, **78,** 1017 (1956).
125. Miller, H. F., and R. G. Flowers, U.S. Pat. 2,445,181 (July 13, 1948).
126. Minsk, L. M., W. J. Priest, and W. O. Kenyon, *J. Am. Chem. Soc.*, **63,** 2715 (1941).
127. Munters, G., and J. G. Tanberg, U.S. Pat. 2,023,204 (Dec. 3, 1935).
128. Mixer, R. Y., and D. L. Bailey, *J. Poly. Sci.*, **18,** 573 (1955).
129. Mochel, W. E., and J. H. Peterson, *J. Am. Chem. Soc.*, **71,** 1426 (1949).
130. Morton, A. A., *Ind. Eng. Chem.*, **42,** 1488 (1950).
131. Morton, A. A., F. H. Bolton, F. W. Collins, and E. F. Cluff, *Ind. Eng. Chem.*, **44,** 2876 (1952).
132. Morton, A. A., B. Darling, and J. Davidson, *Ind. Eng. Chem. Anal. Ed.*, **14,** 734 (1942).
133. Morton, A. A., D. M. Knott, *Ind. Eng. Chem. (Anal. Ed.)*, **13,** 649 (1941).
134. Morton, A. A., R. L. Letsinger, and E. E. Magat, *J. Am. Chem. Soc.*, **69,** 950 (1947).
135. Morway, A. J., and F. L. Miller, U.S. Pat. 2,243,470 (May 27, 1941).
136. Mowry, D. T., U.S. Pat. 2,417,607 (March 18, 1947).
137. Müller-Cunradi, M., and M. Otto, U.S. Pat. 2,203,873 (June 11, 1940).
138. Natta, G., *J. Poly. Sci.*, **16,** 143 (1955).
139. Natta, G., *Angew. Chem.*, **68,** 393 (1956).
140. Natta, G., G. Dall 'Asta., G. Mazzanti, U. Giannine, and S. Cesca, *Angew. Chem.*, **71,** 205 (1959).

141. Natta, G., P. Pino, P. Corradini, F. Danusso, E. Manteca, G. Mazzanti, and G. Moragli, *J. Am. Chem. Soc.*, **77,** 1708 (1955).
142. Newman, M. S., and R. W. Addor, *J. Am. Chem. Soc.*, **75,** 1263 (1953).
143. Newman, M. S., and R. W. Addor, *J. Am. Chem. Soc.*, **77,** 3789 (1955).
144. Nieuwland, J. A., W. S. Calcott, F. B. Downing, and A. S. Carter, *J. Am. Chem. Soc.*, **53,** 4197 (1931).
145. Nystrom, R. F., and W. G. Brown, *J. Am. Chem. Soc.*, **70,** 3739 (1948).
146. Overberger, C. G., D. E. Baldwin, and H. P. Gregor, *J. Am. Chem. Soc.*, **72,** 4864 (1950).
147. Plambeck, L., U.S. Pat. 2,462,422 (Feb. 22, 1949).
148. Plunkett, R. J., U.S. Pat. 2,230,654 (Feb. 4, 1941).
149. Pollach, M. A., U.S. Pat. 2,870,193 (Jan. 20, 1959).
150. Reding, F. P., *J. Poly. Sci.*, **21,** 547 (1956).
151. Reinhardt, R. C., *Chem. Eng. News*, **25,** 2136 (1947).
151a. Renfrow, W. B., Jr., and C. R. Hauser, *Org. Syn.*, coll. vol. II, Wiley, New York, 1943, p. 607.
152. Repp, W., E. Keysner, and E. Dorrer, U.S. 2,072,465 (March 2, 1937).
153. Reppe, W., and Curt Schuster, U.S. Pat. 2,265,450 (Dec. 9, 1941).
154. Roedel, M. J., *J. Am. Chem. Soc.*, **75,** 6110 (1953).
155. Rosenthal, F., U.S. Pat. 2,533,629 (Dec. 12, 1950).
156. Riiber, C. N., *Ber.*, **44,** 2392 (1911).
157. Ruff, O., and O. Bretschneider, *Z. anorg. allgem. Chem.*, **210,** 173 (1933).
158. Ryden, L. L., and C. S. Marvel, *J. Am. Chem. Soc.*, **57,** 2311 (1935).
159. Sargeant, D. E., U.S. 2,560,251 (July 10, 1951).
160. Schulz, R. C., *Makromol. Chem.*, **17,** 62 (1956).
161. Schulz, R. C., and W. Kern, *Makromol. Chem.*, **18/19,** 4–8 (1956).
162. Schildknecht, C. E., S. T. Gross, H. R. Davidson, J. M. Lambert, and A. O. Zoss, *Ind. Eng. Chem.*, **40,** 2104 (1948).
163. Schildknecht, C. E., A. O. Zoss, and C. McKinley, *Ind. Eng. Chem.*, **39,** 180 (1947).
164. Schoene, D. L., U.S. Pat. 2,474,808 (July 5, 1949).
165. Scholoffer, F., and O. Scherer, Ger. Pat. 677,071 (June 17, 1939).
165a. Schulz, R. C., P. Elyer, and W. Kern, *Chimia*, **13,** 235 (1959).
166. Schuster, C., R. Sauerbier, and H. Fikentscher, U.S. Pat. 2,335,454 (Nov. 30, 1943).
167. Scott, N. D., U.S. Pat. 2,181,771 (Nov. 28, 1939).
168. Scott, N. D., J. F. Walker, and V. L. Hansley, *J. Am. Chem. Soc.*, **58,** 2442 (1936).
169. Shashoua, V. E., private communication.
170. Shell Development Company, Report #S-9976, June 25, 1947.
171. Snyder, H. R., H. V. Anderson, and D. D. Hallad, *J. Am. Chem. Soc.*, **73,** 3258 (1951).
172. Sperati, C. A., W. A. Franta, and H. W. Starkweather, *J. Am. Chem. Soc.*, **75,** 6127 (1953).
173. Stamatoff, G. S., U.S. Pat. 2,400,957 (May 18, 1946).
174. Stavely, F. W., et al., The 68th Meeting of the Division of Rubber Chemistry of the American Chemical Society, Philadelphia, Nov. 3, 1955.

175. Stavely, F. W., et al., *Ind. Eng. Chem.*, **48,** 778 (1956).
176. Strain, D. E., R. G. Kennelly, and H. R. Dittmar, *Ind. Eng. Chem.*, **31,** 382 (1939).
177. Szwarc, M., *Nature*, **178,** 1168 (1956).
178. Szwarc, M., M. Levy, and R. Milkovich, *J. Am. Chem. Soc.*, **78,** 2656 (1956).
179. Thomas, R. M., U.S. Pat. 2,873,230 (Feb. 10, 1959).
180. Thomas, R. M., and W. J. Sparks, U.S. Pat. 2,356,128 (Aug. 22, 1944).
181. Ufer, H., U.S. Pat. 2,163,180 (June 20, 1939).
182. Vosburgh, W. G., private communication.
183. Voss, A., and E. Dickhaeuser, U.S. Pat. 2,047,398 (July 14, 1936).
184. Waack, R., A Rembaum, J. D. Coombes, and M. Szwarc, *J. Am. Chem. Soc.*, **79,** 2026 (1957).
185. Walker, H. W., and W. E. Mochel, *Proc. Second Rubber Tech. Conf.*, 69–78 (1948).
186. Walling, C., D. Seymour, and K. B. Wolfstirn, *J. Am. Chem. Soc.*, **70** 1544 (1948).
187. Werkema, T. E., U.S. Pat. 2,658,058 (Nov. 3, 1953).
188. Werntz, J. H., U.S. Pat. 2,497,705 (Feb. 14, 1950).
189. Wieland, H., and E. Sakellarios, *Ber.* **52,** 898 (1919).
190. Wiley, R. H., and J. Moffat, *J. Org. Chem.*, **22,** 995 (1957).
191. Wiley, R. M., U.S. Pat. 2,160,931 (June 6, 1939).
192. Wiley, R. M., U.S. Pat. 2,183,602 (Dec. 19, 1939).
193. Williams, J. L. R., J. Van Den Berghe, K. R. Dunham, and W. J. Dulmage, *J. Am. Chem. Soc.*, **79,** (1716 (1957).
194. Willstatter, R., and Wirth, T., *Ber.*, **46,** 535 (1913).
195. Wilson, D. L., U.S. Pat. 2,399,970 (May 11, 1946).
196. Worrall, B., and S. H. Pinner, *J. Polymer Sci.*, **34,** 229 (1959); *J. Appl. Polymer Sci.*, **2,** 122 (1959).
197. Ziegler, K., and H. Martin, *Makromol. Chem.*, **18/19,** 186 (1956).
198. Ziegler, K., E. Holzlcamp, H. Breil, and H. Martin, *Angew. Chem.*, **67,** 426, 541 (1955).

CHAPTER 5

Ring Opening Polymerizations

I. General Discussion

It is possible in many instances to go directly from a heterocyclic monomer to a linear high polymer by a process of ring opening polymerization. The polymers are condensation-type, although no small molecule is eliminated and no hydrogen transfer is involved. However, ring opening polymerizations may be catalyzed by reagents which typically polymerize vinyl monomers. Most of these are cationic and anionic. Only a few examples of free radical initiation have been reported, and these are not well illustrated.

Although there are many heterocycles which give polymer by ring-opening polymerization, only those which have given polymers fitting the conditions given in Chapter 1 will be considered.

II. Cyclic Amides

An interesting feature regarding ring-opening polymerization, in general, is the relationship between ring size and polymerizability. Caprolactam, a seven-membered ring, polymerizes readily at high temperatures with anionic initiators. Butyrolactam, a five-membered ring, polymerizes anionically also. However, *low* temperatures are required. Above 60–80°C., polymer will revert to monomer in the presence of the catalyst. In direct contrast, valerolactam, a six-membered ring, is configurationally so stable that no satisfactory method for polymerizing it is known. The relationship between polymerizability of cyclic amides and configurational strain in the ring has been studied extensively by H. K. Hall, Jr. (23–27), who has studied polycyclic and bridged monomers as well as the simpler systems. The reader is referred to his papers for a thorough treatment of the subject.

The anionic fast polymerization of caprolactam to 6-nylon

$$\text{(caprolactam ring structure)} \longrightarrow [\text{—NHCH}_2\text{CH}_2\text{CH}_2\text{CH}_2\text{CH}_2\text{CO—}]_n$$

goes very rapidly at elevated temperatures to a polymer with very high viscosity.   If this polymer is maintained at an elevated temperature, the viscosity drops and levels off at a much lower value.   Since degradation of the polymer chain does not appear to be a contributing factor, a change in the molecular weight distribution appears to be the most likely explanation and has been demonstrated recently (28).

190. Fast Polymerization of ε-Caprolactam to 6-Nylon with Anionic Catalyst (14,38)

$$\text{(caprolactam ring structure)} \longrightarrow [\text{—NH—CH}_2\text{CH}_2\text{CH}_2\text{CH}_2\text{CH}_2\overset{\displaystyle O}{\overset{\displaystyle \|}{\text{C}}}\text{—}]_n \longrightarrow$$

Caprolactam is purified before use by recrystallizing twice from cyclohexane. It is then stored in a vacuum desiccator at room temperature over phosphoric anhydride for 48 hr., preferably at pressures below 0.1 mm.   After this treatment, the water content should be below 0.15% as determined by Karl Fischer titration.

A suitable quantity of caprolactam, usually about 25 g., is melted under nitrogen in a polymer tube having a nitrogen capillary inlet, at temperatures of approximately 80–100°C.   To the molten caprolactam is added a quantity of sodium dispersion in xylene corresponding to 0.04–0.08% of sodium based on caprolactam.   The mixture of caprolactam and the sodium salt of caprolactam that results may be maintained in the molten condition for many hours without loss of activity.   In order to polymerize this mixture, it is brought to a temperature of 255–265°C. under nitrogen by a vapor bath as rapidly as possible. From the time of transfer to the high temperature vapor bath to the completion of polymerization will require approximately 5 min.   The course of the polymerization may be judged by observing the rate of rise of nitrogen bubbles issuing from a capillary in the bottom of the liquid.   As polymerization begins, the rate of rise will diminish abruptly and the liquid will take on the consistency of an extremely thick honey.   Polymerization will be complete after 6 min.

and the polymer should have an inherent viscosity of about 2.5 as measured in formic acid at 0.5% concentration.   If the polymer is maintained at the elevated temperature for longer than 6 min., the molecular weight distribution will alter and the viscosity will drop off.   It should level off at an inherent viscosity of about 1.0 after several hours.

This experiment may be carried out using other alkaline catalysts.   For example, lithium, potassium, lithium hydride, sodium hydride, or lithium aluminum hydride may be used in place of the sodium dispersion.   However, metallic sodium dispersion is the most convenient additive to carry out the reaction.

The polycaproamide or 6-nylon which is produced according to the above directions is obtained as a tough, horny plug with a melting point of about 215 °C.   It may be fabricated to a tough film by pressing in a laboratory press at temperatures in excess of 215 °C. or it may be extruded from a spinneret in the form of a filament.   Both filament and film may be stretched over a hot plate to give highly oriented crystalline products which are very tough.

The toughness of the polymer may be illustrated very dramatically by removing the capillary from the viscous mass of polymer after approximately 5 min. of polymerization time, and before cooling.   The viscous mass will be pulled up out of the hot zone and will cool rapidly.   It is possible to draw a long and very strong fiber directly on the tip of the capillary.

191. Polymerization of Caprolactam with Water Catalyst (29,30)

$$\begin{array}{c} \text{CH}_2\text{—CH}_2 \\ \text{CH}_2 \qquad\qquad \text{CH}_2 \\ | \qquad\qquad\quad | \\ \text{CH}_2 \qquad\qquad \text{C}{=}\text{O} \\ \diagdown \text{N} \diagup \\ \text{H} \end{array} \longrightarrow [\text{—NH—CH}_2\text{CH}_2\text{CH}_2\text{CH}_2\text{CH}_2\overset{\overset{\text{O}}{\|}}{\text{C}}\text{—}]_n \longrightarrow$$

The water catalyzed polymerization of caprolactam does not involve hydrolysis of the caprolactam to the amino acid followed by a typical polycondensation reaction.   The polymer grows by reaction of the chain end with additional cyclic monomer (30) in a manner similar to that noted below for the polymerization of carboanhydrides.

The polymerization of caprolactam is carried out in two stages as follows. In a polymer tube is placed 56 g. of purified caprolactam.   Purification of the caprolactam may best be carried out by recrystallization from cyclohexane. To the purified caprolactam is now added 1 ml. of water and the tube is sealed under nitrogen (see Chapter 2, Preparation 3).   The polymer tube is heated to 250 °C. and maintained at this temperature for about 6 hr.   The tube is now cooled, opened cautiously, and reheated under a stream of nitrogen to about 250–255 °C.   During the warm-up period, most of the water added as catalyst will be flushed out of the system.   The polymerization is allowed to proceed under nitrogen for about 2 hr.   At the end of this period the polymer is obtained as an extremely viscous melt which will cool to a tough, horny plug.

Continued heating of the melt will continue to raise the viscosity. In actual industrial practice, it is possible to obtain polymer of too high a melt viscosity for satisfactory fabrication. To obviate this difficulty, small amounts of acetic acid may be added to the original polymerization mixture, to act as a chain terminator, or molecular weight control agent.

It has been noted (5) that the polymerization of cyclic lactams such as butyrolactam and caprolactam is very effectively catalyzed by trace quantities of *N*-acyl lactams. The following experiment will illustrate the **effect of an acetyl lactam on the polymerization of caprolactam** itself.

192. Polymerization of Caprolactam Catalyzed by *N*-Acetyl Caprolactam

In a glass polymer tube is placed 25 g. of caprolactam which is then melted in a steam bath under nitrogen. To the molten caprolactam is added 0.6 g. of sodium hydride which is allowed to dissolve to give the *N*-sodio derivative. This mixture may be maintained at 139°C. in a boiling xylene vapor bath for several hours, but no polymer is produced. To the molten caprolactam containing the sodium derivative is now added 0.33 g. of *N*-acetyl caprolactam at 139°C. The tube is shaken to mix the contents which solidify rapidly. After 30 min. the tube is cooled and broken, the polymer is ground up in, for example, a Wiley mill. The ground product is extracted with hot water and dried to give high molecular weight 6-nylon in yields of the order of 80% and an inherent viscosity of the order of 1.0 as measured in *m*-cresol. Note that the polymerization described here is below the melting point of the polymer, hence on polymerization the caprolactam goes directly from the liquid to the solid polymeric state.

193. Low Temperature Polymerization of γ-Butyrolactam to 4-Nylon (23,24,26,40)

Five hundred g. of freshly distilled γ-butyrolactam is placed in a 1 l., three-necked round bottom flask under dry nitrogen. It is absolutely essential to protect the freshly distilled lactam from moisture, since it is extremely hygroscopic and the absorption of any moisture will interfere with the polymerization. The flask is heated by means of a heating mantle to approximately 80°C. when 5 g. of metallic potassium (**Danger**) weighed under dry hexane is then added over a period of about 1 hr. Approximately 100 ml. of monomer is now distilled from the flask under vacuum to remove byproducts of the reaction of the potassium with the pyrollidone. The flask, which now contains approximately 400 g. of lactam and several grams of catalytic potassium butyrolactam, is allowed to cool to room temperature, still under nitrogen and protected from moisture. Polymerization begins when the contents of the flask reach approximately 50°C. The flask is allowed to stand for 12 hr., then the polymer cake is removed and broken up. The polymer cake should be a solid lump which is very hard and difficult to break up. It is frequently necessary to use a hack saw to reduce the chunk into pieces that can be cut further to a size that will permit easy washing and eventual fabrication. (If the polymerization is less successful at this point, a monomer-polymer slurry will result, which can be filtered directly for recovery of monomer. This polymer, washed thoroughly with water and dried, may still have a high molecular weight for fabrication, but will be obtained in a diminished yield.) The washed polymer cake is dried in a vacuum at 70°C. The yield should be in the range of 300–320 g. The polymer should have an inherent viscosity measured in m-cresol (0.5% concentration) of 1.2–1.8. It is soluble in formic acid and very viscous solutions in this solvent can be cast to tough films or spun into fibers, according to the techniques described in Chapter 2. The polymer is quite crystalline and has a crystalline melting point of 265°C., a value close to 6–6 nylon.

III. N-Carboanhydrides of α-Amino Acids (2,15,16,18,34,59,62)

Many naturally occurring fibers (e.g., wool) are poly-peptides, i.e., polyamides based on naturally occurring amino acids. The synthesis of high molecular weight polypeptides with a predetermined sequence of amino acids is an extremely laborious procedure and not suited to polymer preparation. However, amino acids can be converted to derivatives, according to schemes such as the following:

$$
\begin{array}{c}
\text{R}-\text{CH}-\text{COOH} \longrightarrow \text{R}-\text{CH}-\text{CO}_2\text{H} \longrightarrow \\
\quad | \qquad\qquad\qquad\qquad\quad | \\
\quad \text{NH}_2 \qquad\qquad\qquad\qquad \text{NHCOCl}
\end{array}
$$

These are ring-opening type polymers, since the polymer presumably grows by reaction of an active center on the end of the growing chain with a new cyclic monomer unit by an ionic chain mechanism (62). Homopolymers are usually intractable; copolymers are more readily handled, as shown in the following examples.

194. Preparation of L-4-Isobutyloxazolide-2,5-dione (15,34)

CH₃
  \
   CH—CH₂—CH—CO₂H   ⟶
  / |
CH₃   NH₂

CH₃
  \
   CH—CH₂CH—CO₂H
  / |
CH₃   NHCOCl

CH₃
  \
   CH—CH₂—CH—CO₂H   ⟶
  / |
CH₃   NHCOCl

CH₃
  \
   CH—CH₂—CH—C=O
  / | |
CH₃   NH O
                \C/
                 ‖
                 O

Caution! Phosgene Is Very Dangerous and Must be Used Carefully in a Well Ventilated Hood. All Off-Gases Should be Adequately Scrubbed

Pure L-leucine is recrystallized from water and dried. A sample of this amino acid weighing 32 g. is agitated with purified dioxane (400 ml.) in a three-necked, 2 l. flask. Phosgene is bubbled in a slow stream from a cylinder into the slurry for 45 min. with the temperature maintained at approximately 40°C. After the addition of phosgene is complete, a rapid stream of dry air is passed through the solution for 16 hr. to remove excess phosgene. The dioxane is then removed *in vacuo* at 40°C. The residue crystallizes almost immediately. It is recrystallized immediately prior to use from a mixture of ether and light petroleum. The product melts at 76–77°C. and is very sensitive to moisture. It should be recrystallized and handled in a dry box, preferably.

In this preparation it is essential that pure L-leucine is used and not material which is contaminated with other amino acids such as tyrosine.

195. 4-Benzyloxazolid-2,5-dione (15,16,18)

                     O
                     ‖
C₆H₅CH₂—CH—C   ⟶ C₆H₅—CH₂—CH—C=O
         | \ | \\
         NH₂   OH   NH—C   O
                                    /
                                   ‖
                                   O

Caution! Phosgene Is very Dangerous and Must be Used Carefully in a Well Ventilated Hood. All Off-Gases Should be Adequately Scrubbed.

Twenty g. of DL-phenylalanine is dissolved in 400 ml. of pure dioxane and treated with a slow stream of phosgene for 2 hr. at 40°C. Excess phosgene and solvent is removed with a stream of dry air or nitrogen and the residue is heated at about 40°C. in a vacuum. The residual solid is recrystallized from ethyl acetate–petroleum ether. The yield is about 60% of a material melting at 127°C. It is very moisture sensitive (see Preparation 194).

196. Preparation of 4,4-Dimethyloxazolid-2,5-dione (15,16,18)

Caution! Phosgene Is Very Dangerous and Must be Used Carefully in a Well Ventilated Hood. All Off-Gases Should be Adequately Scrubbed.

Fifteen g. of α-aminoisobutyric acid in 400 ml. of pure dioxane is treated with a slow stream of phosgene at 50°C. for 9 hr. The dioxane and excess phosgene are removed with a stream of dry air or nitrogen. The oily residue solidifies when warmed at 40°C. in a vacuum. The solid is dissolved in the minimum volume of hot chloroform, which should be purified just prior to use to remove moisture and ethanol stabilizer. The chloroform solution is filtered and treated with 3 volumes of petroleum ether. The crystalline product is obtained in about 80% yield and melts at 95–97°C. It must be recrystallized once more just prior to polymerization and should be kept out of contact with moist air.

197. Copolymerization of 4,4-Dimethyloxazolide-2,5-dione and 4-Benzyl DL-Oxazolide-2 5-dione (15,16,18)

A solution of 2.6 g. (0.02 m.) of 4,4-dimethyloxazolide-2,5-dione and 3.8 g. (0.02 m.) of 4-benzyl-DL-oxazolide-2,5-dione in 70 ml. of benzene is treated with a solution of 0.5 ml. of water in 1 ml. of purified dioxane. The solution viscosity increases perceptibly during 6 days. The solution may be poured onto a glass plate and evaporated to a thin polymeric film.

Similarly, a 1:2 copolymer of these reactants may be prepared. Thus, in 70 ml. of benzene is placed 1.3 g. (0.01 m.) of 4,4-dimethyloxazolide-2,5-dione, 3.8 g. (0.02 m.) of 4-benzyl-DL-oxazolide-2,5-dione, and 0.25 ml. of dioxane containing 1% of aniline. Polymerization proceeds over a period of about 10 days. At the end of this period the solution is clear and may be cast to clear, tough film. These films can be stretched and oriented by drawing.

198. Preparation of a Copolymer of L-Leucine and DL-Phenylalanine (15,16,18)

A 1 l., three-necked flask equipped with a stirring shaft, nitrogen inlet tube, and an exit tube is charged with 500 ml. of dry benzene, 3.8 g. (0.02 m.) of 4-benzyl-DL-oxazolide-2,5-dione, and 2.9 g. (0.02 m.) of L-4-isobutyloxazolide-2,5-dione. Some of the benzyl derivative will remain undissolved. To this mixture is now added 0.5 g. of water dissolved in 340 ml. of previously dry benzene. After 5 days the solution will be cloudy and quite viscous. All the glass in contact with the reaction mixture will be coated with a film of polymer. In order to bring the undissolved material into solution, some dry chloroform is added. The resulting clear viscous solution is centrifuged to separate a small amount of insoluble matter.

The polymer solution may be poured onto a glass plate and the solvent evaporated to give polypeptide film of good strength. The resulting dry polymer begins to decompose at about 220–230°C. The polymer may also be precipitated from solution by addition of alcohol or light petroleum ether.

IV. Cyclic Esters

It is interesting to note that although cyclic carboanhydrides of α-hydroxy acids do not polymerize to a high molecular weight it is possible to prepare a polyester by the thermal **polymerization of an anhydrosulfite.** Thus, α-hydroxyisobutyric acid gives, with thionyl chloride, α-hydroxyisobutyric acid anhydrosulfite

which polymerizes when heated, with elimination of sulfur dioxide.

199. Preparation of α-Hydroxyisobutyric Acid Anhydrosulfite (1,7)

In a 3 1., three-necked flask, equipped with a stirrer, a reflux condenser, and a dropping funnel is placed 1000 g. of thionyl chloride. The thionyl chloride is cooled in an ice-salt bath to approximately 0°C. and 312 g. of α-hydroxyisobutyric acid is added. The reaction system is attached to a water pump and a pressure of 100–200 mm. is maintained in the flask with stirring in order to remove the evolved hydrogen chloride. After 18 hr. at 0°C. and 100–200 mm. pressure, the flask is allowed to warm to room temperature at this pressure. Excess thionyl chloride is then distilled rapidly through a short still head, then the anhydrosulfite is obtained boiling at 41–48°C. at 8 mm. The yield of crude product is approximately 309 g. (69%). This crude anhydrosulfite is then distilled through an efficient fractionating column. The boiling point of the pure product is 53–55°C. at 16 mm., $n_D^{25} = 1.4290$–1.4309.

200. Prepolymerization of the Anhydrosulfite

In order to remove chance initiators from the anhydrosulfite the material is maintained at reflux for 140–146 hr. under reduced pressure such that the temperature of reflux is about 55°C. Under these conditions. approximately 10% of the anhydrosulfite will polymerize to low molecular weight material. This effectively removes any chance impurities which might give erratic results during polymerization. Redistillation of unpolymerized material purified in this manner gives a product with a refractive index of 1.4298.

201. Polymerization of α-Hydroxyisobutyric Acid Anhydrosulfite (1)

A 300 ml., round-bottom flask is dried by baking in an oven at 110–150°C. for about 3 hr. To the flask, which is cooled under nitrogen, is added 150 ml. of benzene. In order to make sure that the flask and contents are completely dry, approximately 50 ml. of benzene is then distilled from the reaction vessel. The flask is cooled under nitrogen in an ice bath until the benzene has frozen and 50 g. of the anhydrosulfite with a refractive index of 1.4298 is added. The reaction mixture is refluxed for 52 hr. under nitrogen to give a cloudy colorless gel. This is filtered to give a solid polymer which has a molecular weight in excess of 100,000. It melts at 240°C. and has an inherent viscosity of about 1.5 in a solvent consisting of 58.8 parts of phenol and 41.2 parts of 2,4,6-trichlorophenol. The polymer can be pressed into a clear, colorless film which can be stretched and oriented. It may also be melt-spun to fibrous products.

Chlorobenzene may also be used as a reaction medium. In this case, the polymer remains in solution at the boiling point. Thus, 49.2 g. of the anhydrosulfite is distilled into 275 g. of frozen, dry chlorobenzene. The reaction mixture is maintained at the reflux. The solution becomes more viscous as time progresses. After $7^1/_2$ hr., the polymer solution may be case to a film, or poured into alcohol and precipitated as a white solid, which should also have an inherent viscosity of about 1.5.

It is essential in either of these preparations to have absolutely anhydrous equipment and dry reagents, otherwise polymerization will not proceed to high molecular weight.

In general, unsubstituted **aliphatic polyesters** derived **from lactones** are low melting and tend to revert to monomer. For further information the reader may refer to Carothers' original work (36). Certain lactones, however, deserve mention here.

Propiolactone itself is prepared commercially by the condensation of ketene and formaldehyde

$$CH_2{=}C{=}O + CH_2{=}O \longrightarrow \underset{\underset{CH_2{-}O}{|\qquad|}}{CH_2{-}C{=}O}$$

It polymerizes in the presence of a variety of catalysts, and is, in fact, so liable to spontaneous exothermic polymerization in an unhibited condition as to constitute a laboratory hazard. The

$$\underset{\underset{CH_2{-}O}{|\qquad|}}{CH_2{-}C{=}O} \longrightarrow \left[-OCH_2CH_2{-}\overset{O}{\overset{\|}{C}}-\right]_n$$

melts below 100°C. and is difficult to obtain in high molecular weight (63).

Although poly(trimethylene carboxylate) is low melting, gem-substitution on the α-carbon raises the melting point of the polymer markedly (see Preparation 201). Thus, α,α-**bis-(chloromethyl)-β-propiolactone,** prepared from silver trichloropivalate, polymerizes in the presence of a trace of alkali to a fiber-forming polymer melting over 300°C. (54).

$$\left[-OCH_2{-}\underset{\underset{CH_2Cl}{|}}{\overset{\overset{CH_2Cl}{|}}{C}}{-}\overset{O}{\overset{/\!\!/}{C}}-\right]_n$$

202. Preparation of α α-bis-(Chloromethyl)propiolactone (54)

$$(\text{ClCH}_2)_3\text{C}\cdot\text{CO}_2\text{Ag} \longrightarrow \underset{\underset{\text{CH}_2 \text{———O}}{|}}{\overset{\overset{\text{CH}_2\text{Cl}}{|}}{\text{ClCH}_2\text{—C———C=O}}}$$

Trichloropentaerythritol (47.9 g., 0.25 mole; see Preparation 212) is placed in a 1 l., round-bottom flask, equipped with an efficient wide bore condenser, and set up in an efficient hood. One hundred ml. of concentrated nitric acid is added, and the mixture is warmed cautiously, preferably with an infrared lamp. The chlorohydrin dissolves, then two layers appear and evidence for initiation of a reaction is noted. The flask is rapidly lowered into a cold water bath to moderate the violent reaction which quickly develops. After the reaction moderates and evolution of nitrogen oxides has nearly ceased, the flask is warmed cautiously until no more brown fumes evolve, then the clear, colorless solution is poured into water to give a quantitative yield of crude β,β',β'' trichloropivalic acid, m.p. 108–110°C. Recrystallization from petroleum ether gives a product melting point 112.8–113°C. (38a).

This is a violent reaction and should not be run on a larger scale. The operator should be protected by shields and gauntlets at all times.

Anhydrous, finely powdered silver salt of $\beta,\beta'',''''$ trichloropivalic acid is heated cautiously in an oil-jacketed distillation unit in a slow stream of nitrogen at a pressure of 0.2–0.3 mm. A liquid begins to distill slowly when the jacket temperature reaches 105°C. and somewhat more rapidly when the temperature reaches 110°C. The liquid distillate soon begins to crystallize in the receiver. The jacket temperature is maintained between 110 and 115°C. until distillation slackens and is then raised slowly to 150°C. Very little further distillation occurs above a jacket temperature of 125°C. The solid distillate is collected and consists of pure α,α-bis(chloromethyl)-β-propiolactone melting at 35–36°C. The melting point is unchanged after recrystallization from a mixture of n-hexane and benzene.

203. Polymerization of α α-bis-(Chloromethyl)propiolactone (54)

$$\underset{\underset{\text{O———C=O}}{|}}{\overset{\overset{\text{CH}_2\text{Cl}}{|}}{\text{CH}_2\text{—C—CH}_2\text{Cl}}} \longrightarrow \left[\underset{\underset{\text{CH}_2\text{Cl}}{|}}{\overset{\overset{\text{CH}_2\text{Cl O}}{|}}{-\text{OCH}_2\text{—C——C}}} \right]_n$$

One hundred and fifty g. of α,α-bis-(chloromethyl)-β-propiolactone is heated to 40°C. out of contact with atmospheric moisture until completely molten and 0.1 g. of finely powdered dry potassium hydroxide is added with stirring. Heating and stirring are continued at 40°C. for about 15 min. and then the mixture is heated to 50°C. The mixture soon becomes turbid owing to separation of polymer and within two hours is completely solid. Heating is continued without agitation for a further 4 hr. at 50°C. The product is then heated at 100°C. in a slow stream of nitrogen at a pressure of 0.1 mm. to remove traces of volatile material. The product is a tough, white polymer which has a softening point of about 300°C. and gives a viscous melt from which may be spun filaments which are capable of being cold-drawn.

A dimeric lactone, glycolide, can be polymerized to a **polyester of α-hydroxyacetic acid** in the presence of antimony fluoride. The polyester does not tend to revert to glycolide under normal conditions.

204. Preparation of Lactide (35)

$$HOCH_2CO_2H \longrightarrow$$

Four hundred g. of hydroxyacetic acid is heated at atmospheric pressure in a round-bottom flask until the temperature of the liquid is 175–185°C. The temperature is maintained in this range for 2 hr., or slightly longer, until the water ceases to distill. The pressure is then reduced over a period of $1/2$ hr. to about 150 mm. and the temperature maintained at 175–185°C. for an additional 2 hr. The residue so obtained is poured into an enamel pan where it solidifies to a white, brittle solid. This solid is the low molecular weight polyhydroxyacetic ester which is depolymerized to glycolide. A three-necked reaction vessel is equipped with a stirrer and a neck suitable for introduction of powdered low molecular weight polymer and also equipped with a take-off for distilling the glycolide as it is prepared. The equipment is swept by a steady stream of nitrogen gas and the receiver for the glycolide is cooled in an ice bath. After the ice-cooled receiver, three ice-cooled traps are placed in series in order to catch any glycolide which is carried beyond the receiver by the nitrogen stream. One hundred g. of powdered, low molecular weight polyester (produced as previously described) is thoroughly mixed with 1 g. of antimony trioxide and placed in a supply vessel connected to the inlet neck of the three-neck flask. The polymer is introduced from the supply vessel into the reaction vessel which is maintained at 270–285°C. at a pressure of about 12–15 mm. The solid is added at the rate of about 20 g./hr. to give a 93% yield of glycolide. The glycolide is recrystallized from approximately 2 volumes of ethyl acetate with charcoal.

205. Polymerization of Glycolide to Hydroxyacetic Acid Polymer (35)

A mixture of 50 g. of pure dry glycolide is placed in a reaction vessel under nitrogen in the presence of 0.03% by weight of antimony trifluoride. The reaction vessel is heated to 195°C. by an oil bath and the contents stirred for 1 hr. at this temperature. The viscosity of the melt increases rapidly during this period and at the end of 1 hr. cannot be stirred further. The mixture is heated for an additional hour at this temperature, then the temperature is raised to 230°C. for an additional $1/2$ hr. The resulting polymer has a high molecular weight and can be fabricated into drawable films and fibers.

V. Cyclic Ethers

Practically all **oxiranes** (epoxides) and **oxetanes** (trimethylene oxides) will polymerize.

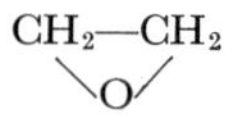

CH₂—CH₂
\O/

Oxirane

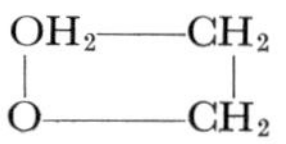

OH₂——CH₂
| |
O————CH₂

Oxetane

CH₂——CH₂
| |
CH₂   CH₂
\O/

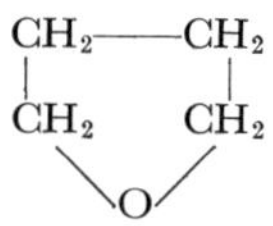

Tetrahydrofuran

Polymers ranging from low molecular weight syrups to tough, high molecular weight solids may be obtained, depending upon the condition and type of catalyst. Normally, ionic catalysts, either cationic or anionic, are the only effective types here. Tetrahydrofuran will polymerize readily, however only in the presence of cationic catalysts. Antimony pentachloride has been the preferred catalyst to polymerize tetrahydrofuran for many years. It is only quite recently that it has been observed that very high molecular weight poly(tetramethylene ether) can be obtained by using phosphorus pentafluoride catalysts (39).

All of the unsubstituted polyethers except the polyacetal derived from formaldehyde melt in the range from 35 to 65°C. As will be seen later, substitution on the chain may tend to raise the melting point. Alkylated derivatives of tetrahydrofuran have resisted polymerization. On the other hand, a **bicyclic epoxide** which may be considered as disubstituted tetrahydrofuran

does polymerize, probably to relieve the strain in the bridge structure (60,61). The melting point of this polymer is very high. (>400°C.). Epoxides will polymerize in the presence of either cationic or anionic initiators and may give linear polymers ranging from a very few units up to molecular weights approaching 1,000,000. Bis-epoxides will give network or cross-linked polymers (13). The lower molecular weight products are normally hydroxyl terminated, hence serve as large difunctional molecules which may be built into high polymers by

further reaction.   See Chapter 3 for examples of polymers based on
large difunctional molecules of this type.   A wide variety of commercial
products is available, and these may be used in the preparations of
higher molecular weight block polymers.

The preparation of **polyethylene oxide** with molecular weight of
the order of several millions has been accomplished recently by workers
at Union Carbide Corp. (4,32,56).   Staudinger and Lohmann found
in 1933 that the oxides and carbonates of strontium and calcium, etc.,
are catalysts for the production of polyethylene oxides.   However, the
rates of polymerization were quite slow and some of their experiments
went as long as 2 years.   The Carbide research team found that very
specially prepared strontium carbonate is capable of polymerizing
purified ethylene oxide fairly rapidly to very high molecular weight
material.   It is necessary that the strontium carbonate prepared be
absolutely free of interfering ions.   For example, nitrate, chlorate,
bisulfate, and other ions in trace quantities completely inhibit the
polymerization.   Furthermore, it is found desirable to maintain at
least $1/2\%$ of water in order to effectively polymerize the ethylene oxide.

206. Preparation of Active Strontium Carbonate Catalyst (32)

$$Sr(OH)_2 + CO_2 \longrightarrow SrCO_2 + H_2O$$

A 22% aqueous solution of pure strontium hydroxide is prepared at 90°C.
in distilled water.   A stream of carbon dioxide gas is introduced under the surface of the solution and allowed to proceed until precipitation of the carbonate
is complete.   The solution is filtered and the filtered solid is washed with distilled water.   The product is dried to a water content of not less than 0.5–
1.0%.

207. Polymerization of Ethylene Oxide (32)

$$CH_2{-}CH_2 \xrightarrow{SrCO_3} [{-}OCH_2CH_2{-}]_n$$

In a polymer tube is placed 50 ml. of redistilled ethylene oxide containing less
than 50 p.p.m. of aldehyde.   To the tube is then added about 0.2 g. of strontium carbonate prepared as before.   The tube is then sealed and heated to
approximately 50°C. and maintained at this temperature.   After an induction
period of approximately 90 min., polymerization will begin.   During the course
of the polymerization the tube should be agitated in some manner, either by a
rocking or rotating mechanism.   After the end of the induction period, polymerization may be extremely rapid.   In some cases reaction is so rapid that the
tube may explode.   Therefore all precautions must be taken to protect the

operator against shattering glass.   Once polymerization is initiated, it should be complete within approximately 2 hr.

A less active catalyst may be obtained by using J. T. Baker's C.P. grade of strontium carbonate as the polymerization initiator.   This again is dried to a water content of not less than 0.5%.   The polymerization is carried out using this material in concentrations of about 1.5 g. per 50 ml. of ethylene oxide. The induction period under these conditions may be as long as 20 hr. or more. Polymerization with the commercial strontium carbonate is much less rapid, and there is less danger of the reaction getting out of hand.

The polymer is soluble in chloroform and ethylene dichloride, as well as in acetonitrile and anisole.   Viscous solutions may be prepared in these solvents. At elevated temperatures the polymer also is soluble in benzene and toluene. It is miscible with water in all proportions at room temperature and extremely viscous solutions can be prepared.   A 20% solution of polymer of high molecular weight in water makes an interesting, elastic, nontacky gel.   These gel lumps may contain as much as 80% water and have the feel and appearance of a clear rubber.   An impressive demonstration of the properties of these materials is to bounce a ball consisting of 80% water and 20% high molecular weight polyethylene oxide.

Tough films may be obtained either by casting a solution, preferably in an organic medium, onto a glass plate or by melt-pressing solid polymer in a Carver Press.   Film obtained in such a manner shows a high degree of cystallinity, sometimes as high as 95%.   The polymer chains may be oriented by stretching in the usual manner.

The polymerization of **propylene oxide** again may be brought about by either basic or acidic catalysts.   The polymer has regularly spaced asymmetric carbon atoms, hence should be capable of existing in either random or stereoregular configuration,

$$(O-CH_2-\overset{\overset{\displaystyle CH_3}{|}}{\underset{*}{CH}}-O-CH_2-\overset{\overset{\displaystyle CH_3}{|}}{\underset{*}{CH}}-OCH_2-\overset{\overset{\displaystyle CH_3}{|}}{\underset{*}{CH}}-)_n$$

just as in the case of polypropylene and other poly(α-olefins) described in Chapter 4.

C. C. Price and his co-workers have shown (46,47) that l-propylene oxide polymerized over solid potassium hydroxide gives solid polymer, whereas dl-propylene oxide gives a liquid product under the same conditions.   Both polymers are of the same molecular weight, albeit quite low.

Using a complex iron catalyst, a research group from Dow Chemical Company has shown that polymerization of dl propylene oxide will give a solid, crystalline, high molecular weight product (48–51).

208. Preparation of a Ferric Chloride Complex Catalyst (48–51)

A complex catalyst is prepared in a polymer tube by dissolving 1.0 g. of anhydrous ferric chloride in 5 ml. of diethyl ether and adding gradually 1.0 g. of liquid propylene oxide with agitation and cooling at temperatures below 60°C. When condensation of the ferric chloride and propylene oxide is completed, the product is warmed in a vacuum to remove volatile matter leaving a semi-solid brown residue.

209. Polymerization of Propylene Oxide (48–51)

$$CH_3 \quad\quad H \qquad\qquad \left[\begin{array}{c} CH_3 \\ | \\ -OCH-CH_2- \end{array} \right]_n \longrightarrow$$

$$\overset{CH_3}{\underset{H}{\diagdown}} C \underset{O}{\overbrace{}} C \overset{H}{\underset{H}{\diagup}} \quad \xrightarrow{Fe^{+3}}$$

To the catalyst residue prepared in the preceding experiment is added 100 g. of propylene oxide. The tube is cooled under nitrogen and sealed. This mixture is heated at 80°C. with agitation for 88 hr., at which time polymerization is complete. There is obtained in this way 94 g. of a brown, rubbery solid polymer. This is dissolved in hot acetone and sufficient concentrated hydrochloric acid is added to convert the iron complex present into soluble ferric chloride. The solution is chilled to −20°C., whereupon solid polymer crystallizes from solution and is separated by filtration. This polymer is reprecipitated twice in acetone in the same manner and about 25 g. of pure white polymer is obtained.

This white solid has a melting point of approximately 70°C. and should have a molecular weight in the range of 100–150,000. It may be dissolved in hot acetone, hot methanol, dioxane, benzene, toluene, tetrahydrofuran, etc. It can be converted by melt-pressing to film which can be cold drawn and oriented.

Epoxides with several symmetrical substituents exhibit a chain stiffening effect noted earlier with poly-α-olefins with branched side groups. The melting points are very high; they are very crystalline and insoluble in all solvents tested.

210. Preparation of 1,1,2,2-Tetramethylethylene Oxide (3)

$$\overset{CH_3}{\underset{CH_3}{\diagdown}} C = C \overset{CH_3}{\underset{CH_3}{\diagup}} \quad \underset{Na_2CO_3}{\overset{CH_3CO_3H}{\xrightarrow{\hspace{1cm}}}} \quad \overset{CH_3}{\underset{CH_3}{\diagdown}} C \underset{O}{\overbrace{}} C \overset{CH_3}{\underset{CH_3}{\diagup}}$$

In a 2 l., three-necked flask, equipped with a stirrer, a condenser, and a dropping funnel and cooled with an ice bath is placed 300 g. of anhydrous sodium carbonate, 300 ml. of methylene chloride and 168 g. of freshly distilled tetramethylethylene. The mixture is stirred and the temperature is held at 5–10°C. To this mixture, is added 372 g. of 40% peracetic acid at such a rate as to keep the temperature below 10°C. Approximately 6 hr. should be required for this addition. The mixture is stirred vigorously during the course of the addition and for 1 hr. after the peracid is all added. Approximately 500 ml. of water is then added and the organic phase is extracted with two 200 ml. portions of methylene chloride. The methylene chloride layer may contain peroxide. It is, therefore, washed with ferrous sulfate solution until it no longer gives a positive peroxide test. The product, tetramethylethylene oxide, boils at 90–91°C. at atmospheric pressure. It has a refractive index at 25°C. of 1.3938. It is obtained in a yield of approximately 70%.

211. Polymerization of 1,1,2,2-Tetramethylethylene Oxide (9)

In a 300 ml., round-bottom flask equipped with a drying tube and a gas inlet and cooled in dry ice are placed 5 ml. of tetramethylethylene oxide and 100 ml. of dry methyl chloride. To this solution is added 1 ml. of redistilled boron trifluoride etherate. The entire mixture is allowed to stand at dry ice temperature for 24 hr. The solid is filtered, washed with methylene chloride, then with alcohol, and dried. The yield of polymer is essentially quantitative. It is a hard, white solid which does not melt below 300°C. It is completely unaffected by boiling with most solvents such as xylene, tetrahydrofuran, dimethylformamide, or dioxane.

Although the polymerization of epoxides dates back to the early days of Staudinger, **oxetanes** have been considered only recently. The parent compound is prone to rearrangement in acid media:

However, Rose (55) has reported the successful polymerization of oxetane to linear **polyether.**

The preparation of this polymer in high molecular weight is quite tedious and will not be described.

Although the polyethers from oxetane and its symmetrically gem disubstituted derivatives are crystalline, the polymer from 3-methyloxetane is not (55).

Substitution of two groups on the 3-position oxetane leads to stiffening of the chain, as described previously for the polymerization of tetramethylethylene oxide. The effect is not so pronounced, however, as is shown in Table 5.1.

TABLE 5.1 Effect of R on Melting Point of Polymer from

$$
\begin{array}{c}
O \!-\!-\! \\
\!||\!-\!R \\
R
\end{array}
$$

R	M.P., °C.	Ref.
—CH$_3$	47	55
—CH$_2$F	135	17
—CH$_2$Cl	180	19
—CH$_2$Br	220	10
—CH$_2$I	290	10

212. Preparation of Trichloropentaerythritol

$$(HOCH_2)_4C \longrightarrow (ClCH_2)_3CCH_2OAc \longrightarrow (ClCH_2)_3CCH_2OH$$

Hydrogen chloride gas is bubbled into a mixture of 600 g. of acetic acid and 100 g. of water at 0°C. until a total of 176 g. (4.9 moles) is absorbed. This mixture is charged into a 1 l. Hastelloy B bomb, together with 200 g. (1.5 moles) of pentaerythritol. The bomb is sealed and heated to 160°C. for 8 hr. Due to the corrosive nature of this mixture, it is best to back the stainless steel rupture disk of the Hastelloy bomb with a thin sheet of Teflon fluorocarbon film resin and then with platinum foil to prevent the rupture from corroding. After 8 hr., the bomb is cooled to room temperature and the reaction mixture diluted with water. The trichloropentaerythritol acetate is isolated by extraction with methylene chloride. The solvent is removed and the residual oil is refluxed overnight with 500 ml. of methyl alcohol and 50 ml. of concentrated hydrochloric acid. The next day the mixture of methyl acetate and methyl alcohol is distilled slowly. The residue of trichloropentaerythritol crystallizes, is filtered, washed with water, and dried. The crude product weighs about 275 g. and melts in the range of 60–63°C. Recrystallization of a small portion from ethyl acetate raises the melting point to 65.5°C. However, the lower melting product is used directly for the preparation of 3,3-bis(chloromethyl)-oxetane.

213. Preparation of 3,3-bis(Chloromethyl)oxetane

$$(ClCH_2)_3CCH_2OH \longrightarrow ClCH_2\!-\!\!\begin{array}{c} CH_2Cl \\ | \\ || \\ O \end{array} \longrightarrow$$

A mixture of 275 g. of trichloropentaerythritol, 500 ml. of methanol, 60 ml. of water, and 80 g. of potassium hydroxide is refluxed 18 hr.   An equal volume of water is added and the heavy oil is separated with two 100 ml. portions of ethyl ether.   The ether extract is dried over calcium chloride and distilled through an efficient distilling column to give about 125 g. of pure cyclic ether, b.p. 101°C. at 27 mm., or 62°C. at 4 mm.   Immediately before polymerization, this product should be fractionated either through an efficient fractionating column, or through a Vigreux column with the first and last 10% being discarded.   It is essential that the monomer be of extremely high purity before the polymerization described in Preparation 217 is attempted.

214. Preparation of 3,3-bis(Fluoromethyl)oxetane (17)

$$ \text{ClCH}_2 - \overset{\text{CH}_2\text{Cl}}{\underset{\text{O}}{\boxed{}}} \xrightarrow{\text{KF}} \text{FCH}_2 - \overset{\text{CH}_2\text{F}}{\underset{\text{O}}{\boxed{}}} $$

In a three-necked, 1 l. flask equipped with a stirrer and a reflux condenser, is placed a mixture of 156 g. of anhydrous powdered potassium fluoride and 156 g. of bis(chloromethyl)oxetane.   To it is added 340 ml. of anhydrous glycol and the mixture is heated with a metal heating bath to a temperature of approximately 160°C. with vigorous and efficient stirring.   The mixture is allowed to reflux and is slowly distilled.   The distillate separates into two layers, the lower layer consisting of the bis(fluoromethyl)oxetane.   The product is obtained in a crude yield of about 70%.   The crude distillate is then mixed with twice its volume of water and the mixture is again distilled.   The organic product is entrained by the water vapor and it is separated and dried over magnesium sulfate.   It then is again distilled in an anhydrous condition to give approximately 40% of pure product, b.p. 56°C. at 29 mm.

215. Preparation of 3,3-bis(Iodomethyl)oxetane (10)

$$ \text{ClCH}_2 - \overset{\text{CH}_2\text{Cl}}{\underset{\text{O}}{\boxed{}}} \xrightarrow{\text{NaI}} \text{ICH}_2 - \overset{\text{CH}_2\text{I}}{\underset{\text{O}}{\boxed{}}} $$

A mixture of 15.5 g. of 3,3-bis(chloromethyl)oxetane, 150 ml. of methyl ethyl ketone, and 35 g. of dry sodium iodide is refluxed for 24 hr.   The solution is then cooled, filtered, and the solvent is partially removed by evaporation.   The residue solidifies on standing and is recrystallized from cyclohexane.   The yield is 30 g. (89%) of coarse, colorless, very dense crystals with a melting point of 50°C.

216. Preparation of Phosphorus Pentafluoride (61)

$$ \text{C}_6\text{H}_5\text{N}_2\text{PF}_6 \longrightarrow \text{N}_2 + \text{PF}_5 + \text{C}_6\text{H}_5\text{F} $$

Caution! Phosphorus Pentafluoride Is Very Toxic.

The most convenient method for the preparation of phosphorus pentafluoride on a laboratory scale is by the thermal decomposition of aryldiazonium hexafluorophosphate (See Chemicals Appendix). The salt in a quantity of 3–12 g. is heated at 150–160°C. in a distillation set-up and the phosphorus pentafluoride is swept into the polymerization vessel with a stream of dry nitrogen. Approximately 1–2 hr. is required to decompose all the diazonium hexafluorophosphate under these conditions.

217. Polymerization of 3,3-bis(Chloromethyl)oxetane (11)

One hundred ml. of anhydrous methyl chloride is condensed into a 500 ml., three-necked flask equipped with a stirrer, a dry ice condenser, and a gas inlet tube. Freshly distilled 3,3-bis-(chloromethyl)oxetane (25 g.) is then added all at once. The dry ice bath is removed and the mixture is allowed to reflux (−25°C.). Into the refluxing reaction mixture is introduced a trace of phosphorus pentafluoride gas. After a short induction period, polymerization takes place very rapidly. Ordinarily, this polymerization is uneventful and the solid polymer precipitates during the course of the first few minutes. Occasionally, however, the polymerization is violent and the content of the reaction flask may be ejected through the top of the condenser. However, no more serious consequences are apt to occur on the scale described.

The methyl chloride is now allowed to evaporate and the solid polymer is isolated and washed several times with methyl alcohol. Poly[3,3-bis-(chloromethyl)trimethylene ether] is obtained as a spongy white solid with an inherent viscosity of about 1.0 in hexamethylphosphoramide. It may be fabricated into clear, tough films by pressing in a Carver press in the range of 175–200°C. These films are highly crystalline and may be stretched and oriented over a hot surface at about 100°C. The polymer has a crystalline melting point of about 177°C. as observed on a polarizing microscope. It may be dissolved to a limited extent in common organic solvents such as hot cyclohexanone or dimethylformamide. It is readily soluble and spinning solutions can be prepared in hexamethylphosphoramide.

3,3-Bis-(fluoromethyl)oxetane, 3,3-bis-(bromomethyl)oxetane, and 3,3-bis-(iodomethyl)oxetane may be polymerized in a like manner.

Compared to the oxetanes and epoxides, the **polymerization of tetrahydofuran** proceeds rather slowly. Ordinarily, the products are viscous oils; however, Muetterties (39) has found that very high molecular weight polyether can be obtained by using phosphorus pentafluoride as a catalyst, instead of boron fluoride or antimony pentachloride.

218. Preparation of Pure Tetrahydrofuran (39)

Tetrahydrofuran is purified by refluxing over solid sodium hydroxide, distilling under nitrogen, then refluxing over lithium aluminum hydride and distilling therefrom immediately prior to use.

219. Polymerization of Tetrahydrofuran (39)

$$\begin{array}{c} \boxed{} \\ O \end{array} \xrightarrow{PF_5} [-OCH_2CH_2CH_2CH_2-]_n$$

To about 350 g. of purified tetrahydrofuran in a suitable sized vessel maintained under nitrogen, is added 1 g. of a solid phosphorus pentafluoride–tetrahydrofuran coordination complex. This material is prepared by saturating tetrahydrofuran with phosphorus pentafluoride (see Preparation 216) at 0°C. and subliming the resulting solid at 70°C. and 0.02 mm. pressure. The mixture of tetrahydrofuran and catalyst is maintained at 30°C. for approximately 6 hr. in order to effect polymerization. The resulting solid, colorless polymer is heated in water to destroy phosphorus pentafluoride residue and is then dissolved in more tetrahydrofuran. The polymer is recovered by pouring the tetrahydrofuran solution into water with violent agitation, preferably in a high speed mixer such as a Waring Blendor. The white shredded polymer is obtained in this manner in a yield of about 59% after air drying. This polymer has an inherent viscosity (0.5% in benzene) of about 3.6, which corresponds to a molecular weight of close to 329,000. The polymer can be molded at temperatures between 100 and 230°C. to a clear, tough film which crystallizes slowly on standing. The crystalline film can be stretched in the usual manner and oriented. The oriented film samples are quite tough. Above the crystalline melting point, which is about 55°C., the polymer films take on a rubbery appearance and feel; however, they maintain their toughness.

Lower molecular weight solid polymer may be prepared by catalysis with antimony pentachloride. Thus, 75 g. of tetrahydrofuran purified as in preceding experiments is cooled in solid carbon dioxide under nitrogen. To this cooled tetrahydrofuran is added 3 g. of freshly distilled antimony pentachloride. The mixture is then stored at 25°C. After 40 min., it has set to a solid; after 24 hr., the polymer is recovered and purified as in the preceding example. Polymer prepared in this manner is a solid, but it is tacky at 40°C. and has an inherent viscosity of only about 0.6.

Poly(tetramethylene oxide) of high molecular weight is crystalline, melting at about 55 °C. Again, the tremendous effect of stiffening a polymer chain on the polymer properties is demonstrated by the polymerization of **1,4-epoxycyclohexane**. The polymer is still highly crystalline, but melts above 400 °C. (60,61).

220. Preparation of 1,4-Epoxycyclohexane (20)

A mixture of cis and trans cyclohexanediols obtained by the hydrogenation of hydroquinone or purchased from a commercial source should be distilled before use in order to obtain a dry product. The diol mixture boils at about 146°C. at 18–20 mm. To 432 g. of the distilled diol is added an equal weight of activated alumina. The intimately mixed solids are placed in an ordinary distillation apparatus and the solids are heated slowly for 6 hr. at such a temperature that a distillate is obtained very slowly during this period. The resulting product which is obtained in roughly 200 g. yield is isolated, dried over anhydrous potassium carbonate, and distilled, preferably through a precision distilling column. The pure 1,4-epoxycyclohexane boils at 119–119.5°C. The yield of product is approximately 41%.

221. Polymerization of 1,4-Epoxycyclohexane (61)

Two catalyst systems have been found effective for the polymerization of 1,4-epoxycyclohexane to high molecular weight, high melting, crystalline polyether.

In the first technique, a mixture of 1 part of epoxycyclohexane and 2 parts of nitrobenzene is cooled to −30°C. To this mixture is added phosphorus pentafluoride (see Preparation 216) gas in a quantity of the order of 1–5 mole %. It is not necessary to accurately measure the amount added. The mixture is maintained at −30°C. for approximately 100 hr. when a solid mass has formed. This solid mixture is taken out and broken up with acetone, filtered, washed repeatedly with water and acetone, and dried. The yield is about 50%; the inherent viscosity is of the order of 1, in a solvent consisting of 66 parts of tetrachloroethane plus 100 parts of phenol.

An alternate method for the polymerization of 1,4-epoxycyclohexane involves use of a catalyst combination such as ferric chloride–thionyl chloride which has been shown to be effective for the polymerization of tetrahydrofuran. Thus, to 50 g. of epoxycyclohexane maintained at 0°C. is added 0.015 g. of anhydrous ferric chloride as a 10% solution in ether, followed by 0.062 g. of thionyl chloride, also added as a 10% solution in anhydrous ether. The mixture is stirred and maintained in a stoppered flask at 0°C. for 18 hr. At the end of 18 hr., the polymer is mixed with alcohol and the solid material is filtered from unreacted monomer. The polymer is washed repeatedly with alcohol and water, and dried. The yield of polymer with an inherent viscosity of about 0.6 is about 37%.

An x-ray diffraction pattern of polymer obtained in either of the above two manners indicates that crystallinity does not disappear below 430°C. The polymer is very insoluble and cannot be dissolved in alcohol, ether, acetone, benzene, dimethylformamide, o-cresol, anisole, or a variety of other organic solvents. It is soluble in a mixture of 66 parts of tetrachloroethane and 100 parts of phenol. It is possible to cast films from this solvent mixture, but the films, even though the inherent viscosity of the polymer is high, are usually brittle and noncoherent.

Up to this point, we have considered strictly organic monomers. There are a number of organo-inorganic and inorganic compounds which exist as polymerizable cyclic monomers.

VI. Silicones

A class of polymers of considerable commercial importance is based on a linear, cyclic, or cross-linked arrangement of alternating silicon and oxygen atoms, where the silicon is substituted with organic radicals or hydrogen. They are called organopolysiloxanes, or simply silicone polymers (52), and can be formulated as

$$\left[\begin{array}{c} R \\ | \\ -Si-O- \\ | \\ R \end{array} \right]_n$$

The usual procedure for preparing silicone polymers is to hydrolyze, either singly or in the appropriate combination, compounds of the type R_3SiCl, R_2SiCl_2, $RSiCl_3$, and $SiCl_4$, depending on the kind of product desired. The intermediates in the reaction are believed to be the corresponding silanols (e.g., $R_2Si(OH)_2$] which condense very rapidly with the elimination of water and formation of the $-Si-O-Si-$ link.

In addition to linear polymer, cyclic forms where n ranges from 3 to 9 are often encountered. These cyclic products can be converted to high molecular weight linear polymer in the presence of alkaline catalysts.

Although many of the silicone "polymers" are of quite low molecular weight, their relationship to the higher molecular weight silicones warrants their inclusion here. The linear silicones, $[(CH_3)_3Si(OSi-$

$(CH_3)_2]_n$—$OSi(CH_3)_3$, where n is fairly small, form the basis of the well-known silicone oils. The **cyclic silicones,** formed in hydrolysis reactions of the silane dihalides, especially $[(CH_3)_2SiO]_{3-4}$, **are convertible to** high molecular weight **linear silicone elastomers.** Various curing techniques are available for converting linear and cyclic materials to cross-linked elastomers and resins.

222. Preparation of Cyclic Polysiloxanes (44)

$$CH_3\!-\!\underset{\underset{Cl}{|}}{\overset{\overset{Cl}{|}}{Si}}\!-\!CH_3 \quad\xrightarrow{H_2O}\quad -\!\!\left(\underset{\underset{CH_3}{|}}{\overset{\overset{CH_3}{|}}{Si}}\!-\!O\!-\!\right)_{\!3-9}$$

A. From a dropping funnel protected with a drying tube, 200 ml. of dimethyldichlorosilane is added slowly to 600 ml. of vigorously stirred water maintained at 15–20°C. When the addition is finished, the oily, organic layer is taken up in 150 ml. of ethyl ether, separated from the water phase, and dried over magnesium sulfate. The ether solution is filtered and the ether removed by evaporation. The oily residue contains cyclic products of the type shown in the preceding reaction, plus some high molecular weight materials, probably linear as well as cyclic.

The material obtained from the ether layer, about 100 ml., is fractionated with precision in order to isolate the individual components of the mixture. The approximate percentages of the components and their boiling points are: $n = 3$, 0.5%, 134°C./760 mm. (m.p. 64°C.); $n = 4$, 42%, 175°C./760 mm., 74°C./20 mm. (m.p. 17.5°C.); $n = 5$, 6.7%, 101°C./20 mm. (m.p. −38°C.); $n = 6$, 1.6%, 128°C./20 mm. (m.p. −3°C.). The trimer and tetramer can be distilled conveniently at atmospheric pressure. Trimer to hexamer constitute about half the total product.

B. The higher molecular weight residue in the still pot is a viscous oil which is pyrolyzed to trimer and tetramer by heating in a slow stream of nitrogen by means of a metal bath to 350°C. with a Claisen head and condenser set for distillation. Up to 350°C. only trace quantities of distillate appear. From 350 to 400°C. the liquid in the flask begins to boil, with the distillate temperature being 135–210°C. Continued heating at 400°C. causes almost the entire contents of the flask to distill. The distillate, totaling about 40 ml., forms a mixture of crystals and liquid and consists of about 44% of the cyclic trimer and 24% of the cyclic tetramer, with the remainder being pentamer and above. This mixture can be fractionated to its components, as described in A.

These reactions demonstrate the tendency of the $(R_2Si$—$O)$ unit to form cyclic structures under the conditions given. The reverse of this latter process, namely the **formation of low molecular weight linear polymer from low molecular weight cyclic siloxanes** can be accomplished by an equilibration reaction in the presence of sulfuric acid, and is demonstrated in the following way.

223. Preparation of Linear Polysiloxanes (44)

$$[(CH_3)_2SiO]_4 \xrightarrow{\text{H}_2\text{SO}_4} [(CH_3)_2SiO]_n$$

Twenty ml. of octamethylcyclotetrasiloxane is placed in a stoppered flask or bottle with 3.7 ml. of concentrated sulfuric acid and 10 ml. ethyl ether and shaken at room temperature for 1 day. The mixture becomes very viscous. Then 20 ml. ether and 10 ml. water are added and the mixture is shaken for 1 hr. The lower aqueous layer is drawn off and the ether solution is washed three times with 10 ml. portions of water and is then dried over anhydrous potassium carbonate. The ether is distilled from the solution through a Claisen head and the temperature of the distilling flask is raised by means of a metal bath to 310°C., during which time a small quantity of distillate forms. The residue in the distilling flask is a clear, viscous oil, soluble in various hydrocarbon or ether solvents. If purified tetramer, $[(CH_3)_2SiO]_4$, is used as the starting material, a cryoscopic molecular weight determination in cyclohexane indicates a value of about 2740, or 37 $(CH_3)_2SiO$ units.

By carrying out the above reaction on the cyclic tetramer in the presence of a definite amount of hexamethyldisiloxane, one can prepare linear polymers of the structure $(CH_3)_3SiO[(CH_3)_2SiO_n]Si(CH_3)_3$, where n is determined by the amount of chain terminating $(CH_3)_3$-$SiOSi(CH_3)_3$ used. It is these linear polysiloxanes that form the basis of methyl silicone oils. A variety of products is possible having a wide range of viscosities, depending on the value of n in the above formula. They are distinguished by their small change in viscosity over a wide range of temperatures, quite unlike petroleum oils.

The other linear polysiloxanes mentioned are terminated with hydroxyl groups which may condense further on heating and alter the molecular weight and viscosity as a result. The advantage of the **$(CH_3)_3$—SiO terminated polysiloxanes** over these is the stability to heat conferred by the trimethylsiloxy group.

224. Preparation of a Linear Polysiloxane Terminated with Trimethyl Siloxy Groups (44)

$$[(CH_3)_2SiO]_4 + [(CH_3)_3Si]_2O \xrightarrow{\text{H}_2\text{SO}_4} (CH_3)_3SiO[(CH_3)_2SiO]_nSi(CH_3)_3$$

Twenty ml. of the cyclic tetramer from Preparation 222 is mixed with 0.4 ml. of hexamethyldisiloxane and shaken for 24 hr. with 0.8 ml. of concentrated sulfuric acid. After this time, 5 ml. of water is added and shaking continued another hour. The mixture is centrifuged, and the two layers separated. The viscous upper layer of silicone oil has a viscosity of about 130 cs. at 40°C.

Linear silicone polymers, which may have molecular weights of 1,000,000 or more, are conveniently prepared from a **base-catalyzed** ring opening polymerization of the cyclic tetramer or trimer, $[(CH_3)_2SiO]_3$ or $_4$. The gummy products are soluble in aromatic hydrocarbons, and may be compounded, molded and cured, much as a natural rubber might be.

225. The Preparation of Poly(dimethylsiloxane) (58)

A catalyst solution is prepared by dissolving 1.0 g. of potassium hydroxide (dried at 70°C. in vacuum overnight) in 400 ml. of dry isopropanol in a flask protected with a drying tube and equipped for distillation. Isopropanol is distilled until the volume of the solution is reduced to 250 ml. One-tenth ml. of this solution is then transferred by a pipette to a 100 ml. three-necked flask purged with nitrogen and fitted with a good mechanical stirrer and a nitrogen inlet. The isopropanol is removed in a stream of nitrogen with moderate heating. Then 29.6 g. of octamethylcyclotetrasiloxane is added, the flask is equipped with a drying tube, and heated by means of an oil bath to 165°C. with stirring for 1–5 hr., without the nitrogen, during which time the reaction mass will become a highly viscous gum. The polymer is transferred to an evaporating dish and heated in an oven at 150°C. for 3 hr. The polymer is soluble in benzene and toluene and has an inherent viscosity in the latter of about 0.7 (0.5% concentration at 25°C.). Catalyst residues may be removed by washing a solution of the polymer with very dilute hydrochloric acid, then with water.

An estimation of number average molecular weight can be made from a determination of the intrinsic viscosity in toluene (6):

$$[\eta] = 2 \times 10^{-4} \, \bar{M}_n^{0.66}$$

Silicone rubbers are noted for their flexibility over a wider range of temperatures (−90 to 300°C.) and their resistance to moisture, air, and weathering. The polymer so obtained must be properly compounded with fillers and curing agents in order to form a cross-linked, or vulcanized product. If a rubber mill or some similar set of differential rolls is available, the polysiloxane prepared may be compounded as follows to obtain a rubber which resists deformation under compression at elevated temperatures (45). The following ingredients are blended: 20 g. poly(dimethylsiloxane), 12 g. diatomeceous earth, 17.5 g. titanium dioxide, 0.3 g. benzoylperoxide, and 2.0 g. 2,5-di-*t*-butylquinone. The mix may then be molded or shaped, and cured by heating at 250° in an oven for 24 hr.

Cross-linked silicone resins are the result of replacing the hydrocarbon R groups in $(R_2SiO)n$ units (either in cyclic or linear materials) with oxygen bridges. This can be accomplished by cohydrolysis of tri- or tetrahalosilanes with the dihalosilanes, or by oxidation of linear silicones. In the methylsilicone resins, for instance, the C/Si ratio is less than 2.0; the smaller the ratio, the greater the degree of cross-linking.

226. Preparation of a Methylsilicone Resin by Oxidation (33)

Twenty ml. of dimethyldichlorosilane is hydrolyzed as described in Preparation 222. The resulting oil is heated at 225°C. for 10 hr. in a small distilling flask while a slow stream of air is passed through the liquid. The resulting glassy solid is infusible and insoluble, but is somewhat flexible.

227. Preparation of a Methylsilicone Resin by Cohydrolysis (53)

A mixture of 4.5 g. dimethyldichlorosilane and 1.95 g. methyltrichlorosilane in 50 ml. ether is hydrolyzed by pouring onto 100 g. of cracked ice. The ether solution is evaporated and the oil is heated at 75°C. in air until it becomes a hard, glassy solid. The C/Si ratio of the resin is 1.3 as calculated from the mixture of chlorosilanes. The resin is infusible and insoluble. It is stable in air at 200°C. showing no apparent change over a long period. Heating at 300–400°C. causes rapid oxidation leaving only silica.

VII. Preparation and Polymerization of Phosphonitrilic Chloride

Phosphonitrilic chloride is obtained by the reaction of phosphorus pentachloride and ammonium chloride. It does not exist in the monomeric state but is isolated in the form of ring compounds, predominately the trimer and tetramer.

$$NH_4Cl + PCl_5 \longrightarrow$$

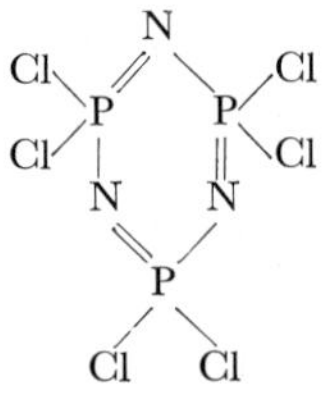

$$+ (PNCl_2)_4$$

The purified cyclic materials can be polymerized quite readily to linear polymer with the structure

$$\left[\begin{array}{c} Cl \\ -P{=}N- \\ Cl \end{array} \right]_n$$

which is very similar in properties to ordinary rubber (8,41,42). It has been called inorganic rubber. The polymer will swell in benzene, but will not dissolve. Pieces of film can be stretched and will give a typical fiber diagram (37). This polymer is unique in that it is the only known example of a completely stable inorganic polymeric substance with the plastic properties usually associated with organic polymers.

228. Preparation of Phosphonitrilic Chloride (8)

$$NH_4Cl + PCl_5 \longrightarrow (PNCl_2)_3 + (PNCl_2)_4$$

To a solution of 450 g. of phosphorus pentachloride in 1200 ml. of dried *sym*-tetrachloroethane is added 140 g. of dry ammonium chloride. This mixture is refluxed for about 12 hr. or until evolution of hydrogen chloride has ceased. A calcium chloride tube is now attached to the open end of the condenser and the mixture is cooled. The unreacted ammonium chloride is filtered and the solvent is distilled under water pump vacuum, the temperature not exceeding 50–60°C. The residual mass is now transferred to an open dish and allowed to cool. The oily material and traces of excess solvent are removed by suction on a funnel, and the product is now washed with a little 50% aqueous ethyl alcohol. The residual powder, which consists almost entirely of phosphonitrilic chloride trimer, is recrystallized from benzene for purification. Before polymerization, the monomer should be recrystallized an additional two times. The product melts at 114°C.

229. Polymerization of Phosphonitrilic Chloride (8)

A sample of phosphonitrilic chloride weighing from 5 to 10 g. is placed in a polymer tube and sealed under nitrogen. The tube and contents are now heated to 300°C. for 4–6 hr. The tube is cooled, broken open, and the product is obtained in the form of a milky-white, rubbery plug.

VIII. Polymerization of Sulfur (S_8)

Another inorganic cyclic monomer which will open to give linear polymer which is not usually considered as such is ordinary sulfur (S_8). This may be converted to a linear high polymer with molecular weights of the order of 1,500,000 or more. The melted sulfur can be drawn out into fiber with surprisingly good tensile properties, provided the melt is quenched rapidly in water. It will crystallize to give a typical fiber diagram. Unfortunately, this extremely inexpensive high polymer does not remain in the polymeric condition at room temperature, but reverts rapidly to the cyclic S_8 monomer and loses all its polymer characteristics (3,37,57).

230. Polymerization of Sulfur

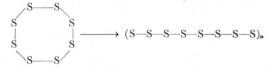

Ordinary rhombic sulfur is heated in a test tube gradually to 180°C. Melting of the rhombic material occurs at about 113°C., and at 180°C. the previously fluid material turns brown and becomes extremely viscous. The viscosity reaches its maximum at about 187°C. Fibers may be drawn from the viscous mass at that temperature and after quenching have surprisingly good tensile strength. As a variation on this experiment, a Carver press is heated to 180–187°C., and a lump of the polymeric sulfur prepared above and quenched in ice water is immediately pressed out into a film. The film is removed from between the two sheets of aluminum used for pressing and quenched rapidly in an ice water mixture. A rubbery tough, dark brown film is obtained.

IX. Polymerization of Sulfur Nitride

The chemistry of sulfur nitrides has been examined by Goehring (21). Tetrasulfur tetranitride is a cyclic compound made most readily by reaction of sulfur chloride and ammonia:

The tetranitride can be pyrolyzed to disulfur dinitride, $S = N - \overset{\oplus}{S} = \overset{\ominus}{N}$, which polymerizes,

The polymer represents a unique type of structure. It has not been fully characterized, therefore directions for its preparation are not included.

REFERENCES

1. Alderson, T., U.S. Pat. 2,811,511 (Oct. 29, 1957).
2. Astbury, W. T., *Nature*, **162**, 596 (1948).
3. Bacon, R. F., and R. Fanelli, *J. Am. Chem. Soc.*, **65**, 639 (1943).
4. Bailey, Jr., F. E., G. M. Powell, and K. L. Smith, *Ind. Eng. Chem.*, **50**, 8 (1958).
5. Barnes, C. E., W. O. Ney, and W. R. Nummy, U.S. Pat. 2,809,958 (Oct. 15, 1957).
6. Barry, A. J., *J. App. Phy.*, **17**, 1020 (1946).
7. Blaise, E. E., and M. Montagne, *Compt. rend.*, **174**, 1173, 1553 (1922).
8. Brown, C. J., *J. Polymer Sci.*, **5**, 465 (1950).
9. Cairns, T. L., and R. M. Joyce, U.S. Pat. 2,455,912 (Dec. 14, 1948).
10. Campbell, T. W., *J. Org. Chem.*, **22**, 1029 (1957).
11. Campbell, T. W., U.S. Pat. 2,831,825 (April 22, 1958).
12. Campbell, T. W., and W. R. Sorenson, unpublished data.
13. Canadian Industries, Ltd., British Pats. 642,799 and 642,983 (Sept. 13, 1950).
14. Coffman, D. D., W. L. Cox, E. L. Martin, W. E. Mochel, and F. J. Van Natta, *J. Polymer Sci.*, **3**, 85 (1948).
15. Coleman, D., *J. Chem. Soc.*, **1950**, 3222.
16. Coleman, D. and A. C. Farthing, *J. Chem. Soc.*, **1950**, 3218.
17. Etienne, Y., *Ind. des Plastique Moderne*, **9**, 37 (1957).

18. Farthing, A. C., *J. Chem. Soc.*, **1950**, 3213.
19. Farthing, A. C., *J. Chem. Soc.*, **1955**, 3648.
20. Fehnel, E. A., S. Goodyear, and J. Berkowitz, *J. Am. Chem. Soc.*, **73**, 4978 (1951).
21. Goehring, M., *Quart. Rev.*, **10**, 437.
22. Grubb, W. T., and R. C. Osthoff, *J. Am. Chem. Soc.*, **77**, 1405 (1955).
23. Hall, H. K., Jr., *J. Am. Chem. Soc.*, **80**, 6404 (1958).
24. Hall, H. K., Jr., *J. Am. Chem. Soc.*, **80**, 6412 (1958).
25. Hall, H. K., Jr., M. K. Brandt, and R. M. Mason, *J. Am. Chem. Soc.*, **80**, 6420 (1958).
26. Hall, H. K., Jr., and A. K. Schneider, *J. Am. Chem. Soc.*, **80**, 6409 (1958).
27. Hall, H. K., Jr., and R. Zbinden, *J. Am. Chem. Soc.*, **80**, 6428 (1958).
28. Hamann, A., *Faserforsch u. Textiltech.*, **9**, 351 (1958).
29. Hanford, W. E., and R. M. Joyce, *J. Polymer Sci.*, **3**, 167 (1948).
30. Hermanns, P. H., D. Heikens, and P. F. van Velden, *J. Polymer Sci.*, **30**, 81 (1958).
31. Hickinbottom, W. J., and D. R. Hogg, *J. Chem. Soc.*, **1954**, 4200.
32. Hill, F. N., F. E. Bailey, and J. T. Fitzpatrick, *Ind. Eng. Chem.*, **50**, 5 (1958).
33. Hyde, J. F., and R. C. Delong, *J. Am. Chem. Soc.*, **63**, 1194 (1941).
34. Leuchs, H., and E. Geiger, *Ber.*, **41**, 1721 (1908).
35. Lowe, C. E., U.S. Pat. 2,668,162 (Feb. 2, 1954).
36. Mark, H., G. S. Whitby, ed., High Polymers, vol. I, *The Collected Papers of Wallace H. Carothers*, Interscience, New York, 1940.
37. Meyer, K. H., *Natural and Synthetic High Polymers*, Interscience, New York, 1950.
38. Mighton, H. R., U.S. Pat. 2,647,105 (July 28, 1953).
38a. Mooradian, A. and J. B. Cloke, *J. Am. Chem. Soc.*, **67**, 942 (1945).
39. Muetterties, E. L., U.S. Pat. 2,856,370 (Oct. 14, 1958).
40. Ney, W. O., W. R. Nummy, and C. E. Barnes, U.S. Pat. 2,638,463 (May 12, 1953).
41. Patat, F., *Angew. Chem.*, **65**, 173 (1953).
42. Patat, F., and K. Frombling, *Monatsh.*, **86**, 718 (1955).
43. Patat, F., and F. Kollinsky, *Makromol. Chem.*, **6**, 292 (1957).
44. Patnode, W., and D. F. Wilcock, *J. Am. Chem. Soc.*, **68**, 358 (1946).
45. Pfeifer, C. W., U.S. Pat. 2,666,041 (Jan. 12, 1954).
46. Price, C. C., and M. Osgan, *J. Am. Chem. Soc.*, **78**, 4787 (1956).
47. Price, C. C., M. Osgan, R. E. Hughes, and C. Shambelan, *J. Am. Chem. Soc.*, **78**, 690 (1956).
48. Pruitt, M. E., and J. M. Baggett, U.S. Pat. 2,706,181 (April 12, 1955).
49. Pruitt, M. E., and J. M. Baggett, U.S. Pat. 2,706,189 (April 12, 1955).
50. Pruitt, M. E., and J. M. Baggett, U.S. Pat. 2,811,491 (Oct. 29, 1957).
51. Pruitt, M. E., J. M. Baggett, R. J. Bloomfield, and J. H. Templeton, U.S. Pat. 2,706,182 (April 12, 1955).
52. Rochow, E. G., *An Introduction to the Chemistry of the Silicones*, John Wiley, New York, 1957.
53. Rochow, E. G., and W. F. Gillian, *J. Am. Chem. Soc.*, **63**, 798 (1941).
54. Reynolds, R. J. W., Canadian Pat. 549,347 (Nov. 26, 1957).

55. Rose, J. B., *J. Chem. Soc.*, **1956,** 542, 546.
56. Smith, K. L., and R. Van Cleve, *Ind. Eng. Chem.*, **50,** 12 (1958).
57. Tobolsky, A. V., and A. Eisenberg, *J. Am. Chem. Soc.*, **81,** 780 (1959).
58. Warrick, E. L., U.S. Pat. 2,634,252 (April 7, 1953).
59. Wiley, S. G., J. Watson, and W. E. Hanby, *Nature*, **161,** 132 (1948).
60. Wittbecker, E. L., Paper presented at 129th Meeting of the American Chemical Society, Dallas, Texas, April 1956.
61. Wittbecker, E. L., H. K. Hall, and T. W. Campbell, *J. Am. Chem. Soc.*, **82,** 1218 (1960).
62. Woodward, R. B., and C. H. Schramm, *J. Am. Chem. Soc.*, **69,** 1551 (1947).
63. Zaugg, H. E., *Org. React.*, **8,** 305 (1954).

CHAPTER 6

Nonclassical Routes to Polymers

There are a number of polymer-forming reactions which cannot be properly classified as members of any of the previously described general categories. These are grouped in this chapter.

I. Cyclopolymerization

It is possible for certain structurally favorable **unconjugated dienes** to **copolymerize** according to the equation:

where X = C, O, S, N, etc.

Polymerizations of this type were first reported by Butler (9). Others who published at about the same time are Marvel (22) and Jones (13). The following example is due to the latter author.

231. Preparation of Linear Poly(acrylic anhydride) by Cyclopolymerization

267

A solution of 20 g. of acrylic anhydride of at least 98% purity in 200 ml. of anhydrous benzene is mixed with 0.4 g. of benzoyl peroxide in a polymer tube, and sealed under an atmosphere of nitrogen (see Chapter 2). The tube is agitated at 50°C. for 25 hr., then the resulting thick polymer slurry is cooled to room temperature and the polymer is isolated by suction filtration under nitrogen. It is dried at 50°C. in a high vacuum for 24 hr. The yield is 20 g. with an inherent viscosity of about 2 measured in dry dimethylformamide. This viscosity number corresponds to a molecular weight in the range of 200,000.

Although the monomer from which the polymer is made is a divinyl compound, the polymer obtained is linear, as evidenced by the fact that it is completely soluble at room temperature in such solvents as dimethylformamide, γ-butyrolactone, and N-methyl pyrrolidone. It is insoluble in most nonpolar solvents such as benzene and hexane. The polymer can be pressed to bars or to thin films at 180°C. Thin films of polyacrylic anhydride hydrolyze quite readily and the product is identical in every respect with polyacrylic acid.

II. Polymerization of the Carbonyl Group

With few exceptions, the only unsaturated compounds polymerizable to high molecular weight are those containing $C{=}C$ linkages. One notable exception is the carbonyl group.

The polymerization of monomeric formaldehyde has been known and described for many years (39). The earlier researches of Staudinger (31,32) produced films and fibrous material. However, it is only recently that tough, high molecular weight material has been obtained. Schneider (28) has shown that the cyclic monomer **trioxane**

$$\text{trioxane} \xrightarrow{\text{SbF}_3} CH_2O \longrightarrow [-CH_2O-]_n$$

can be polymerized by a variety of Friedel-Craft type catalysts, particularly antimony trifluoride, to a high molecular weight film-forming material which can be cold-drawn and oriented. Furthermore, MacDonald (17) has shown that high molecular weight linear polymer with a high degree of thermal stability and toughness can be obtained. First, **paraformaldehyde,** is pyrolyzed to gaseous monomeric formaldehyde.

$$\text{Paraformaldehyde} \longrightarrow CH_2O \longrightarrow [-CH_2O-]n$$

The monomeric formaldehyde is then passed into a solution containing one of a variety of different catalysts. The monomeric formaldehyde under these conditions polymerizes to high molecular weight linear materials.

Interesting polymers have been prepared from **acetaldehyde** (16,24) and **fluorinated aldehydes** (12). These products are unstable and have not been completely evaluated.

232. The Polymerization of Trioxane to High Molecular Weight Polyformaldehyde, or Polyoxymethylene (28)

$$\underset{\underset{\displaystyle CH_2}{\underset{\displaystyle |}{O}}}{\overset{\displaystyle O}{\diagup \diagdown}} \quad \xrightarrow{\quad SbF_3 \quad} \quad [-O-CH_2-]_n$$

The following polymerization must be carried out under completely anhydrous conditions. Trioxane is purified by recrystallizing twice from methylene chloride. Trioxane (10 g.) and antimony trifluoride (0.1 g.) are placed in a "Pyrex" Carius tube, previously washed with 10% sodium bicarbonate, rinsed ten times with distilled water and dried under nitrogen. After charging, the tube is pumped under high vacuum until there is an observable evaporation of trioxane. The tube is then sealed and placed in an oven at 120°C. for 48 hr. The cooled tube is cut in the middle, and the solid deposits at both ends collected. These fractions are exposed to moving air for 48 hr. to evaporate monomeric trioxane. From the top of the tube about 6 g. polymer is obtained, while about 3 g. is recovered from the bottom. That portion at the top is noticeably tougher than the bottom fraction. The polymer may be pressed at 170–190°C. to give glossy, tough film. Strips of this film may be stretched at room temperature and exhibit the typical necking-down phenomenon. The strips become highly oriented.

Trioxane may be polymerized by a variety of acidic catalysts as disclosed in the patent literature (28). However, antimony trifluoride seems to be the most satisfactory for this purpose.

233. Polymerization of Anhydrous Formaldehyde to Polyoxymethylene (17)

$$CH_2O \xrightarrow{\quad\quad} [-OCH_2-]_n$$

Anhydrous monomeric formaldehyde is prepared by pyrolyzing 100 g. of anhydrous paraformaldehyde according to techniques described by Walker (39). The vapors are passed through 2 traps, maintained at −15°C. The formaldehyde monomer is then passed through a vigorously stirred reaction medium consisting of 600 ml. of anhydrous pentane and 0.2 g. of triphenyl phosphine at 25°C. Polymerization occurs as rapidly as the formaldehyde is introduced, yielding a total of about 90 g. of a snow-white powdery product. The inherent viscosity is about 2 in p-chlorophenol. This product gives translucent films when compression molded at 180–220°C. The films are quite tough and are oriented by stretching.

234. Polymerization of Monomeric Formaldehyde Vapor to High Molecular Weight Polyoxymethylene (17)

$$CH_2O \longrightarrow [-OCH_2-]_n$$

Seventy-five g. of anhydrous paraformaldehyde is pyrolyzed (39) over a 2 hr. period to produce monomeric gaseous formaldehyde, which is passed through two traps at −15°C. and then into a reaction vessel containing 800 ml. of carbon tetrachloride, 0.05 g. of diphenylamine, and 0.078 g. of tributylamine. The reaction mixture is stirred vigorously and maintained at approximately 25°C. Polymerization proceeds throughout the addition of the monomeric formaldehyde to give a slurry of polymer. This is filtered, washed with ether, and air dried to give about a 35% yield of snow-white, high molecular weight polyformaldehyde. This polymer should have an inherent viscosity of about 1.8 as measured in p-chlorophenol. Again, tough, translucent films can be compression molded at about 190°C. and then stretched and oriented.

III. Polymerization of Monoisocyanates

For many years, isocyanates have been known to trimerize in the presence of certain basic catalysts according to the equation:

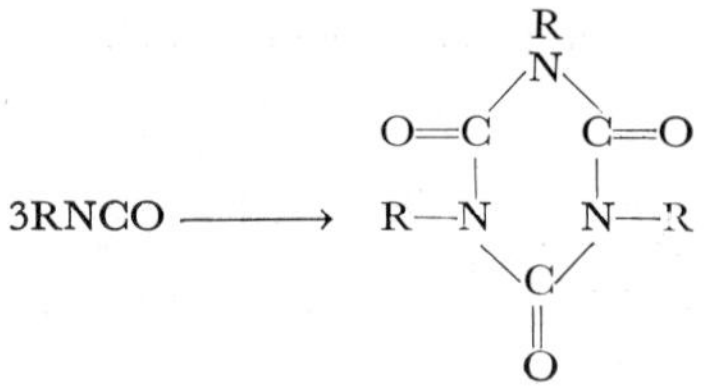

However, polymerization to a linear product without cyclization was not observed until 1959, when Shashoua, Sweeny, and Tietz (29) showed that **basic catalysts** such as sodium cyanide in dimethylformamide **will polymerize the C≡N group to a linear high polymer,** provided the reaction is carried out at **low temperatures:**

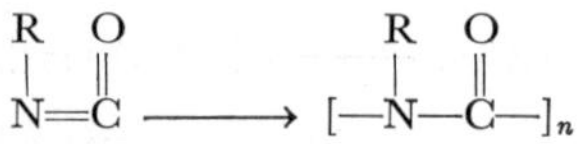

Structurally, the products are **1-nylons**, i.e., polyamides of the hypothetical N-substituted carbamic acids.

The polymers can be obtained with molecular weights approaching 1,000,000. If R is sufficiently large, e.g., n-butyl, the polymers are soluble in benzene, and tough films can be cast. The polymer where R is n-butyl melts over 200°C. and is crystalline.

1-Nylons tend to depolymerize in the melt, or in solution at room temperature in the presence of catalyst. High molecular weight products may have inherent viscosities as high as 15. Very dilute solutions (2–3%) are viscous enough to cast to very thin films.

235. Polymerization of *n*-Butyl Isocyanate (29)

$$CH_3CH_2CH_2CH_2N{=}C{=}O \longrightarrow [\ {-}\overset{\displaystyle \overset{C_4H_9}{|}}{N}{-}\overset{\displaystyle \overset{O}{\diagup}}{C}{-}\ ]_n$$

The monomer is prepared by the Curtius reaction from the corresponding acid chloride. It should be distilled immediately before use, b.p. 113–115°C., and should be stored under nitrogen. The catalyst for the polymerization is prepared by saturating dry dimethylformamide with anhydrous sodium cyanide under nitrogen for about 1 hr. The resulting solution is a powerful anionic catalyst, see Chapter 4, Preparation 145.

A 250 ml., three-necked flask is now equipped with a stirrer and two side-arm adapters. To one of these is attached a calcium chloride tube and a low temperature immersion thermometer to determine the temperature of the reaction medium. The other is fitted with a nitrogen "T" inlet tube, the vertical arm of which is sealed with a rubber bulb. The empty flask is flamed out under nitrogen and allowed to cool in an inert atmosphere. Dimethylformamide (30 ml.) is now added and the flask and contents cooled to about -58°C. which is close to the melting point of pure DMF. Ten ml. of freshly distilled *n*-butyl isocyanate is added and the mixture is stirred and allowed to cool again to -58°C. The rubber bulb is pierced with a hypodermic needle and 1 ml. of the catalyst solution is added dropwise over a period of 3 min. with vigorous stirring. After stirring for approximately 15 min. at -58°C., 50 ml. of methanol is added to inactivate the catalyst and precipitate the polymer. The polymer is filtered and washed repeatedly with methanol, then dried at 40°C. in a vacuum. The molecular weight is extremely high, and inherent viscosities of the order of 15 in benzene should be obtained routinely. The yield is about 75%. The polymer is soluble in benzene, however, only to the extent of 2–3%. The viscosity is so high that solutions of this concentration can be successfully cast to film. These films are clear and tough. In appearance, they are very similar to polyethylene.

Poly(*n*-butyl-1-nylon) has a softening temperature of about 180°C. and a melting point of about 209°C. It gradually reverts to monomeric products when maintained at this melting point for any period of time.

236. Polymerization of *p*-Methoxyphenol Isocyanate (29)

Polymerization of this monomer is carried out essentially in the same manner as in the previous example. Thirty five g. of p-methoxyphenyl isocyanate, b.p. 82°C./2 mm., is mixed with 100 ml. of dry dimethylformamide at -58°C. and treated with 12 ml. of a saturated solution of sodium cyanide in anhydrous dimethylformamide. After polymerization is completed at -58°C., the polymer is isolated as described in the previous example in a yield of about 35%. The molecular weight is somewhat lower, the viscosity being in the range of 0.7 in dimethylformamide. In the case of p-methoxyphenyl isocyanate, the polymer tends to revert to dimer in the presence of the polymerization catalyst, so the polymerization should be quenched as soon as high molecular weight has been reached. Poly(N-p-methoxyphenyl-1-nylon) is soluble in dimethylformamide at fairly high concentrations and films can be cast from this solvent and viscosity determinations carried out. The polymer melt temperature is approximately 212°C.

IV. Polymerization of Diazo Compounds

An interesting type of polymerization is the **conversion of a diazoalkane to a polyhydrocarbon** in the presence of a catalyst such as boron fluoride. The reaction proceeds according to the equation:

$$RCHN_2 \longrightarrow N_2 + [-\overset{\overset{\textstyle R}{|}}{C}H-]_n$$

A wide variety of catalysts will bring about this polymerization. Several different mechanisms may be involved, depending on the catalyst. For example with boron fluoride or borate esters, an intermediate such as $BF_3 . CH_2^+$ may be involved, while with copper powder, or colloidal gold, a carbene structure may be important (5,8,23).

It has been found possible to prepare high molecular weight **polymethylene** by polymerization of **diazomethane.** Laterally substituted polyhydrocarbons have not been prepared in as high molecular weights as has polymethylene. There are, apparently, steric factors working against the growth of high molecular weight polymer chains. Because of the unusual nature of this polymerization, several examples will be given even though the molecular weights obtained in some of them are not particularly high.

The synthesis of **isotactic polyethylidene** has been carried out, using finely divided gold as catalyst. This polymer has the structure:

$$CH_3CHN_2 \longrightarrow [-\overset{\overset{\textstyle CH_3}{|}}{C}H-\overset{\overset{\textstyle CH_3}{|}}{C}H-\overset{\overset{\textstyle CH_3}{|}}{C}H-\overset{\overset{\textstyle CH_3}{|}}{C}H-]_n$$

and is reported to have a crystalline melting point of 195°C. (22,25).

Although the structure of polymers from diazo decomposition are represented as polymethylenes, the polymers contain small amounts of nitrogen, making the absolute structure uncertain.

The diazoalkanes are toxic and potentially explosive and the following experimental examples should be carried out using due safety precautions.

237. Polymerization of Diazomethane (8)

$$CH_2N_2 \longrightarrow (-CH_2-)_n$$

A solution of 13.7 g. of diazomethane in about 700 ml. of ether is treated with 0.3 g. of freshly distilled trimethyl borate at approximately 0°C. Nitrogen evolves slowly and a precipitate begins to form in the solution. After 24 hr., the diazomethane is entirely decomposed as shown by the lack of color in the solution. The rubbery solid is obtained by filtration and weighs about 3–5 g. It may be pressed to a thin film in a Carver Press at 180–200°C.

Polymerization may also be carried out as above, but with 0.1 ml. of boron fluoride etherate as catalyst (14).

238. Preparation of Diazododecane (8)

$$C_{11}H_{23}CH_2NHCONH_2 \longrightarrow C_{11}H_{23}CHN_2$$

A mixture of 160 g. of dodecyl urea and 640 ml. of glacial acetic acid is heated on a steam bath until a clear solution is obtained. This solution is cooled to 0°C. with vigorous stirring, and a solution of 200 g. of sodium nitrite in 350 ml. of water with stirring is added over a period of 15 min. After 15 min at 0°C. an equal volume of ice water is added and the precipitated nitro-sododecylurea is collected on a filter at 0°C. Aqueous potassium hydroxide (250 ml., 40%), ethanol (500 ml.), and ligroin (500 ml.) are mixed and cooled to 0°C. The crude nitrosododecylurea is then added during 30 min. with vigorous agitation. After a further 15 min. stirring at 0°C., the upper layer is removed and filtered. This solution of 1-diazododecane is used without purification in Preparation 239. For estimation of the concentration of diazododecane, an aliquot of about 30 ml. is added to 0.5 g. of benzoic acid in benzene. Nitrogen is evolved and the color of the diazo compound is discharged. The excess benzoic acid is then titrated with standard sodium hydroxide solution and the quantity of diazododecane present in the original aliquot is calculated. One molecule of benzoic acid is equivalent to one of diazo compound. The yield of diazo compound is low, about 5.2 g./l.

239. Preparation of a Copolymer of Diazomethane and Diazododecane (8)

$$CH_2N_2 + C_{11}H_{23}CHN_n \longrightarrow Copolymer$$

To a solution of 2.2 g. of diazododecane and 6 g. of diazomethane in a total of about 700 ml. of ether-ligroin is added 0.5 g. of freshly distilled trimethyl borate. The mixture is allowed to stand for 24 hr. and the precipitated polymer is collected, washed, and dried. The yield is about 2 g. of a translucent rubbery solid soluble in chloroform, benzene, and other similar solvents. It becomes soft at about 250°C. but does not decompose completely until 370°C. It is very high molecular weight with an intrinsic viscosity in the range of 6–7 in chloroform.

240. Preparation of Diazohexane

$$C_5H_{11}CH_2NHCONH_2 \longrightarrow C_5H_{11}CHN_2$$

This material is synthesized from 100 g. of hexylurea, using the conditions given for diazododecane.

241. Preparation of a Copolymer from Diazomethane and Diazohexane (25)

$$CH_2N_2 + C_5H_4CHN_2 \longrightarrow Copolymer$$

Six g. of diazomethane and 1 g. of diazohexane are diluted to 500 ml. with anhydrous ether. One g. of triphenyl borate is then added and the mixture is allowed to stand at room temperature for 24 hr. under nitrogen. The precipitate is collected, washed with ether, and dried. It consists of about 2 g. of a rubbery, elastomeric product which is soluble in cold chloroform but not in alcohol. The crystallinity of a film cast from chloroform is relatively high. The product should have an inherent viscosity of 2.0–2.5 in chloroform.

242. Preparation of Phenyldiazomethane (31)

$$C_6H_5CH{=}NNH_2 \longrightarrow C_6H_5CHN_2$$

Nine g. of benzalhydrazine is suspended in 50 ml. of low boiling petroleum ether and shaken with 15 g. of yellow mercuric oxide with external cooling. When all of the mercuric oxide appears to have reacted, the reddish brown petroleum ether solution is decanted from the residue and most of the petroleum ether is removed in a vacuum at 0°C. For purification, the phenyldiazomethane is distilled in a vacuum of at least 1 mm. The product is explosive and high temperatures must be avoided. Phenyldiazomethane is a brown-red liquid which boils at about 35° at 1 mm. pressure. For polymerization, the product should be repeatedly distilled. The yield from 9 g. of benzalhydrazine should be approximately 4–5 g.

243. Polymerization of Phenyldiazomethane (6)

$$C_6H_5CHN_2 \longrightarrow \left[-\overset{\displaystyle C_6H_5}{\underset{\displaystyle |}{CH}}- \right]_n$$

A solution of 4 g. of phenyldiazomethane (Preparation 242) in 100 ml. of toluene is cooled to −80°C. To this solution is added 2 ml. of a 0.4 molar solution of boron trifluoride dissolved in toluene. The temperature is maintained at −80°C. for 2–3 days. The polymer is isolated by pouring the toluene solution into methyl alcohol and is purified by dissolving in benzene and reprecipitating into methanol. The yield of polymer should be about 80–85%. This polymer melts in the range of 220–240°C. It is brittle and of relatively low molecular weight.

V. Preparation of Poly-p-xylene

Two novel syntheses for **poly-p-xylylene** have been developed. The first method, discovered by Szwarc (35,36), involves the thermal **dehydrogenation of p-xylene at high temperature** to quinonedimethide, which on quenching polymerizes spontaneously.

An interesting by-product is the dimer, di-p-xyllyene,

The second method of synthesis for poly-p-xylylene is the **decomposition of a p-xylylene ammonium salt in strong, hot alkali** (10,40,41).

The latter technique is claimed to give a less cross-linked, more stable product.

Poly-p-xylylene is stable at elevated temperatures (>300°C.), and is crystalline. It is hard to fabricate, and only weak, brittle fibers have been obtained. Tough, clear, drawable films may be obtained directly, however, when the monomer is quenched on the interior surface of the collection flask in the pyrolytic method.

244. Preparation of Poly-p-Xylylene by the Pyrolysis of Xylene (3,4,27)

$$CH_3-\!\!\!\left\langle\begin{array}{c}\end{array}\right\rangle\!\!\!-CH_3 \xrightarrow{\;H_2\;} CH_2=\!\!\!\left\langle\begin{array}{c}\end{array}\right\rangle\!\!\!=CH_2 \longrightarrow$$

$$\left[-CH_2-\!\!\!\left\langle\begin{array}{c}\end{array}\right\rangle\!\!\!-CH_2-\right]_n$$

The successful dehydrogenation of p-xylylene requires high temperatures (700–1100°C.) and reduced pressures (1–5 mm.). The most suitable technique for converting p-xylene to transient quinonedimethide, which then polymerizes on cooling, is to pass vapors of p-xylene through a quartz tube heated by an external electric heater to temperatures in the range of about 900–1000°C. The monomer is vaporized by boiling at reduced pressure and the vapors are passed first through a capillary tube in order to give a constant flow of gas and then into the quartz pyrolysis tube, 19 in. long and 2 in. in diameter, held at the required polymerization temperature (900–1000°C.), preferably by the use of a multiple unit furnace. A furnace such as is used in combustion analyses in satisfactory. The exit gases are passed from the hot tube directly into a series of four traps. The first consists of a one l., round bottom standard taper flask held at room temperature, followed by three cold traps maintained at dry ice temperature. The entire system is kept at a pressure of 1–5 mm. by the use of an oil pump.

The p-xylene vapors are passed through the quartz tube where they are dehydrogenated. On exiting into the flask maintained at room temperature, the monomer will polymerize on the surface of the flask wall as a continuous tough, clear film. In addition, smaller amounts of polymer will be collected as a solid fluff in the succeeding traps maintained at -80°C. Unreacted xylene also collects in the traps as well as gaseous by-products, exclusive of hydrogen. The polymerization is surprisingly efficient under the conditions described. Xylene will be converted to poly-p-xylylene in conversions varying from 12 to 20%, the remaining xylene being recovered as such.

Ordinarily, the film of polymer laid down on the inside walls of the collecting flask may be removed in one piece. This film can be stretched at very high temperatures to give oriented product. Inherent viscosities may be determined at very high temperatures (305°C.) in benzyl benzoate. The viscosities obtained are often anomalously low because polymers prepared in this manner are not strictly linear, but are at least partially cross-linked.

245. Purification of Trimethyl(p-methylbenzyl)ammonium Bromide (38,39)

$$CH_3-\!\!\!\left\langle\begin{array}{c}\end{array}\right\rangle\!\!\!-CH_2Br + N(CH_3)_3 \longrightarrow CH_3-\!\!\!\left\langle\begin{array}{c}\end{array}\right\rangle\!\!\!-CH_2\overset{+}{N}(CH_3)_3Br$$

This salt is prepared in approximately 90% yield by quaternization of p-methylbenzyl bromide with trimethylamine. Purification of the salt is carried out as follows. Three hundred g. of the salt is disolved in 200 ml. of boiling absolute alcohol. This hot solution is filtered and cooled to about 1°C. in an ice bath. The product is then filtered, air dried, and oven dried at 110°C. in a vacuum. Approximately 65% of the crude salt is recovered as a white, pure product, m.p. 201–203.5°C.

246. The Preparation of Poly-*p*-xylene from Trimethyl(*p*-methylbenzyl) ammonium Bromide (41)

$$CH_3-\langle\bigcirc\rangle-CH_2-\overset{+}{N}(CH_3)_3 \xrightarrow{\ NaOH\ } \left[-CH_2-\langle\bigcirc\rangle-CH_2-\right]_n$$
$$Br^-$$

A 3 l., three-necked flask is equipped with a paddle type stirrer, a reflux condenser, a nitrogen inlet with a stoppered opening for rapidly adding chemicals to the flask. In the flask is placed a solution of 800 g. of sodium hydroxide in 1200 g. of distilled water. This alkali solution is heated to the boiling point with stirring. To the boiling alkali, blanketed with nitrogen, is added all at once a solution of 234 g. of trimethyl(*p*-methylbenzyl)ammonium bromide dissolved in 250 ml. of water. The resulting mixture is allowed to reflux for $3^1/_2$–4 hr. during which time the solid poly-*p*-xylylene is formed as a suspended white solid. The reaction mixture is poured into 10 l. of water and the resulting polymer suspension is filtered. The solid polymer is washed on the filter with several portions of hot water, then is extracted with 250 ml. portions of boiling ethyl alcohol. The extracted polymer is then washed with ether and dried in a vacuum. The yield of poly-*p*-xylylene should be about 60 g. Poly-*p*-xylylene is soluble in benzyl benzoate at 305°C. The inherent viscosity may be measured on a solution of the polymer at the specified temperature. A technique for determining the viscosity of solutions at elevated temperatures will be found in Chapter 2.

Poly-*p*-xylylene prepared in this manner is also a very high melting crystalline polymer which is rather difficult to fabricate. However, it can be pressed to films in a laboratory press at temperatures in excess of 350°C. Films are ordinarily highly crystalline and rather brittle.

VI. Polymerization of Norbornylene

The polymerization of olefins by organometallic titanium catalysts (cf. Chapter 4, Section VIII) proceeds uneventfully in virtually all reported cases, without rearrangement of the carbon skeleton. However, in the case of **norbornylene** it is possible to get two types of polymer, the structures of which depend on the ratio of catalyst components. With a molar ratio of titanium tetrachloride to lithium aluminum tetraheptyl greater than one, a low yield of a stiff brittle polymer (A) is produced. However, with an excess of lithium aluminum tetraheptyl, a polymer (B) is formed by an unique ring-opening polymerization (1,2,37):

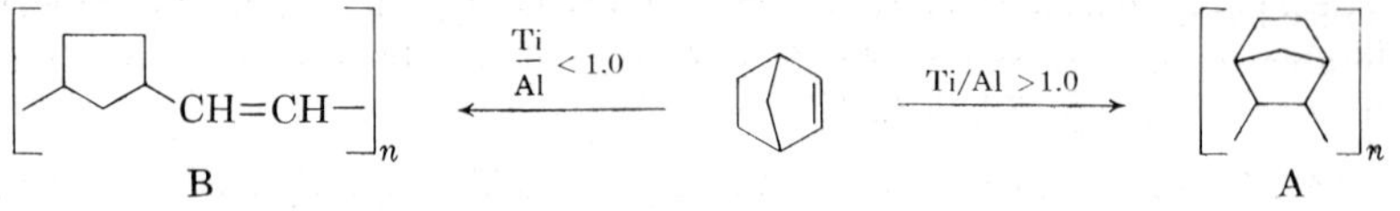

The mechanism of formation of B is believed to be the following:

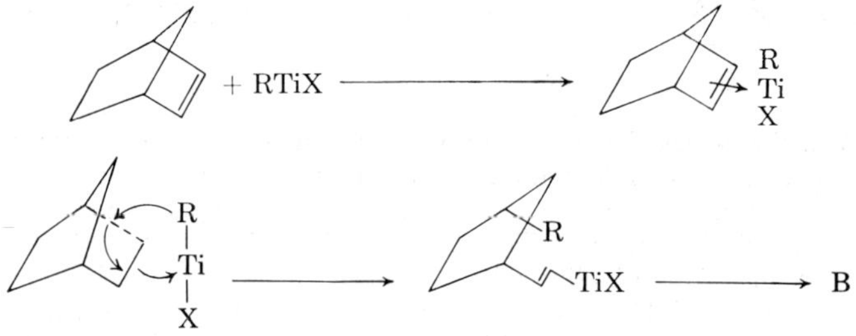

247. Lithium Aluminum Tetraheptyl (37)

$$LiAlH_4 + CH_3(CH_2)_5CH{=}CH_2 \longrightarrow LiAl(C_8H_{16})_4$$

A mixture of 13 g. (0.34 mole) of lithium aluminum hydride, 285 ml. (2.0 moles) of 1-octene, and 300 ml. of decahydronaphthalene is heated to reflux under nitrogen in a 1 l., three-neck flask, fitted with a stirrer, reflux condenser and, Glascol heater. The temperature gradually rises from 115 to 135°C. over a period of 5 hr., at which time the reaction is complete. The reaction mixture is filtered with suction through paper while hot under a nitrogen atmosphere to remove unreacted solid. The insoluble residue is pyrophoric and should be quickly quenched in isopropanol. Upon cooling, the filtered solution deposits crystals which are conveniently freed of solvent by forcing nitrogen in the flask and removing the solvent by means of a filter stick. The last trace of solvent is removed by drying under vacuum at room temperature. The white crystalline solid is dissolved in about 1 l. of xylene and standardized by titration of an aliquot with standard acid using a pH meter. The concentration of the solution usually ranges from 0.35 to 0.40 molar in lithium aluminum tetraheptyl. Exposure of the solution or solid to air or moisture leads to a loss of activity.

248. Polymerization of Norbornylene (37)

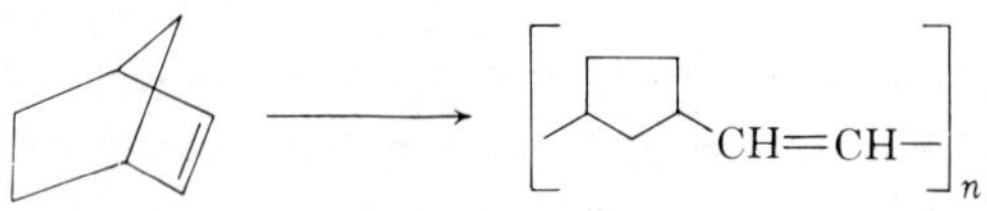

The following polymerization is carried out in an inert atmosphere in any convenient equipment. A solution of 0.02 moles of lithium aluminum tetraheptyl in xylene (prepared above and standardized) is added to 1.1 ml. (0.01 mole) of titanium tetrachloride in 50 ml. of decahydronaphthalene.

The mixture is allowed to stand for 10 min. and then 47 g. (0.5 mole) of nor-bornylene in 94 ml. of benzene is added. After standing for 24 hr., the polymer is worked up (see Chapter 4, Section VIII) to give 14.5 g. (31%) of a white powder. The powder can be pressed to a clear, stiff, tough film at 225°C. Low molecular weight benzene-soluble polynorbornylene can be separated by extraction of 34 g. of the high molecular weight polymer using 300 ml. of benzene in a Soxhlet extractor. The extraction is performed under a nitrogen atmosphere.

VII. 1-*n*-Polyamides

Polyamides based on methylenediamine may be prepared **by the reaction of formaldehyde with dinitriles** (18–21) in a strongly acidic medium. The products are **1-*n*-nylons**, where n is the number of carbons in the nitrile. The polymerization is catalyzed by strong acids and is thought to take place by the following mechanism:

$$CH_2O + H^+ \rightleftharpoons {}^+CH_2OH$$

$$^+CH_2OH + -R-CN \rightleftharpoons -R-\overset{+}{C}=N-CH_2OH$$
$$I$$

$$I + H_2O \rightleftharpoons -R-\overset{\overset{\displaystyle OH}{|}}{C}=N-CH_2-OH + H^+$$
$$II$$

$$II + H^+ \rightleftharpoons -R-\overset{\overset{\displaystyle OH}{|}}{C}=N-CH_2{}^+ + H_2O$$
$$III$$

$$III + -R-CN \rightleftharpoons -R-\overset{\overset{\displaystyle OH}{|}}{C}=N-CH_2-N=\overset{+}{C}-R-$$
$$IV$$

$$IV + H_2O \rightleftharpoons -R-\overset{\overset{\displaystyle OH}{|}}{C}=N-CH_2-N=\overset{\overset{\displaystyle OH}{|}}{C}-R- + H^+$$
$$V$$

$$V \rightleftharpoons -R-\overset{\overset{\displaystyle O}{||}}{C}-NHCH_2-NH-\overset{\overset{\displaystyle O}{||}}{C}-R$$

All the reactions involved are reversible, and the reaction product must be washed free of acid, or fairly rapid degradation will result from prolonged contact with the aqueous acids used.

Although the polymer structure is mostly that of a linear polymethyl-eneamide, there is evidence for some chain branching and the presence of an unaccountably large number of —CN groups. The polymer melt temperature is around 300°C. for 1–6 nylon, some 35°C. higher than 6–6 nylon. The difference is due at least in part to the closer arrangement of the amide groups in 1–6 nylon.

249. Preparation of Poly(methyleneadipamide) (1–6 Nylon)

$$NC—(CH_2)_4—CN + CH_2O + H_2O \longrightarrow$$

$$\left[\begin{matrix} O \\ \| \\ —C—(CH_2)_4—C—NH—CH_2—NH— \\ \| \\ O \end{matrix} \right]_n$$

In a 5 l., three-neck flask equipped with a stirrer and dropping funnel are placed 78.0 g. (0.50 m.) of adiponitrile, 15.4 g. (0.171 m.) of trioxane, and 600 ml. 98% formic acid. The solution is cooled to 10°C. and 200 g. (2.0 m.) of concentrated sulfuric acid is added with stirring and cooling during 10 min. The solution is then stirred for about 1 hr. at 26–28°C. At this point a gel forms, to which is then rapidly added, with vigorous stirring, 4 l. of water. The white powder is filtered, washed successively with dilute sodium carbonate solution, water, and ethanol. After drying in vacuum at 70°C., the yield of polymer having an inherent viscosity in m-cresol (0.5% conc. at 25°C.) of 0.6–1.2 is obtained in a yield 31–47 g. (40–60%). The polymer melt temperature is about 290–300°C. with decomposition. Other solvents are formic acid and phenol.

VIII. Polyphenylene Ethers

The preparation of high molecular weight **polyphenylene ethers**.

$$\left[\begin{matrix} R \\ —\bigcirc—O— \end{matrix} \right]_x$$

has been of interest to polymer chemists for some time. Hunter and his students (11a), and later Staffin and Price (30) studied the ferri-cyanide oxidation of 2,6-dialkyl-4-halophenols to polymers of moderate molecular weight. This was presumed to involve displacement of halogen by an aryloxy radical:

A more sophisticated **oxidation of a 2,6-disubstituted phenol** was reported later by Hay, Blanchard, Endres, and Eustance (11). These workers found that passing air through a vigorously agitated solution of a 2,6-dialkyl phenol in an organic solvent containing an amine and a copper (I) catalyst gave polymer. The reaction is rapid and high molecular weight polyphenylene ethers are obtained when R is not too large.

250. Preparation of Poly(2,6-Dimethyl-p-phenylene Ether)

A mixture of 9 ml. of pure pyridine and 30 ml. of pure nitrobenzene and 0.04 g. of cuprous chloride is shaken in an atmosphere of oxygen until the Cu (I) is converted to Cu (II). This occurs fairly rapidly; if desired, this reaction and the subsequent polymerization may be followed quantitatively by using a closed system and a gas burette. After the catalyst is prepared, 0.977 g. (0.008 m.) of pure 2,6-dimethylphenol is added, and vigorous agitation is continued. The absorption of oxygen is complete in about $1/2$ hr. The polymer is precipitated by pouring into 1% concentrated aqueous hydrochloric acid in methanol (150 mol). The solid is filtered, slurried with 5% concentrated hydrochloric acid in methanol, filtered, dissolved in chloroform, filtered, and reprecipitated into methanol. The yield is about 0.8 g. of a polymer with an inherent viscosity of about 1.0, as measured in chloroform, and an osmotic molecular weight of 28,000.

References

1. Anderson, A. W., and N. G. Merckling, U. S. Pat. 2,721,189 (Oct. 1 1955).
2. Anderson, A. W., N. G. Merckling, and P. A. Settlage, German Pat. 1,037,103 (Aug. 21, 1958).
3. Auspos, L. A., L. A. R. Hall, J. K. Hubbard, W. Kirk, Jr., J. R. Schaefgen, and S. B. Speck, *J. Polymer Sci.*, **15**, 9 (1955).
4. Auspos, L. A., C. W. Burnam, L. A. R. Hall, J. K. Hubbard, W. Kirk, Jr., J. R. Schaefgen, and S. B. Speck, *J. Polymer Sci.*, **15**, 19 (1955).
5. Bawn, C. E. H., and A. Ledwith, *Chem. and Ind.*, **1957**, 1180.
6. Bawn, C. E. H., S. Ledwith, and P. Matthies, *J. Polymer Sci.*, **33**, 21 (1958).
7. Bawn, C. E. H., A. Ledwith, and P. Matthies, *J. Polymer Sci.*, **34**, 93 (1959).
8. Buckley, G. D., and N. H. Ray, *J, Chem. Soc.*, **1952**, 3701.
9. Butler, G. B., and R. J. Angelo, *J. Am. Chem. Soc.*, **79**, 3128 (1957).
10. Fawcett, F. S., U. S. Pat. 2,757,146 (July 31, 1956).
11. Hay, A. S., H. S. Blanchard, G. F. Endres, and J. W. Eustance, *J. Am. Chem. Soc.*, **81**, 6335 (1959).
11a. Hunter, W. H., and M. J. Morse, *J. Am. Chem. Soc.*, **55**, 3701 (1933).
12. Husted, D. R., and A. A. Ahlbrecht, British Pat. 719,877 (1954).
13. Jones, J. F., *J. Polymer Sci.*, **33**, 15 (1958).
14. Kantor, W., and R. C. Osthoff, *J. Am. Chem. Soc.*, **75**, 931 (1953).
15. Ledwith, A., *Chem. and Ind.*, **1956**, 1310.
16. Letort, M. J. A., and P. Mathis, *Compt. rend.*, **241**, 1765 (1958).
17. MacDonald, R. N., U. S. Pat. 2,768,994 (Oct. 30, 1956).
18. Magat, E. E., B. F. Faris, J. E. Reith, and L. F. Salisbury, *J. Am. Chem. Soc.*, **73**, 1028 (1952).
19. Magat, E. E., L. B. Chandler, B. F. Faris, J. E. Reith, and L. F. Salisbury, *J. Am. Chem. Soc.*, **73**, 1031 (1951).
20. Magat, E. E., and L. F. Salisbury, *J. Am. Chem. Soc.*, **73**, 1035 (1951).
21. Magat, E. E., *J. Am. Chem. Soc.*, **73**, 1367 (1951).
22. Marvel, C. S., and R. D. Vest, *J. Am. Chem. Soc.*, **79**, 5771 (1957).
23. Nasini, A. *et al.*, *J. Polymer Sci.*, **34**, 106 (1959).
24. Petry, J. E. E., and M. J. A. Letort, German Pat. 933,785 (1955).
25. Ray, N. H., U. S. Pat. 2,670,333 (February 23, 1954).
26. Saini, G. *et al.*, *Gazz.* **87**, 342 (1957); also, XVI Inter. Cong. of Pure and Applied Chemistry, Paris 1957. Handbook vol. II, p. 184.
27. Schaefgen, J. R., *J. Polymer Sci.*, **15**, 203 (1955).
28. Schneider, A. K., U.S. Pat. 2,795,571 (June 11, 1957).
29. Shashoua, V. E., W. Sweeny, and R. F. Tietz, *J. Am. Chem. Soc.*, **82**, 866 (1960).
30. Staffin, G., and C. C. Price, *Rubber World*, **139**, 408 (1958).
31. Staudinger, H., and A. Gaule, *Ber.*, **49**, 1897 (1916).
32. Staudinger, H., and R. Signer, *Helv. Chim. Acta.*, **11**, 1847–51 (1958).
33. Staudinger, H., and R. Signer, H. Johner, O. Schweitzer, M. Luthy, W. Kern, and D. Russidis, *Ann.*, **474**, 145 (1929).
34. Sweeny, W., private communication.

35. Szwarc, M., *J. Polymer Sci.*, **6,** 319 (1951).
36. Szwarc, M., *J. Chem. Phys.*, **16,** 128 (1948).
37. Truett, W. L., D. R. Johnson, I. M. Robinson, and B. A. Montague, *J. Am. Chem. Soc.*, **82,** 2337 (1960).
38. von Braun, J., and W. Leistner, *Ber.*, **59B,** 2323–9 (1926).
39. Walker, J. F., *Formaldehyde*, Reinhold, New York, 1953, Chapter 2.
40. Winberg, H. E., F. S. Fawcett, W. E. Mochel, and C. W. Theobald, *J. Am. Chem. Soc.*, **82,** 1428 (1960).
41. Young, T. E., British Pat. 807,196 (Jan. 7, 1959).

CHAPTER 7

Synthetic Resins

The term "resin" had its original usage in connection with certain naturally occurring materials, obtained in most cases from evergreen trees, which found use as hard, protective coatings when solutions of these materials in organic solvents were allowed to dry in air. The most widely used natural resin is rosin (or colophony). "Resin" was then applied to any of the synthetic materials which were developed to supplement or replace the natural products, and eventually to most of the early synthetic materials which were products of organic chemistry, but were without the strictly definable structure and typical properties of crystalline organic solids. The concepts of modern polymer chemistry were as yet undeveloped, and the growth of the synthetic materials parallel to the usage of the natural materials kept the term "resin" in continual application to a wider spectrum of products. Today, "resin" covers a multitude of polymer types, including the classical phenol-formaldehyde condensates and the relatively recent epoxy resins, vinyl polymers such as polystyrene and poly(methyl methacrylate), and condensation polymers of the polyamide or polyester class. Most of the application of the term "resin" is to those linear or cross-linked (or cross-linkable) polymers that are used in molding, casting, or extruding operations and in surface coatings; and, to most cross-linked (or cross-linkable) polymers, no matter what the end use (as in adhesives, textile finishes, etc.). Thus, poly(methyl methacrylate) and various polyamides, both essentially linear polymers, are termed molding resins when directed to a molding end use. However polyamides would not be termed resins by the synthetic fiber industry in their usage of the material.

While almost any polymer may find itself classed as a resin at one time or another, and while many of the polymers prepared in other sections of this book may be resins to some readers, we have arbitrarily chosen to limit the designation to certain well-known classes of wholly synthetic condensation polymers which are usually characterized by a high degree of cross-linking.   In most of the world of polymer chemistry, they will be found to have the term "resin" in their descriptive title, as urea-formaldehyde resins, epoxy resins, alkyd resins, etc. Several reference works are available on the synthetic and natural resins generally and may be consulted for further information (3,13,16, 21,24,27,28,31,32).

I. Cross-Linked Polyesters

Polyesters (1) which have been rendered insoluble and infusible by cross-linking are commercially important types of polymeric materials. Cross-linking may be accomplished in several ways.   One of these is to start with an unsaturated polyester made by conventional esterification of a glycol with an unsaturate such as maleic acid.   The double bonds in the polyester can be used, then, as sites for copolymerization with vinyl monomers, of which styrene is typical and the most widely used.   The resulting polymer is something of a hybrid, therefore, of condensation and vinyl type polymers.

$$\left[R-O-\overset{O}{\overset{\|}{C}}-CH=CH-\overset{O}{\overset{\|}{C}}-O\right] + \phi-CH=CH_2 \longrightarrow$$

$$\left[-R-O-\overset{O}{\overset{\|}{C}}-CH-\overset{\overset{\displaystyle -CH-\phi}{\overset{\displaystyle |}{CH_2}}}{\underset{\underset{\displaystyle \phi}{\overset{\displaystyle |}{CH-CH_2}}}{CH}}-\overset{O}{\overset{\|}{C}}-O-\right]$$

The final product is complex in structure* and can be only generally indicated by equations such as this.   Usually, the linear unsaturated polyester is prepared and mixed with the vinyl monomer to give a viscous solution which is treated with a free radical catalyst to initiate the cross-linking polymerization step.   The latter step is generally

* In this chapter, the subscript n is often omitted, since the indicated structures may not be true repeat units.

carried out after the polymer solution has been placed in the casting, laminating, or other operational process from which the desired product is to be obtained.

The possible **combinations of unsaturated polyester and vinyl monomer** are very great. Copolyesters of various diols or mixtures of saturated, unsaturated, and aromatic acids (6) permit a wide range of properties to be obtained with the use of any one vinyl monomer. However, the most widely used unsaturated acids are maleic and fumaric (14). Tetrahydrophthalic and endomethylenetetrahydrophthalic acids are diene adducts of maleic acid which also find use (38). Ethylene-, propylene-, and diethylene glycols are widely used in the ester polymerization. In addition to styrene, diallyl phthalate is useful as the vinyl component, but others, such as triallyl cyanurate and diallyl diglycol carbonate, can be used which may be better suited to particular processing applications.

251. Preparation of a Polyester Resin Based on Poly-(oxydiethylene maleate) and Styrene (9)

$$HOCH_2CH_2OCH_2CH_2OH + \underset{\underset{O}{\overset{\displaystyle C}{\diagup}}\overset{O}{\diagdown}\underset{O}{\overset{\displaystyle C}{\diagdown}}}{CH{=\!\!=}CH} \longrightarrow$$

$$\left[OCH_2CH_2OCH_2CH_2O{-}\overset{\displaystyle O}{\overset{\|}{C}}{-}CH{=}CH{-}\overset{\displaystyle O}{\overset{\|}{C}} \right]$$

(I)

$$(I) + CH_2{=}CH{-}\phi \longrightarrow \left[OCH_2CH_2OCH_2CH_2O{-}\overset{\displaystyle O}{\overset{\|}{C}}{-}\underset{\underset{\phi}{\overset{|}{CH_2CH{-}}}}{CH}{-}CH{-}\overset{\displaystyle O}{\overset{\|}{C}} \right]$$

A 1 l. four-necked flask is equipped with a stirrer, siphon, nitrogen inlet, and thermometer, all reaching below the surface of the solution and a side arm with condenser set for distillation (Fig. 7.1). In the flask is placed 233.4 g. (2.2 moles) diethylene glycol, which is heated to 80°C. by means of a Glas-Col heater while nitrogen is passed through in a slow stream, and stirring is begun. Then, 196.1 g. (2.0 moles) maleic anhydride is added. The temperature is raised to 150°C. over 1 hr., then to 190°C. over 4 hr. An exothermic reaction occurs at about 100°C. and the heat should be removed until the reaction subsides. The temperature is maintained at 190°C. for 1 hr., and a vacuum of 100–200 mm. is applied. The temperature is then lowered to, and maintained at, 170°C. until the acid number of a sample of the polyester removed through the siphon is 50 or less. This requires about 1 hr. The acid number is determined as described in Chapter 3, Preparation 76, using 75 ml. acetone as solvent. The vacuum is removed and the reaction product permitted to cool to 100°C. under nitrogen. About 0.02 g. hydroquinone or *p-t*-butyl-catechol is added as an inhibitor. At 100°C. the liquid, slightly yellow poly-ester, is poured with good stirring into a sufficient quantity of styrene at 25°C. to give a 70% solution of the polyester. The solution is relatively stable at room temperature when stored under nitrogen in a brown bottle.

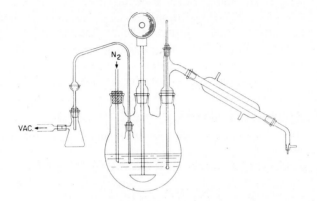

Fig. 7.1. Preparation of an unsaturated polyester.

Copolymerization of the solution can be effected by adding 4.0 g. benzoyl peroxide to 200 g. of the polyester-styrene mixture. This mixture forms a hard, tough solid in about 2 hr. at room temperature. Castings can be obtained if the mixture is poured into a suitable mold or container and allowed to set up.

252. Preparation of a Polyester Resin Based on Poly(ethylene-oxy-diethylene maleate-phthalate-adipate) and Styrene (9)

In the same apparatus as described in the preceding preparation, but using a 2 l. reaction flask, are placed 170 g. (2.75 moles) ethylene glycol and 292 g. (2.75 moles) diethylene glycol. The temperature is raised to 80°C. and 343 g. (3.5 *m.*) maleic anhydride, 111 g. (0.75 *m.*) phthalic anhydride, and 109 g. (0.75 *m.*) adipic acid are added. The temperature is raised to 150°C. over 1 hr., then increased at the rate of 10°C./hr. to 210°C. It is maintained at this level until the acid number (see Preparation 251) of a sample of the poly-ester is 60 or less. A vacuum of about 100 mm. is applied and the temperature dropped to 180°C. When a sample of polyester has an acid number of 20–30, the product is allowed to cool to room temperature under nitrogen and a trace of *t*-butylcatechol is added as an inhibitor.

A solution of the polyester is made in styrene containing a trace of inhibitor in the proportion of 100 g. polyester to 43 g. styrene. A casting can be made in the following way. One-half g. of a 6% commercial solution of cobalt naphthenate is added to 100 g. of the polyester–styrene varnish and carefully mixed to avoid the formation of a large number of air bubbles. Then, 1.5 g. of a 60% solution of methyl ethyl ketone hydroperoxide in dimethyl phthalate (Lupersol DDM) is dispersed carefully and thoroughly into the solution. The solution will cure in a mold at room temperature in about 2 hr. to give a hard, tough casting.

The term **"alkyd,"** a blend of the first part of the word alcohol and the last of acid, is generally applied to the **polyesters from reaction of alcohols and acids** where the total functionality is capable of causing crosslinking directly. Such a combination would be glycerol with phthalic anhydride, a reaction product sometimes termed a **glyptal resin.** As is evident, no additional cross-linking agent is needed. The functionality of the reactants assures cross-linking when the reaction has been carried sufficiently far.

In practice, the polycondensation is taken just far enough to provide a polyester which is still fusible and soluble, and which can be easily poured into a mold. Application of heat then causes conversion to the final insoluble, infusible polyester in the finished form. The final cross-linking is a slow process, however, and the inclusion of unsaturated monoacids is a frequent modification of the process to overcome this deficiency.

Fundamental studies of the unmodified **glycerol–phthalic anhydride reaction** have been made by Kienle (17), who found that gelation can occur at as little as 75% esterification. Intraesterification and anhydride formation occur to a small extent along with the primary reaction of interesterification. The molecular weight of the molecules formed at gelation was found to be rather low; products of molecular weight corresponding only to tetramers had been formed immediately prior to gelation. Further reaction can still occur past the gel point to form, eventually, giant molecules. Thus, gelling apparently occurs when a suitable concentration of highly complex, but low molecular weight, molecules are formed.

253. Preparation of Poly(glyceryl phthalate) (17)

In a 600 ml. beaker immersed in a silicone oil or Wood's metal bath, and equipped with a thermometer and stirrer are placed 148.1 g. (1.0 m.) phthalic anhydride and 61.4 g. (0.67 m.) glycerol. The mixture is stirred and the temperature raised to 200°C., where it is maintained for $1^{1}/_{2}$ hr. The acid value should be about 127–132, determined in acetone (Preparation 251). At this point, the product is still soluble in acetic acid, acetone, and others. Continued heating at 200°C. for about 15 min. causes the mixture to set to an immobile gel.

The possible **combinations of glycerol with dibasic acids other than phthalic or in combination with phthalic** is evident. In most cases, the acids used are limited primarily to phthalic, or phthalic plus a limited quantity of acids such as adipic or sebacic. Maleic anhydride also may be substituted wholly, or in part, for phthalic anhydride. In some cases, it is possible to include rosin with the maleic-containing polymerizates. Reaction of the dienic abietic acid and other unsaturated portions of the rosin with maleic anhydride in a Diels-Alder reaction leads to products with different and desirable properties. Pentaerythritol also has been used in place of glycerol.

A widely used modification of the basic polymerization technique is the addition of an air-drying unsaturated fatty acid or oil to the glycerol–phthalic anhydride such that the adduct becomes incorporated in the polyester. Such polymers are soluble in the hydrocarbon or ester solvents used in the paint and varnish industry. These drying oil-modified alkyds have been extremely important in surface coating uses.

The following is an example of an **oil-modified alkyd resin.** Free fatty acids are used as the modifying agent, hence the term **Fatty Acid Process** (6). The unsaturated acids are esterified by the glycerol and become part of the poly(glyceryl phthalate) molecule. Structural formulas for such polymers can only be representative of typical groupings, rather than an accurate delineation of molecular structure.

254. Preparation of a Drying Oil-Modified Poly(glyceryl phthalate) Alkyd by the Fatty Acid Process (10)

where R = $CH_3(CH_2)_4CH=CHCH_2CH=CH(CH_2)_7-$, and related unsaturates.

In a 1 l. beaker immersed in a silicone oil bath and equipped with a stirrer is placed 206 g. phthalic anhydride. An excess of anhydride is used to compensate for an anticipated 15% loss by sublimation. The anhydride is melted by raising the bath temperature to 130–135°C. and 200 g. linseed oil fatty acids is added. The mixture is stirred and heated at 135–140°C. until miscible. Then 92 g. of glycerol is added to the solution and the reaction heated at a rate of about 1°C./min. until a temperature of 240°C. is reached. This temperature is maintained for 10–15 min. Water is evolved during heating and some phthalic anhydride may sublime; for this reason, the reaction should be run in a hood. The product, when cooled, is a clear solid which is soluble in butyl acetate/toluene (75/25 volume). A 50% solution of the resin in this solvent mixture can be cast onto a glass plate, smoothed out with a doctor knife or glass rod, and heated at 150°C. for 2 hr. A hard, tough, cross-linked coating results. If cobalt naphthenate drier (0.2 g. per 100 ml. of resin solution) is added, a film can be air-dried at room temperature.

The fatty acid may be replaced in certain formulations by the fatty oil from which it is derived, obviating the need for freeing the acid from its glyceryl ester.   Such a variation is called the **Alcoholysis Process** (21) **or the Fatty Oil Process.**   It involves, first, an ester exchange reaction between glycerol and the triglyceride fatty oil, giving mono- and diglycerides of the fatty acid component of the original fatty oil.   The remaining hydroxyls of the glycerides formed are further esterified with a polybasic acid such as phthalic acid.

255. Preparation of a Drying Oil-Modified Poly(glyceryl phthalate) by the Fatty Oil or Alcoholysis Process (41)

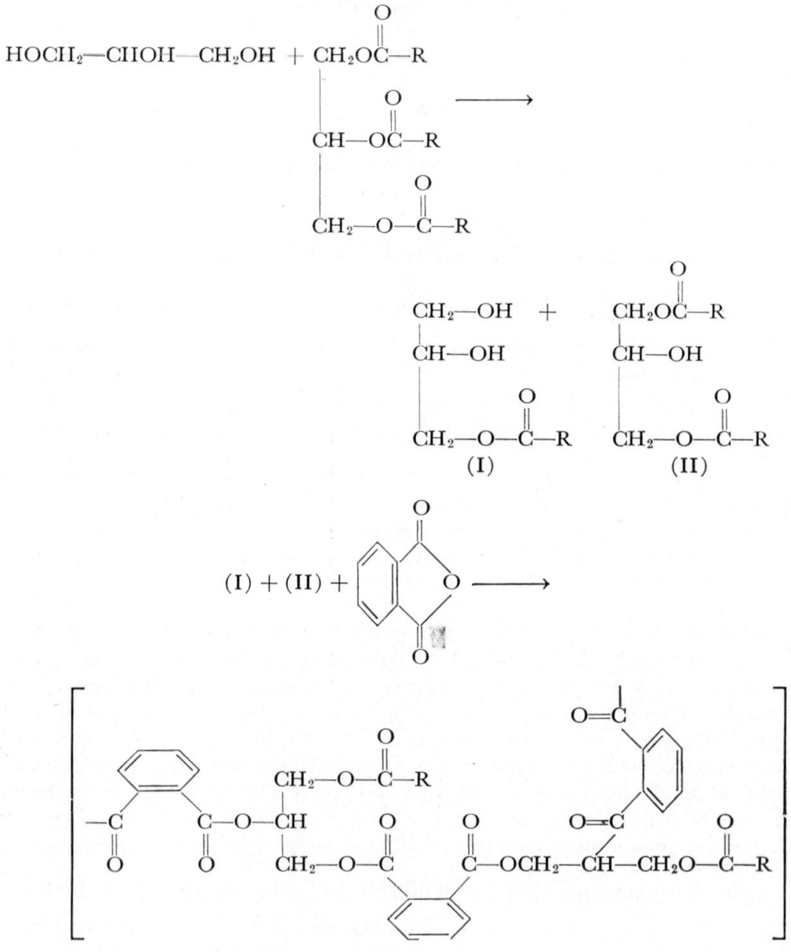

$$
HOCH_2\text{—}CHOH\text{—}CH_2OH \;+\;
\begin{array}{l}
CH_2O\overset{\displaystyle O}{\overset{\|}{C}}\text{—}R \\[2mm]
CH\text{—}O\overset{\displaystyle O}{\overset{\|}{C}}\text{—}R \\[2mm]
CH_2\text{—}O\text{—}\overset{\displaystyle O}{\overset{\|}{C}}\text{—}R
\end{array}
\;\longrightarrow
$$

$$
\begin{array}{l}
CH_2\text{—}OH \\
CH\text{—}OH \\
CH_2\text{—}O\text{—}\overset{\displaystyle O}{\overset{\|}{C}}\text{—}R \\
\quad (I)
\end{array}
\;+\;
\begin{array}{l}
CH_2O\overset{\displaystyle O}{\overset{\|}{C}}\text{—}R \\
CH\text{—}OH \\
CH_2\text{—}O\text{—}\overset{\displaystyle O}{\overset{\|}{C}}\text{—}R \\
\quad (II)
\end{array}
$$

$$(I) + (II) + \text{[phthalic anhydride]} \longrightarrow$$

A 500 ml. resin kettle is equipped with stirrer, thermometer, dropping funnel, reflux condenser, and nitrogen inlet reaching to the bottom of the vessel. To the reactor, which has been flushed with nitrogen, is charged 118.4 g. of linseed oil. The oil is then heated under nitrogen to 235°C. and, after first adding 0.5 g. lead oxide, 25.6 g. of glycerol is added slowly from the dropping funnel over a period of about 20 min. with vigorous agitation. In about 30 min., the glycerol and linseed oil become miscible. Fifty-four g. of phthalic anhydride is then added all at once, preferably molten so that air is not introduced. The dropping funnel is replaced by a siphon for sampling. The mixture is heated and stirred at 250°C. until an acid number of 5 or less is reached. (See Chapter 3, Preparation 76; acetone is used as a solvent in this case.) Nitrogen flow is fairly rapid during this part of the reaction. The final product is a pale yellow, viscous liquid, soluble in aromatic hydrocarbons, butyl acetate, and acetone.

A 50% solution of the resin in benzene, to which is added 1.5% of a cobalt naphthenate drier, forms a tough lacquer when cast as a thin coating on a metal surface and dried at room temperature. A white enamel can be made from a mixture of 100 g. of the resin, 150 g. lithopone, 50 g. zinc oxide, 55 g. turpentine, and 1 g. cobalt naphthenate drier.

II. Resins from the Reaction of Formaldehyde with Phenols

Formaldehyde condenses readily with phenols (21,13,7,27) primarily in the ortho and para positions, **to give,** eventually, **cross-linked polymers having aromatic rings linked together by methylene or oxydimethylene bridges.** The reaction is usually carried out only to such a point that a soluble, meltable intermediate condensate is formed which can be formed readily. It is converted to an insoluble, infusible final polymeric product by a later treatment, usually heat plus additional catalyst or formaldehyde.

The intermediate condensation products are of low or moderate molecular weight and may be of one of two types. The first is often called a **"resol,"** and is formed by the reaction of excess formaldehyde with phenol, about 1:1.5 mole ratio, in the presence of base. It contains hydroxymethyl groups which can condense further on heating. A typical resol may be indicated by the structure:

Some of the links between rings may be —CH_2OCH_2—.   The resol-type products are mixtures of much more complex structures than that above.

The second type of intermediate is called a **"novolak."** It arises from the reaction of less than equivalent amounts of formaldehyde with phenol, about 1:0.8 mole ratio, in an acid catalyzed reaction. There are then essentially no hydroxymethyl groups present for further condensation, and the structure may be represented by:

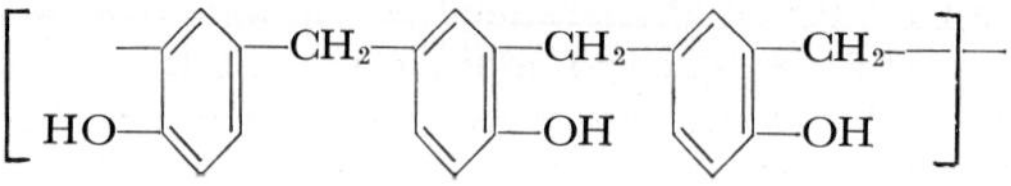

The novolaks may have molecular weights up to 1200–1500.   The resols are lower molecular weight, about 300–700.   Novolaks do not condense further without the addition of a catalyst and more formaldehyde.   Hexamethylenetetramine is frequently used as a catalyst; it may also take part in the condensation, by providing formaldehyde by hydrolysis, or in formation of dibenzylamine bridges:

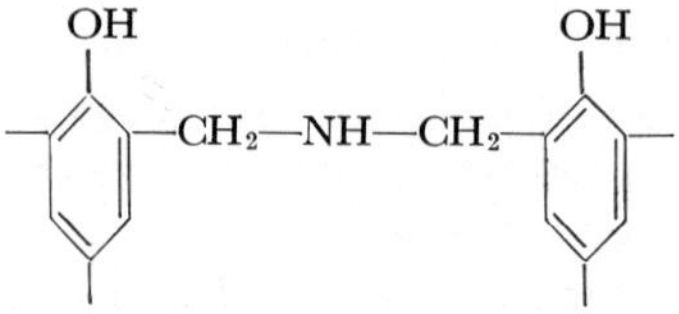

For the following, and similar resin preparations, use of a resin kettle rather than a round-bottom flask is recommended for greater ease of product removal.

256. Preparation of a Resol from Formaldehyde and Phenol (23)

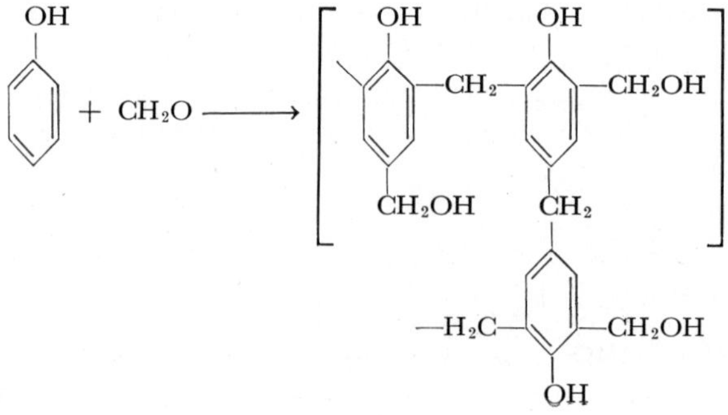

A 500 ml. resin kettle is equipped with a reflux condenser, stirrer, thermometer, and siphoning tube leading to a collecting trap for the removal of samples for testing. To the reaction vessel is added 94 g. (1 *m.*) of distilled phenol, 123 g. of aqueous formaldehyde, 37% by weight, (1.5 *m.* formaldehyde), and 4.7 g. barium hydroxide octahydrate. The reaction is stirred and heated in an oil bath at 70 °C. for 2 hr. Two layers form if stirring is stopped. Sufficient 10% sulfuric acid is added to bring the pH to 6–7. Vacuum is then applied by means of a water aspirator (pressure regulated at about 30–50 mm.) and water is removed through the condenser, which is now set for distillation. The temperature is not permitted to exceed 70 °C. Samples (1–2 ml.) are withdrawn every 15 min. through the vacuum siphon take-off and tested for gel time; by working with a spatula on a hot plate at 160 °C., gel time is taken as the time required for the resin to set up to a rubbery infusible solid. A portion of each sample removed from the reaction mixture should be cooled to room temperature and its brittleness noted. The dehydration should be stopped when the gel time is less than 10 sec., or the resin is brittle and non-tacky at room temperature. This product has been termed **"A stage" resin.** Further heating forms a resin which softens with heat but doesn't melt, and is no longer soluble. It is referred to as "**B stage**" resin. The final product from continued heating, "**C stage**" resin, is hard, insoluble and infusible. Resin at the first stage can be mixed with wood flour, lime, and pigments, and used as a molding powder for conversion to the final stage C by means of heat. Much industrial use is made of the "A" stage resin in laminates, adhesives and varnishes.

To observe the eventual hardening to the "C stage" resin, the resin prepared above should be removed at the A stage and heated in test tubes or small beakers at 100 °C.

257. Preparation of a Novolak from Formaldehyde and Phenol (23)

A 500 ml. resin kettle is equipped as described in the preceding preparation and charged with 130 g. phenol (1.38 *m.*), 13 ml. water, 92.4 g. 37% aqueous formaldehyde (1.14 *m.*), and 1 g. oxalic acid dihydrate. The mixture is stirred and refluxed for 30 min. An additional 1 g. of oxalic acid dihydrate is then added, and refluxing is continued for another hour. At this point, 400 ml.

water is added and the mixture cooled.   The resin is permitted to settle for
30 min. and the upper layer of water decanted or withdrawn through the
siphon.   Heating is then begun with the condenser set for vacuum distillation.   Water is distilled at 50–100 mm. pressure until the pot temperature
reaches 120°C., or until a sample of the resin is brittle at room temperature.
The resulting novolak resin is soluble in alcohol.   About 140 g. of resin is obtained.   It can be used in the following preparation.

258. Preparation of a Molding Powder from a Novolak Resin (25)

A mixture of 46 g. of finely ground novolak (Preparation 257), 44.6 g. of
dry wood flour filler (80–100 mesh), 6.7 g. hexamethylenetetramine, 2.0 g.
magnesium oxide, and 1.0 g. magnesium or calcium stearate is blended by
tumbling in a jar or a ball mill.   The blended material can then be placed
in a mold and heated under 2000 p.s.i. at 160°C. for 5 min.   A hard, cured
solid results.

259. Preparation of a Cast Phenolic Resin (25)

In a 1 l. resin kettle equipped with a stirrer, condenser, thermometer, and
vacuum siphon for sampling, is placed 100 g. phenol (1.06 $m.$), 203 g. of 37%
aqueous formaldehyde (2.5 $m.$), and 3.0 g. of 20% aqueous sodium hydroxide.
The reaction is stirred and heated to 70–80°C. by means of an oil bath for
about 3 hr.   The reaction mixture is then concentrated at 30 mm. pressure
until a pot temperature of 65°C. is reached.   Then, 6.5 g. lactic acid is added,
followed by 15 g. glycerol.   The removal of water is then continued at 30 mm.
until a sample of the resin withdrawn through the vacuum siphon forms a
ball that will just barely yield to pressure between the fingers when a drop is
placed in 11–13°C. water.   This may require that a pot temperature of
about 85°C. be reached.   Samples of this finished resin, a viscous liquid, may
then be poured while hot into test tubes or beakers and heated at 80°C. for
4–8 days to give hard castings which are clear if sufficient water was removed
from the resin during preparation.

Because formaldehyde preferentially condenses at the ortho and para
positions of phenol, it should be theoretically possible to prepare only
linear, soluble high polymers from formaldehyde and a phenol with
either an ortho or para position blocked.   In practice, however, some
condensation apparently takes place at open meta positions, since o-
and p-cresol will eventually give an infusible, thermoset material,
although times involved are very long (21).   However, other **para
substituted phenols,** such as p-t-butylphenol and p-phenylphenol, are
used to **give oil soluble condensates with formaldehyde** which are
useful in varnish applications.   Linear polymers of relatively low
molecular weight have also been prepared and studied, using **formaldehyde** and o- and p-chlorophenol (4).   These polymers are too
brittle to give useful products, however.

260. Preparation of a Polymer from *o*-Chlorophenol and Formaldehyde (4)

A solution of 25.71 g. (0.20 *m.*) *o*-chlorophenol, 6.12 g. *s*-trioxane (0.204 *m.* formaldehyde), 0.40 g. *p*-toluene sulfonic acid monohydrate 10 ml. bis(2-ethoxyethyl)ether is sealed in a thick-walled polymer tube and heated at 150°C. for 24 hr. in an oil bath.   The sealed tube must be properly shielded in case of rupture.   The tube is then permitted to cool to room temperature and is opened cautiously after wrapping in a towel.   The mixture is poured into 100 ml. acetone and filtered through a coarse, sintered glass funnel.   The filtrate is added slowly with vigorous stirring to 3 l. of distilled water containing 20 ml. concentrated hydrochloric acid.   The light tan solid is filtered, washed with distilled water, and dried over phosphorus pentoxide at 60°C./0.5 mm. for 24 hr.   The inherent viscosity in dimethylformamide (at 0.5% concentration, 25°C.) is about 0.4.   The polymer recovered is about 80% of the theoretical, the remainder being insoluble in acetone.   On a melting point block, the polymer softens around 90–100°C., starts to char around 120°C., and decomposes without melting at 200°C. or more.   On a preheated hot bar, the polymer melts around 145–155°C., if placed immediately in this range.

Five g. of polymer is dissolved in 48 ml. dry pyridine and the solution treated with 14 ml. acetic anhydride.   After the solution stands at room temperature for 5 days, the acetylated polymer which is formed is recovered by pouring into 1 l. of distilled water containing 10 ml. concentrated hydrochloric acid.

The polymer acetate softens around 140°C. and melts without decomposition around 150–165°C. on a heated bar.

The **linear formaldehyde-*o*-chlorophenol polymer can be dechlorinated** with sodium in liquid ammonia to give an essentially halogen-free polymer with the ortho position now open (5).

261. Dechlorination of an *o*-Chlorophenol–Formaldehyde Polymer

A solution of 7 g. of sodium in 200 ml. liquid ammonia is prepared in a 500 ml., three-necked flask, cooled in dry ice–methanol and equipped with a dry ice condenser, stirrer, and dropping funnel. To it is added slowly, with stirring, a solution of 10 g. of the *o*-chlorophenol–formaldehyde polymer, prepared as before, dissolved in 140 ml. of tetrahydrofuran which has been dried by distilling from sodium. Stirring is continued for 24 hr., at which time the excess sodium is destroyed by the addition of ammonium chloride. The reaction mixture is poured slowly with stirring into 10 l. of ice and water containing 600 ml. of concentrated sulfuric acid. The temperature is kept below 10°C. and the pH below 4. The light tan polymer is filtered, washed we l with distilled water, and air-dried. It is then dissolved in 75 ml. of dimethylformamide and added slowly with stirring to 1 l. of distilled water containing 10 ml. concentrated hydrochloric acid. The solid is filtered, washed well with distilled water and dried at 60°C./0.5 mm. over phosphorus pentoxide in a drying pistol for 24 hr. The chlorine content should be 0.5–0.6%. Further chlorine can be removed by repeating the above procedure, using 5 g. sodium for 10 g. of once dechlorinated polymer. After similar work-up, the polymer contains 0.01% chlorine or less. Dechlorinated polymer softens at about 120°C. when placed on a preheated block. The acetyl derivative (see Preparation 260) softens around 100°C. and melts at 120–125°C.

If 0.5 g. of dechlorinated polymer (once treated with sodium) is dissolved in 5 ml. dimethylformamide and treated with 0.2 g. hexamethylenetetramine at reflux, a precipitate forms via cross-linking within 1 hr. If bis(2-ethoxyethyl)ether is used as solvent, a precipitate forms in 3 min. at reflux. In either solvent, no precipitate occurs if the original chlorine containing polymer is used, due to the blocking effect of the chlorine in the ring.

III. Reaction of Formaldehyde with Urea and Melamine

Formaldehyde and **urea** react under alkaline conditions to give isolatable **mono- and di-methylolureas** (21,13,36,27).

$$\underset{\text{H}_2\text{N--C--NHCH}_2\text{OH}}{\overset{\text{O}}{\|}} \qquad \underset{\text{HOCH}_2\text{NH--C--NHCH}_2\text{OH}}{\overset{\text{O}}{\|}}$$

Such compounds are precursors in the formation of **cross-linked urea-formaldehyde resins.** The mechanism of the polymerization is still not known with certainty; one suggestion is that of Marvel (20), wherein urea is considered as an aminoacid amide. Thus, the two –NH$_2$ groups are not identical; one is considered an amino, the other an amide, –NH$_2$. The amide –NH$_2$ is thought to react with formaldehyde to give the monomethylolurea which trimerizes with loss of water. Further reaction occurs with the –CONH$_2$ of the trimer with formaldehyde to produce a cross-linked material. The stoichiometry of the mechanism requires a urea:formaldehyde ratio of $1:1.5$, which is about what is generally used in commercial resin production.

$$3H_2N-\overset{\overset{\textstyle O}{\|}}{C}-NHCH_2OH \longrightarrow \quad H_2N\overset{\overset{\textstyle O}{\|}}{C}-N \underset{\smile}{\overset{\overset{\textstyle NH_2}{\overset{\textstyle |}{\overset{\textstyle O=C}{\overset{\textstyle |}{N}}}}}{\quad}} N-\overset{\overset{\textstyle O}{\|}}{C}-NH_2 \quad \xrightarrow{\ CH_2O\ }$$

$$\left[\; HN-\overset{\overset{\textstyle O}{\|}}{C}-N \underset{\smile}{\overset{\overset{\textstyle NH-}{\overset{\textstyle |}{\overset{\textstyle O=C}{\overset{\textstyle |}{N}}}}}{\quad}} N-\overset{\overset{\textstyle O}{\|}}{C}-NH-CH_2-NH-\overset{\overset{\textstyle O}{\|}}{C}-N \underset{\smile}{\overset{\overset{\textstyle -NH}{\overset{\textstyle |}{\overset{\textstyle C=O}{\overset{\textstyle |}{N}}}}}{\quad}} N-\overset{\overset{\textstyle O}{\|}}{C} \; \right]$$

Cyclic units are not a requisite for ultimate crosslinking, however. Later evidence has indicated that a noncyclic methylene urea having linear and branched segments is the correct structure (11a), with few or no rings present.

$$\left[\begin{array}{c} -H_2CNH\overset{\overset{\textstyle O}{\|}}{C}-NH-CH_2-N-\overset{\overset{\textstyle O}{\|}}{C}-NH- \\[2mm] \overset{\overset{\textstyle O}{\|}}{}\; \overset{\textstyle CH_2}{} \\ -NH\overset{\overset{\textstyle O}{\|}}{C}-N \\ CH_2 \\ NH-\overset{}{C}-N-CH_2- \\ \overset{\overset{\textstyle }{\|}}{O}\;\;\overset{\textstyle CH_2}{} \end{array} \right]$$

The commercial preparation of urea-formaldehyde resins usually involves the formation of soluble methylol-urea derivatives with basic catalysts. This intermediate condensate is then compounded with various fillers, pigments, and an accelerator. The latter is either an acidic material or one capable of functioning as an acid at a high temperature. The product so obtained can then be placed in a mold and heated to effect the final thermosetting, cross-linking (21) reaction. Urea-formaldehyde condensates can also be used as additives for wet strength in papers and as finishes for fibers to impart crease resistance, and as adhesives.

262. Preparation of a Urea-Formaldehyde Resin (33)

To a 500 ml., three-necked flask equipped with a stirrer and reflux condenser is charged 130 g. of 37% aqueous formaldehyde (1.6 m.) which is brought to a pH of about 7.5 by the addition of 10% sodium hydroxide solution. Then, 60 g. (1.0 m.) urea is added and the mixture gently refluxed and stirred for 2 hr. The mixture is then concentrated to 70% solids by distillation of 40 ml. of water under water aspirator pressure. The resulting syrup, after acidifying with acetic acid, can be heated further at 100°C. for several hours to effect gelation.

263. Preparation of a Urea-Formaldehyde Adhesive (33)

To prepare a plywood adhesive, 100 g. of the unacidified concentrated syrup prepared as in Preparation 262, can be mixed with 28 g. furfuryl alcohol, 16 g. wood flour (80–100 mesh), 1 g. calcium phosphate, and 0.35 g. triethanolamine by stirring, while raising the temperature to 90°C. over $^1/_2$ hr. This temperature is held for 15 min., then the mixture is cooled slowly to room temperature. The mixture will set to a solid at room temperature if mixed with 2 g. of ammonium chloride and 3 ml. water in a beaker. The ammonium chloride and water function as a hardening catalyst, providing a working life for the adhesive of about 6 hr. Before addition of the catalyst, the adhesive resin is stable for weeks.

264. Preparation of a Urea-Formaldehyde Molding Powder

The resin solution prepared in Preparation 262 may be used without concentrating in the preparation of a molding powder. Fifty g. of the resin solution is mixed with 40 g. of alpha flock cellulose and 0.5 g. zinc stearate in a dough mixer or by hand in a metal beaker or dish until all the lumps are broken up. The mix is dried in a circulating air oven for 2–4 hr. at 70°C. and is ground in a mechanical mill or by hand in a mortar to a powder. The material can then be pressed in a mold or laboratory press at 145°C. for 2–3 min. at 2000 p.s.i. to give solid pieces.

The methylolurea groupings in the soluble first stage of the urea-formaldehyde reaction reduce the compatibility of the product with many nonpolar organic solvents and oils. **Solubility** in such solvents can be achieved by carrying out the initial reaction in the presence of an alcohol. The **methylol groups are partially etherified,** and the solubility of the product depends on the chain length of the alcohol used. Methanol, for instance, gives an etherified intermediate which is still water soluble. Butanol will produce a toluene-soluble product. Etherification of the methylols reduces the likelihood of gelation at moderate temperatures.

265. Preparation of a Urea-Formaldehyde Resin Modified with Butanol (15)

$$NH_2CONH_2 + CH_2O \longrightarrow -\overset{|}{N}CH_2OH \xrightarrow{\text{BuOH}} -N-CH_2OBu(n)$$

$$-NCH_2OBu(n) \longrightarrow \text{Crosslinked Polymer} + n-BuOH + H_2O$$

In a 1 l. three-necked flask equipped with reflux condenser, thermometer, and stirrer are placed 243 g. of 37% aqueous formaldehyde (3.0 m. formaldehyde) and 4–6 g. of concentrated ammonium hydroxide to bring the pH to 7.5–8.5. Sixty g. (1.0 m.) urea is added with stirring and the mixture heated to 100°C. over a 1 hr. period by means of a Glas-Col mantle. This temperature is maintained for $^1/_2$ hr. One hundred forty-eight g. (2.0 m.) n-butanol is added, followed by enough phosphoric acid to bring the pH to 5.5. The reaction is heated and stirred for $^1/_2$ hr. at 100°C. The resin is freed of water by heating at 60–70°C. under a water aspirator pressure of 100–200 mm. The hot resin is pourable, but becomes tacky at room temperature. The resin can be dissolved in butanol or toluene to give a 50–60% solution. When this solution is flowed onto glass or metal plates which are then heated for $^1/_2$ hr. in an oven at 150°C., a hard, clear coating results.

Melamine reacts with **formaldehyde** in much the same way as urea, forming compounds of varying degrees of N-methylol substitution depending on the mole ratio of reactants.

III

The tri- and hexamethylol compounds (I and II) are readily prepared and isolated, and may be polymerized to cross-linked products. The structure of the final polymer is presumably that obtained from elimination of water between N-methylol groups and remaining $-NH-$ groups. From the hexamethylol melamine, reaction may be through inter-etherification of methylol groups, or elimination of some formaldehyde followed by the first described condensation. As in the case of the urea-formaldehyde reaction, it is possible that cyclic structures may also be formed in the melamine reaction (III).

In practice, the initial reaction is carried to a soluble syrup, which can be mixed with fillers or used as such in molding or casting under conditions of heating, to give hard, insoluble, infusible products.

266. Preparation and Polymerization of Hexamethylol Melamine (39)

In a 500 ml., three-necked flask equipped with stirrer and condenser are placed 37.8 g. (0.3 m.) melamine and 195 g. of 37% aqueous formaldehyde (2.4 m.) which has been made slightly basic (pH 7.5) with dilute sodium hydroxide. The mixture is stirred and heated on the steam bath until a solution results. Heating is continued for 10 min.; then the reaction is cooled. A solid separates which is filtered, washed well with ethanol, and dried at 50°C. The melting point is about 150°C. The clear melt resolidifies on further heating to a clear, hard, insoluble product.

267. Preparation of a Melamine-Formaldehyde Molding Powder (39)

In a 1 l. resin kettle equipped with condenser and stirrer are placed 126 g. (1.0 m.) melamine and 365 g. (4.5 m.) of 37% neutralized aqueous formaldehyde. The mixture is stirred and heated at reflux for 40 min. Dilution of a sample of the solution with an equal volume of water should give a precipitate of resin. The undiluted solution is cooled to room temperature and 235 g. of the reaction mixture is kneaded with 50 g. of alpha flock and 0.5 g. zinc stearate in a dough mixer, if available, or by hand in a metal beaker or dish, making sure any lumps are broken up. The mass is then dried in a circulating air oven for 2–4 hr. at 70–80°C It is ground to a uniform powder in mechanical mill or by hand in a mortar to give a solid, which, if pressed in a mold or laboratory press at 145°C. for 2–3 min. at 2000 p.s.i., gives a hard, lustrous, water insensitive material.

268. Preparation of a Melamine-Formaldehyde Casting Resin

The method of the preceding preparation is used to condense 126 g. (1.0 m.) of melamine and 243 g. (3.0 m.) of 37% aqueous formaldehyde. At the end of the 40 min. reflux period, the solution is concentrated to about 70% solids by distilling about 60 ml. of water at water aspirator pressure. As a softening agent, 20 g. of glycerine is stirred into the resin. The resulting syrup can be solidified in a mold, or in a beaker, by gradually raising the temperature to 150°C. to give a clear, hard product.

269. Preparation of Melamine-Formaldehyde Resin Modified with Butanol (39)

Fifty g. of the hexamethylolmelamine (Preparation 266) is added to 80 g. of n-butanol and 0.5 g. concentrated hydrochloric acid in 250 ml. flask equipped with a condenser. The reaction mixture is heated to reflux for 15 min. A clear solution is obtained which forms a hard, clear coating when a portion of it is evaporated to dryness on a surface, then heated at 150°C. for 30 min.

Mixtures of melamine with urea or phenol may be condensed with formaldehyde. Such compositions contain the structural features of the "homopolymers" that comprise them in a network system of crosslinked molecules. From melamine and phenol with formaldehyde, a representation of the structure is:

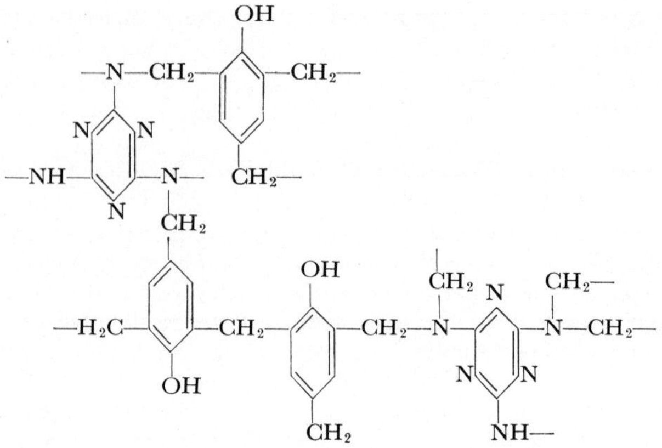

270. Preparation of a Melamine-Phenol-Formaldehyde Molding Powder (39)

In a 500 ml. resin kettle with stirrer, thermometer, and condenser are placed 50 g. (0.4 *m.*) melamine, 37.3 g. (0.4 *m.*) phenol and 130 g. (1.6 *m.*) of 37% aqueous formaldehyde. The mixture is acidified to pH 5.5–6.5 with acetic acid and is heated at 95°C. with stirring for 30 min. Two layers form. To the mixture at room temperature is added 60 g. of alpha flock cellulose, which is kneaded in until the mass is homogeneous. The mass is dried at 60°C. in a vacuum oven and ground up. When heated under pressure at 150°C., the resin is thermoset to a hard, infusible solid.

IV. Ion Exchange Resins from Formaldehyde Condensations

Ion exchange resins can be **prepared by condensing formaldehyde with a phenol, a urea or a melamine** in such a way as to introduce ionic sites in the final resin (18). This can be achieved by **using an ionic coreactant** which enters into the polymer structure, by using a phenol carrying an ionic substituent, or by after treatment of the resin (e.g., sulfonation). Ion exchange resins are fundamentally of two types: (a) those having **basic groups capable of exchanging anions,** and (b) those having **acidic groups capable of exchanging cations.** The types of reactions are shown below, with the exchangeable ion boxed:

$$\text{(a) } \sim\text{N} + \text{HCl} \longrightarrow \sim\text{NH}^{\oplus} \boxed{{}^{\ominus}\text{Cl}}$$

$$\text{(b) } \sim\text{CH}_2\text{—SO}_3\text{Na} \longrightarrow \sim\text{CH}_2\text{—SO}_3{}^{\ominus} \boxed{\text{Na}^{\oplus}}$$

In the first type, various basic nitrogen-containing compounds can be used as coreactants. Among these are dimethylamine, guanidine, 2-aminopyridine, diethanolamine, and tetraethylenepentamine. To introduce anionic groups, sodium bisulfite, *p*-hydroxybenzene sulfonic acid, glycine, taurine, and others have been used.

In the following preparation, sodium bisulfite and sulfite are the coreactants in a phenol-formaldehyde condensation. This introduces $-CH_2SO_3Na$ groups into the final resin.

271. Preparation of a Cation Exchanging Resin Based on Phenol, Sodium Bisulfite and formaldehyde (11)

In a 500 ml., three-necked flask equipped with stirrer and reflux condenser are placed 94 g. (1.0 *m*.) phenol, 26 g. (0.25 *m*.) anhydrous sodium bisulfite, 31.5 g. (0.25 *m*.) anhydrous sodium sulfite, 75 g. (2.5 *m*.) paraformaldehyde, and 11.3 g. water. An exothermic reaction occurs as the mass is stirred and the temperature rises to about 100°C. When the initial reaction subsides, the mixture is heated to reflux until a viscous syrup results. The syrup is then poured into a shallow glass tray and heated in a circulating air oven at 100°C. for 3 hr., followed by 16 hr. at 150°C. Heating effects the curing of the resin to an insoluble state. It is then ground to about 24–30 mesh. It has a capacity for the removal of cations from solution equivalent to about 17.8 kgr. (1.15 kg., or 11.5 *m*. of divalent cation) of calcium carbonate per ft.³ of resin of density 25.3 pounds/ft.³

The **acidic grouping** of a resin **may be a substituent on the phenol,** as in the subsequent preparation where *p*-**hydroxybenzen sulfonic acid** is prepared and then **condensed with formaldehyde.**

Cross-linking probably results from additional condensations meta to the hydroxyl, from incomplete sulfonation which leaves unsubstituted "trifunctional" phenol, and formal linkage through the phenolic hydroxyl.

272. Preparation of a Cation Exchange Resin from Phenol Sulfonic Acid and Formaldehyde (37)

In a 500 ml., three-necked flask having a stirrer, dropping funnel, and condenser is placed 94 g. (1.0 m.) phenol. The flask is heated to 90°C. by means of a water bath, and a mixture of 98 g. (1.0 m.) sulfuric acid and 18 g. (1.0 m.) water is added with stirring over a period of 1 hr. The mixture is stirred for another hour at 90°C. It is then diluted with 170 ml. water. With the temperature of the solution maintained at 90–100°C., 150 g. (5.0 m.) paraformaldehyde is added portionwise. The mixture is heated at 90–100°C. for about 10 hr. The black resin which results is washed with water and ground up to 24–30 mesh. It will absorb 5% of its weight of calcium, calculated as calcium oxide, from an aqueous calcium chloride solution. When the sites for exchange are exhausted, they can be regenerated by washing with a solution of hydrochloric acid.

When the strong base **guanidine** is **incorporated in a melamine-formaldehyde resin,** the resulting material is capable of anion exchange at the basic centers which are introduced, probably by a reaction of the following type:

273. Preparation of an Anion Exchanging Resin Based on Melamine and Formaldehyde (34)

In a 1 l. resin kettle equipped with a thermometer and condenser is placed a mixture of 126 g. (1.0 m.) melamine, 122 g. guanidine nitrate (1.0 m.), and 324 g. (4.0 m.) of 37% aqueous formaldehyde. The mixture is adjusted to a pH of 9–10 by the addition of 30.5 g. sodium carbonate, refluxed for 2 hr., then acidified at 80°C. with 30 g. concentrated hydrochloric acid diluted with 25 ml. water. The syrup gels almost immediately to a white, opaque mass. It is cut up to pea size and air-dried overnight at 60–65°C. The resin is cured at 100°C. for 2 hr. The product is ground again to a finer size (24–30 mesh) and washed with a 5% sodium hydroxide solution. The resin will remove chloride ions from acidic solutions, and can be regenerated by treatment with aqueous sodium hydroxide, through reactions of the type below:

$$\begin{array}{c}\diagdown \\ \diagup\end{array}C = NH_2^{\oplus} \quad OH^{\ominus} \quad \underset{NaOH}{\overset{HX}{\rightleftarrows}} \quad \begin{array}{c}\diagdown \\ \diagup\end{array}C = NH_2^{\oplus} \quad X^{\ominus} \quad + H_2O$$

V. Epoxy Resins

Epoxy resins (27,35,19,26) are **prepared by the base-induced condensation of a polyhydroxy compound,** usually a bisphenol, **with,** in most cases, **epichlorohydrin** to give as an intermediate a low molecular weight, essentially linear polymer, having terminal epoxide groups and pendant hydroxyls. An excess of epichlorohydrin in the reaction accounts for the termination of chains with epoxy groups. The following reactions are believed to occur in the one-step operation leading to the fusible prepolymer:

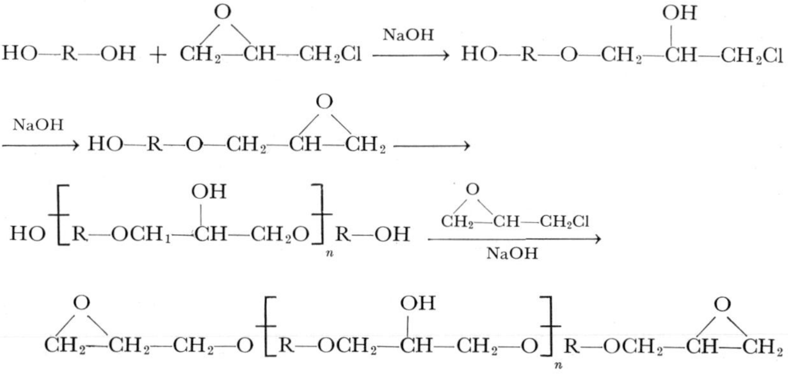

$$HO-R-OH + CH_2-CH-CH_2Cl \xrightarrow{NaOH} HO-R-O-CH_2-\underset{\overset{|}{OH}}{CH}-CH_2Cl$$

$$\xrightarrow{NaOH} HO-R-O-CH_2-CH-CH_2 \longrightarrow$$

$$HO\left[R-OCH_1-\underset{\overset{|}{OH}}{CH}-CH_2O\right]_n R-OH \xrightarrow[NaOH]{CH_2-CH-CH_2Cl}$$

$$CH_2-CH_2-CH_2-O\left[R-OCH_2-\underset{\overset{|}{OH}}{CH}-CH_2-O\right]_n R-OCH_2-CH-CH_2$$

I

The value of n in the polyether formula above can vary from 0 to 20, and the intermediate resin (I) can range from a liquid to a high melting (150°C.) solid, accordingly. The final cross-linking, to give an infusible, insoluble, hard product, can be carried out in a variety of ways, which usually involve either ring-opening of the terminal epoxides and/or esterification of the chain hydroxyls. Among the more widely used cross-linking, or curing, agents are amines and dicarboxylic acids or their anhydrides. The reactions are presumed to be of the addition type in the case of the primary amines.

$$RNH_2 + \underset{CH_2-CH}{\overset{O}{\diagup\diagdown}}\sim\!\!\sim\!\!\sim\underset{CH-CH_2}{\overset{O}{\diagup\diagdown}} \longrightarrow$$

$$
\begin{array}{c}
\overset{\displaystyle\xi}{CH-OH} \\
| \\
OH\ \ OHCH_2 \\
|\ \ \ || \\
CH_2-CH\!\!\sim\!\!CH-CH_2-N-R \\
\diagup \\
R-N \\
\diagdownR \\
| \\
CH_2-CH\!\!\sim\!\!CH-CH_2-N-CH_2-CH\!\!\sim \\
|\ \ \ || \\
OH\ \ OHOH
\end{array}
$$

[where $R = -C_6H_4C(CH_3)_2C_6H_4-$]

The tertiary amines are believed to operate by a catalytic ring-opening polymerization mechanism involving epoxy groups rather than a simple addition reaction, which is unavailable to the R_3N compounds. Secondary amines function in the same way after an initial single step addition reaction.

Anhydrides of dibasic acids react first with a chain –OH. The free carboxyl can then esterify an –OH of another chain (path A) or open a terminal epoxide (path B):

The epoxy resins are very stable to heat and have little tendency to cross-link before a curing agent has been added. After compounding with a suitable curing agent, the epoxy resin is then used in its soluble, fusible state for a variety of applications (adhesives, surface coatings, potting of electrical assemblies, laminates, foams, etc.). Curing to the final hard resin is effected either by the application of heat or, more slowly, at ambient temperatures.

274. Preparation of Epoxy Resins from 2,2-bis(4-hydroxyphenyl)-propane (bisphenol A) or Glycerol and Epichlorohydrin (30, 40)

Resins of the formula I can be prepared in a variety of average molecular weights. The following examples are typical of the conditions used and products obtained. The latter are designated below by the arbitrary assignment of letters to permit ease of later reference.

Resin A: Molecular Weight 370. In a 2 l. resin kettle equipped with stirrer, thermometer, condenser, and dropping funnel is placed a mixture of 228 g. (1 m.) of bisphenol A, 925 g. (10 m.) epichlorohydrin, and 5 ml. of water.

A total of 82 g. (2.05 m.) solid sodium hydroxide is added in portions. First, 13 g. of the base is added and the mixture is heated with stirring. The heating is stopped when the temperature reaches 80 °C., and the Glas-Col heating mantle replaced by an ice water bath so that the temperature does not exceed 100°C. When the reaction temperature falls to 95°C., another 13 g. of sodium hydroxide is added. Temperature control is exercised as above. The remainder of the sodium hydroxide is added in 13–14 g. increments. After the final addition of base, no cooling is applied. When the exothermic reaction subsides, the excess epichlorohydrin is distilled at a pressure of about 50 mm. with a pot temperature not exceeding 150°C. The residue is then cooled to about 70°C. and 50 ml. benzene is added to precipitate the salt present. The salt is removed by vacuum filtration and washed with benzene (50 ml.). The benzene solutions are combined and the benzene distilled. When the pot temperature reaches 125°C. a vacuum of about 25 mm. is applied and the distillation continued until a pot temperature of 170°C. is reached. The resulting clear, highly viscous liquid epoxy resin has an average molecular weight of about 370, as determined ebullioscopically in ethylene dichloride. It has a softening point of about 9°C. by the Durrans' mercury method (see Chapter 2).

The epoxide content is determined by heating 1 g. of resin at reflux for 20 min. with 25 ml. of a standardized solution prepared from 16 ml. concentrated hydrochloric acid diluted with pyridine to 1 l. After cooling, the excess hydrochloric acid is back-titrated with 0.1 N sodium hydroxide in methanol to a phenolphthalein endpoint. One HCl is considered equivalent to one epoxide group. For the resin prepared above, the epoxy content per 100 g. is about 0.5, which corresponds to 1.85 epoxy groups per molecule for a molecular weight of 370. The epoxide equivalent weight (the grams of resin containing 1 g. mole of epoxide) is, therefore, 200. In general:

Epoxy Content = number of epoxy groups per 100 g. of resin

Epoxy Equivalent Weight = grams resin per epoxy group = 100/epoxy content

Thus, Resin A corresponds closely to the epoxy resin product (I) in the preparative equation, where $n = 0$, which has a calculated molecular weight of 340, an epoxy functionality of 2.0, and an epoxide equivalent weight of 170. In resin derived from diols, there shall be between 1 and 2 epoxides per molecule, if the experiment is run correctly.

Resin B: Molecular Weight 900. In a 1 l. resin kettle equipped as in procedure for Resin A, with added provision for a siphon, are placed 228 g. (1 m.) bisphenol A and 75 g. (1.88 m.) sodium hydroxide as a 10% aqueous solution, and the mixture heated to 45 °C. Then, 145 g. (1.57 m.) epichlorohydrin is added rapidly with stirring. The mixture is then heated to a temperature of about 95 °C. where it is maintained for 80 min. The mixture separates into two phases. The aqueous layer can be siphoned from the taffy-like product. The latter is washed with hot water with stirring while molten until the wash water is neutral to litmus. The resin is then removed while hot and is dried by heating in an air oven at 130 °C. The solid product has a softening point (Durrans' mercury method) of about 69°C., and molecular weight (ebullioscopic in ethylene dichloride) of about 900. The epoxy content per 100 g. is about 0.2, hence an epoxy functionality of 1.8 groups per molecule. The epoxide equivalent weight is, therefore, 500. The resin corresponds approximately to formula I, where $n = 2$; the calculated molecular weight is 908.

Resin C: Molecular Weight 1400. The procedure for Resin B is followed except that 54.8 g. (1.37 m.) of sodium hydroxide (10% solution) and 113 g. (1.22 m.) epichlorohydrin are used. The product is a brittle solid with a softening point (Durrans' mercury method) of about 98 °C., and an ebullioscopic (ethylene dichloride) molecular weight of about 1400. The epoxy content per 100 g. is about 0.1. Thus, there are 1.44 epoxide groups per molecule and the epoxide equivalent weight is 970. The resin corresponds approximately to I with $n = 3.7$.

Resin D: Molecular Weight 2900. One hundred g. of Resin C (0.071 m., containing 0.103 m. epoxy groups) in 250 ml. beaker is heated with stirring to 150 °C. by means of an oil bath. Then 5 g. (0.022 m.) bisphenol A is added and the mixture heated to 200 °C. over a 2 hr. period. The resulting resin has a softening point of about 130 °C. (Durrans' mercury method) and a molecular weight (as in the preceding examples) of about 2900. There are approximately 0.05 epoxy groups per 100 g. grams, hence, 1.45 epoxy groups per molecule, and epoxide equivalent weight of 2000. The resin is approximately represented by I where $n = 9$.

Resin E (From Glycerol): Molecular Weight 324. This resin is prepared from glycerol and epichlorohydrin in an acid-catalyzed reaction. The main reaction may be indicated in the following way:

$$\underset{\displaystyle |}{\overset{\displaystyle OH}{HOCH_2CHCH_2OH}} + \overset{\displaystyle O}{\overset{\diagup\;\diagdown}{CH_2-CH-CH_2Cl}} \xrightarrow{\ BF_3\ }$$

$$\underset{\displaystyle |}{\overset{\displaystyle HO}{ClCH_2CH}}-CH_2(OCH_2\underset{\displaystyle |}{\overset{\displaystyle OH}{CHCH_2}})_nOCH_2\underset{\displaystyle |}{\overset{\displaystyle OH}{CHCH_2Cl}}$$

$$\xrightarrow[NaAlO_2]{}\ \overset{\displaystyle O}{\overset{\diagup\;\diagdown}{CH_2-CHCH_2}}(OCH_2\underset{\displaystyle |}{\overset{\displaystyle OH}{CHCH_2}})_nOCH_2\overset{\displaystyle O}{\overset{\diagup\;\diagdown}{CH-CH_2}}$$

Epoxy resins based on glycerol will usually have between two and three epoxides per molecule, depending on the excess of epichlorohydrin used. Thus, the secondary hydroxyls in the above equation may bear glycidyl groups to some extent.

In a 2 l. resin kettle equipped with stirrer and condenser are placed 276 g. (3 m.) glycerol and 828 g. (9 m.) epichlorohydrin. To this stirred mixture is added 10 g. of an etheral solution of boron trifluoride etherate containing about 0.5 g. boron trifluoride. The temperature of the reaction rises and is maintained between 50 and 75°C. over a 3 hr. period by means of intermittent ice cooling.

About 370 g. of the resulting viscous liquid condensate is dissolved in 900 ml. of dioxane in a 2 l. resin kettle equipped with stirrer and condenser. Three hundred g. of sodium aluminate is added and the mixture heated to reflux and stirred for 9 hr.   After cooling the mixture to room temperature, the solids are filtered with vacuum and the filtrate concentrated by returning to a 2 l. resin kettle and distilling the solvent and any other volatiles by heating to a temperature of 205°C. at 20 mm. pressure.   The resulting epoxy resin is a pale yellow, viscous liquid, having an ebullioscopic (dioxane) molecular weight of about 324.   The epoxide content per 100 g. is about 0.67.   There are, therefore, 2.18 epoxide groups per molecule and the epoxide equivalent weight 150.

275. The Curing of Epoxy Resins

The method of choice in curing an epoxy resin is determined by a combination of factors.   The end use of the resin, whether as a casting or potting material, a surface coating, an adhesive, etc., fixes certain limitations on cure temperature and time.   The effect of curing agents on color, or stability to heat, light or moisture of the final form of the product is critical also.   Moreover, the strength and hardness of the end product often depends on the type of curing agent and the quantity used.   The following examples demonstrate only a few of the **types of curing agents** that have been used for the epoxies and, only some of the variations of technique in using them.   Resins used in the following examples are those prepared above.

A. With a Tertiary Amine (22,29).   An epoxy resin adhesive formulation can be made by mixing 34 g. of Resin A, 12 g. of Resin E, and 4 ml. of acetonitrile.   To the mixture is added 7 g. of triethylamine.   The resulting mixture can be applied to the surfaces to be joined, which are then clamped together. Cure is effected at 75–80 °F. in 6 days to give a strong bond.   Phenolic cloth laminate blocks or panels can be so joined, as can aluminum sheets also, particularly if the above formulation has 40 g. of powdered bauxite (alumina containing 17% iron oxide) mixed into it thoroughly.

A surface coating can be made from a solution of 10 g. Resin C and 1 g. of benzyldimethylamine in 5 ml. each of xylene and methyl cellosolve acetate. The solution is flowed onto a glass plate.   The solvent is evaporated in air and the plate heated at 100°C. for $1/2$ hr.   A hard film coating results.

B. With a Secondary Amine (30).   To 142 g. of diethylamine in a 1 l. resin kettle equipped with stirrer, condenser, and thermometer is added 125 g. of Resin A in 125 g. of dioxane, with stirring.   A slightly exothermic reaction occurs.   The mixture is then heated to reflux (55–60 °C.) for 3 hr.   The resulting mixture is poured into 750 ml. water in a 2 l. beaker and the sticky product washed repeatedly with water by stirring and decantation to remove excess amine and dioxane.   The resin is then dissolved in 500 ml. diethyl ether, and the solution extracted with 500 ml. portions of water until the washings are neutral to litmus.   The etheral solution is dried over Drierite and the ether removed by distillation on the steam bath.   The product (about 92 g.) is a very viscous liquid at room temperature, but fluid at 60°C.

The resin is still soluble in methyl ethyl ketone and chloroform.   The large amount of diethylamine used provides for a one-to-one reaction of amine with epoxy groups, and no cross-linking is, therefore, possible.   If, however, 50 g.

of Resin A is mixed with 2.5 g. of diethylamine and kept at room temperature for 60 hr. followed by 65°C. for 24 hr., a solid, insoluble product is obtained. In this case, each amine group, present in low quantity, effects the catalytic polymerization of several epoxides, with cross-linking as the result. If now 50 g. of Resin A is mixed with 7.5 g. of the soluble resin prepared above from Resin A and excess of diethylamine, the mixture will cure to a hard, clear solid in 1–2 hr. at 60°C. The combined amine groups in the amine-modified Resin A serve to cross-link the mixture through the epoxides of the added Resin A.

C. With an Acid (2). A solution is prepared in a 50 ml. Erlenmeyer flask by dissolving 10 g. of Resin C in 12 ml. of ethyl ketone, to which is then added 1 g. oxalic acid dihydrate. The mixture is gently warmed on the stream bath to assist in dissolving the acid. The solution is cast on a glass plate with aid of a doctor knife and the solvent allowed to evaporate at room temperature. The glass plate is then heated in an oven at 150 °C. for 30 min. to an hour to give a cured coating of considerable hardness.

D. With an Anhydride (8,12). Fifty g. of Resin B is placed in a 200 ml. tall-form beaker in an oil bath. The resin is heated to 120 °C. Fifteen g. of molten phthalic anhydride is added and stirred into the resin. Part of the phthalic anhydride will precipitate if the resin is cooled at this point to 60 °C. or below, but reheating will dissolve it. The beaker is covered with a glass plate and the resin-phthalic anhydride mixture is held at 120 °C. for 1 hr., at which point it is still soluble in acetone and chloroform. Heating at 170–180 °C. will effect the final cure and produce a clear, hard, insoluble resin in one to two hours.

If 0.5 g. N,N'-dimethylaniline is added to the reaction immediately after or along with the phthalic anhydride, the resin will cure in about 1 hr. at 120°C. Tertiary amines function as accelerators for anhydride curing of epoxy resins.

REFERENCES

1. Bjorksten Research Laboratories, Inc., *Polyesters and Their Applications*, Reinhold, New York, 1956.
2. Bradley, T. F., U.S. Pat. 2,500,449 (Mar. 14, 1950).
3. Burk, R. E., H. E. Thompson, A. J. Weith, and I. Williams, *Polymerization*, Reinhold, New York, 1937.
4. Burke, W. J., and S. H. Ruetman, *J. Poly. Sci.*, **32**, 221 (1958).
5. Burke, W. J., S. H. Ruetman, and H. P. Higginbottom, *Linear Phenol-Formaldehyde Polymers*, ASTIA Report AD 202, 138 (Aug., 1958); *J. Polymer Sci.* **38**, 513 (1959).
6. Carlston, E. F., G. B. Johnson, F. G. Lum, D. G. Huggins, and K. T. Park, *Ind. Eng. Chem.*, **51**, 253 (1959).
7. Carswell, T. S., *Phenoplasts: Their Structure, Properties, and Chemical Technology*, Interscience Publishers, New York, 1947.
8. Castan, P., U.S. Pat. 2,324,483 (July 20, 1943).
9. *Composition and Utilization of Polyesters*, National Aniline Division, Allied Chemical and Dye Corporation (1954).

10. Dawson, E. S., U.S. Pat. 1,888,849 (Nov. 22, 1932).
11. Day, H. M., U.S. Pat. 2,477,328 (July 26, 1949).
11a. de Jong, J. I., and J. de Jonge, *Rec. trav. chim.* **72,** 1027 (1953).
12. Dearborn, E. C., R. M. Fuoss, A. K. MacKenzie, and R. G. Shepherd, *Ind. Eng. Chem.*, **45,** 2715 (1953).
13. Ellis, C., *The Chemistry of Synthetic Resins*, Reinhold, New York, 1935.
14. Ellis, C., U. S. Pat. 2,195,362 (Mar. 26, 1940).
15. Hodgins, T. S., and A. G. Hovey, U.S. Pat. 2,226,518 (Dec. 24, 1940).
16. Houwink, R., ed., *Elastomers and Plastomers*, Elsevier, New York, 1949.
17. Kienle, R. H., P. A. Van Der Meulen, and F. E. Petke, *J. Am. Chem. Soc.*, **61,** 2258 (1939).
18. Kunin, R., *Ion Exchange Resins*, second edition, Wiley, New York, 1958.
19. Lee, H., and K. Neville, *Epoxy Resins: Their Applications and Technology*, McGraw-Hill, New York, 1957.
20. Marvel, C. S., J. R. Elliott, F. E. Boettner, and H. Yuska, *J. Am. Chem. Soc.*, **68,** 1681 (1946).
21. Morrell, R. S., ed., H. M. Langton, ed., third edition, *Synthetic Resins and Allied Plastics*, Oxford University Press, London, 1951.
22. Newey, H. A., and E. C. Shokal, U.S. Pat. 2,553,718 (May 22, 1951).
23. Office of Tech. Serv., U.S. Dept. of Commerce, Washington, D.C. (1945) (P.B. Report 25,642).
24. Ott, E., H. M. Spurlin, and M. W. Grafflin, *Cellulose and Cellulose Derivatives*, second edition, Interscience Publishers, New York (1954).
25. Pantke, O., U.S. Pat. 1,909,786 (May 16, 1933).
26. *Reports on the Progress of Applied Chemistry*, Vol. XLII, Society of Chemical Industry, London (1957), p. 462.
27. Schildknecht, C. E., ed., *Polymer Processes*, Interscience Publishers, New York, 1956.
28. Schlack, W., ed., *A Manual of Plastics and Resins*, Chemical Publishing, Brooklyn, 1950.
29. Shokal, E. C., and A. C. Mueller, U.S. Pat. 2,548,447 (April 10, 1951).
30. Shokal, E. C., H. A. Newey, and T. F. Bradley, U.S. Pat. 2,643,239 (June 23, 1953).
31. Simonds, H. R., A. J. Weith, and M. H. Bigelow, *Handbook of Plastics*, D. Van Nostrand, New York, 1949.
32. Simonds, H. R., *A Concise Guide to Plastics*, Reinhold, New York, 1957.
33. Simons, W. G., U.S. Pat. 2,518,388 (Aug. 8, 1950).
34. Swain, R. C., U.S. Pat. 2,285,750 (June 9, 1942).
35. Technical Bulletins on epoxy resins, Shell Chemical Corp.
36. Vale, C. P., *Aminoplastics*, Cleaver-Hume Press, London, 1950.
37. Wasseneger, H., and K. Jaeger, U.S. Pat. 2,204,539 (June 11, 1940).
38. Weith, G. S., U.S. Pat. 2,475,731 (July 12, 1949).
39. Widmer, G., and W. Fisch, U.S. Pat. 2,328,592 (Sept. 7, 1943).
40. Wiles, Q. T., and D. W. Elam, U.S. Pat. 2,681,901 (June 22, 1954).
41. British Pat. 359,365 (Oct. 22, 1931); British Pat. 316,914 (Aug. 6, 1929).

Sources of Equipment

Most of the equipment used in this book is conventional; however, some is not. Of the nonconventional items, many are best fabricated by the experimenter. The following items are in this category: shear disk stirrers; pressure filter; pipe autoclave; polymerization flasks, specially shaped; salt bath; and doctor knives.

The remaining items are best purchased, although some of them (marked with an *) may be home-made.

TABLE A.1

Wiley mill	Arthur H. Thomas Co., Philadelphia, Pennsylvania
Koefler hot stage	Arthur H. Thomas Co., Philadelphia, Pennsylvania
Serum-type rubber stoppers	A. S. Aloe and Co., Aloe Scientific Division, St. Louis 12, Missouri
Filter cloth (pressure filter use)	Circles cut from undyed cotton blanketing may be used.
Hydraulic press	Fred S. Carver, Inc., Summit, New Jersey
Pressure bottles	Arthur H. Thomas Co., Phi!adelphia, Pennsylvania
Glass cloth tubing (shield)	Bentley, Harris Manufacturing Co., Conshohocken, Pennsylvania
*Dennis bar	Arthur H. Thomas Co., Philadelphia, Pennsylvania
Microscopes for crystalline melting point	Inexpensive and satisfactory microscopes for this purpose are models #78 and 79 of the American Optical Co., instrument division, Buffalo, New York
*Polymer tubes (These should be made only by a competent glassblower.)	Labglass, Inc., Vineland, New Jersey
Viscometers	Cannon Instrument Co., Box 812, State College, Pennsylvania
*Dry box	Air-Shields, Inc., Hatboro, Pennsylvania
Rubber mill (small)	Farrell-Birmingham Co., Inc., Ansonia, Connecticut

Sources of Chemicals and Raw Materials

There are numerous sources for fine organic chemicals, monomers, and other raw materials required for the reactions described in this book. Many of them are quite common and can be found in any laboratory. Others may be obtained readily from fine chemical suppliers. A partial list of such sources would include the following:

1. Distillation Products Industries, Division of Eastman Kodak Co., Rochester, New York.
2. Aldrich Chemical Co., Inc., Milwaukee, Wisconsin.
3. Research Laboratories of Monomer-Polymer, the Borden Co., Leominster, Massachusetts.
4. Matheson, Coleman and Bell, Inc., East Rutherford, New Jersey.
5. Anderson Chemical Co., division of Stauffer Chemical Co., Weston, Michigan.
6. Brothers Chemical Co., Orange, New Jersey.
7. K & K Laboratories, Inc., Jamaica, New York.

Other items not specifically listed in one or more of these catalogs are noted individually in Table B.1. Not all suppliers are given when the compound is relatively common. Intermediates not available commercially must be synthesized. Synthetic methods are given in the text for some of these. Others may be made simply by common methods.

TABLE B.1

Aerosol OT (sodium salt of sulfosuccinic acid diethyl ester)	Union Carbide Corp., New York, New York
Aluminum triisobutyl	Texas Alkyls, New York
Amyl diazonium fluoborate (Phosphorogen A)	Ozark Mahoning, Tulsa, Oklahoma
m-Benzenedisulfonyl chloride	Tennessee Corp., Atlanta, Georgia
Benzyldimethylamine	Rohm & Haas Co., Philadelphia, Pennsylvania
Bisphenol A [2,2-Propane-bis-(4-hydroxybenzene)]	Monsanto Chemical Co. St. Louis, Missouri; Dow Chemical Co. Midland, Michigan
Chloroprene (in xylene)	E. I. du Pont de Nemours & Co., Inc., Wilmington, Delaware
Cobalt naphthenate	Frederick A. Stressen-Reuter, Inc., Bensonville, Illinois
Cyclohexanedimethanol-1,4	Available as 70% methanolic solution from Eastman Chemical Products, Kingsport, Tennessee
3,3'-Diaminobenxidine	J. T. Baker Chemical Co., Phillipsburg, New Jersey
4,4'-Diaminophenyl ether	Dow Chemical Co., Midland, Michigan
2,5-Dimethylpiperazine	Wyandotte Chemical Co., Wyandotte, Michigan
N,N'-Diethylethylenediamine	Ames Laboratories, South Norwalk, Connecticut
"Duponol" ME and C detergent	E. I. du Pont de Nemours & Co., Inc., Wilmington, Delaware
Emulsifier—MP-189-EF	E. I. du Pont de Nemours & Co., Inc., Wilmington, Delaware
Eutectic salt mixtures	E. I. du Pont de Nemours & Co., Inc., Wilmington, Delaware
α-Flock	International Filler Corp., North Tonawanda, New York
Hexamethylene diisocyanate	Delta Chemical Works, New York, New York
Isophthaloyl chloride	Hooker Chemical Corp., Niagara Falls, New York; E. I. du Pont de Nemours & Co., Inc., Wilmington, Delaware
Li dispersion	Foote Mineral Co., Philadelphia, Pennsylvania
Linseed oil fatty acids	G. S. Ziegler & Co., Great Neck, New York
Melamine	American Cyanamid Co., industrial chemicals division, New York, New York
3-Methyl-1-butene	Phillips Petroleum Co., Bartlesville, Oklahoma

4-Methyl-1-pentene	Phillips Petroleum Co., Bartlesville, Oklahoma
Methyl ethyl ketone hydroperoxide	Lucidol division, Wallace & Tiernan, Inc., Buffalo, New York
Methylene bis(4-phenylisocyanate)	General Aniline & Film Co., New York, New York; E. I. du Pont de Nemours & Co., Inc., Wilmington, Delaware
Norbornylene	Roberts Chemicals, Inc., Nitro, West Virginia
Phenylphosphonyl dichloride	Victor Chemical Works, Chicago, Illinois
Polyethyleneoxide glycols	Union Carbide Corp., New York, New York
Polypropyleneoxide glycols	Dow Chemical Co., Midland, Michigan
Pyromellitic dianhydride	E. I. du Pont de Nemours & Co., Inc., Wilmington, Delaware
Sodium "Lorol" sulfate	E. I. du Pont de Nemours & Co., Inc., Wilmington, Delaware
Sodium salt of a sulfonated paraffin oil	American Cyanamid Co., dyes department, Bound Brook, New Jersey
Tergetol	Union Carbide Corp., New York, New York
Terephthaloyl chloride	Hooker Chemical Corp., Niagara Falls, New York
Triphenyl borate	R. W. Greeff & Co., Inc., New York 20, New York
"Triton" 720	Rohm & Haas Co., Philadelphia, Pennsylvania
Vinyl chloride	Dow Chemical Co., Midland, Michigan; The Matheson Company, Inc., East Rutherford, New Jersey
Vinylidene chloride	Dow Chemical Company, Midland, Michigan
Wood flour	American Colloid Company, Skokie, Illinois

SUBJECT INDEX

A. Index of Initiator Systems

B. Index of Reaction Systems

C. Index of Polymerizations Through Functional Groups

D. General Index